Marine Botany

An Introduction

Marine Botany

An Introduction

E. YALE DAWSON

Smithsonian Institution
United States National Museum

Holt, Rinehart and Winston, Inc.
NEW YORK / CHICAGO / SAN FRANCISCO / TORONTO / LONDON

4567   090   987

Copyright © 1966 by Holt, Rinehart and Winston, Inc.
Library of Congress catalog card number: 66-16952
ISBN: 0-03-055590-6

Printed in the United States of America

*Dedicated to the memory of William Albert Setchell,
my teacher, who inspired me with his knowledge of
marine plants and led me into the thrills of the
sea quest;
and to Mrs. N. Floy Bracelin, beloved, persevering
Bracie, my living link with the classical past of Farlow
and Agardh, of Madame Weber and Herr Kützing,
through him who was our mentor and friend, our
"Uncle Bill."*

Preface

Today, the general public is aware of the widespread economic significance of marine vegetation resources. But this recognition does not go back very far. Before the two World Wars the study of marine plants was a matter of little more than academic interest; it became one of national urgency. The crisis caused by the cut-off of German potash supplies during World War I and a similar crisis with respect to Japanese agar during World War II awoke the United States to the industrial utilization of seaweeds and therefore gave useful purpose to marine botany in the public eye.

The interest in marine plants has now expanded greatly with the recognition of economic importance not only of larger seaweeds, but of marine fungi, marine bacteria, and the fundamental food producers of the oceans — the phytoplankton. Increasing pollution of the sea along urban shores has focused attention on the conservation of industrial kelp resources and on the various destructive effects of ocean outfalls. Experimental biologists have begun to put marine plant organisms to use as experimental subjects in physiological and biochemical research. The widely successful cultivation of food seaweeds in Japan has pointed to potentials in that field untapped in the Western world.

While the economic development of marine botany has been gaining momentum, the public awareness of marine plants has markedly increased through vastly improved transportation. This has brought the seashore within reach of the most inland dweller. Increased living standards have brought to many the opportunity for a seaside vacation, while sporting trends have put thousands on the sea in small yachts and under the sea with the "aqua-lung." Familiarity with seaweeds is now common to a large segment of our population, and is no longer confined to a relatively few seashore residents.

Despite this broadened interest in marine plants, there have been few published materials on the subject made available to the public, and none designed to present to the advanced college undergraduate a survey of the field of marine botany. Colleges and universities, in recognition of the growing importance of marine science, are encouraging students to obtain specific training in marine biology. Numerous small seaside laboratories have opened in recent years for summer classwork, and some larger and older ones now are endeavoring to provide year-round marine biological teaching and research programs. These expanded seashore facilities for summer collecting and study, and the increased availability of instructional specimens and slides from supply houses, make possible the presentation of marine botany in almost any inland institution in which an enthusiastic teacher may assemble his materials.

It is, then, to that need for instruction of the advanced undergraduate (or beginning graduate), whether at a seaside or an inland school, whether botany major, beginning oceanographer, marine zoologist, marine geologist, or interested student of another discipline, that this book is directed. It is intended to emphasize those plants that are most readily and widely available as examples for instructional purposes on the coasts of the United States, although the book as a whole will have a wider application. It is further intended that this book be used in conjunction with one of the pertinent American regional marine floras listed in the bibliography (Appendix A) and with the writer's illustrated artificial key to the American seaweeds: "How to Know the Seaweeds."

To the end that his instructional aims may be met, the author invites inquiry from interested teachers toward provision of exemplary marine plant materials for laboratory class study.

A large number of individuals and institutions have assisted in the preparation of this book. The writer especially wishes to thank the following. For reading and editing manuscript: George F. Papenfuss, Shirley R. Sparling, G. J. Hollenberg, and Isabella A. Abbott; for critical reviews of the entire text: Michael Neushul, Chapters 1, 7, 11; Harold J. Humm, Chapters 1–8, 11–18; Francis T. Haxo, Chapter 13; Thomas D. Brock, Chapter 2; Ralph A. Lewin, Chapter 2; C. den Hartog, Chapter 14; Howard C. Whisler, Chapter 3. For contribution of illustrations or of special information: Richard L. Steele, Don Ollis, Joseph H. Powell, David J. Chapman, Bruce C. Parker, Mary Belle Allen, Robert F. Scagel, W. R. Taylor, Wheeler J. North, Francis Drouet, Ruth Patrick, Kathleen Cole, Claude E. Zobell, Clinton J. Dawes, Mary Parke, Walter Plaut, Richard D. Wood, Irene Manton, Michael Neushul, Kelco Company, The New York Botanical Garden. For permission to use copyrighted materials: H. E. Jaques, J. Cramer.

The following figures are reprinted from Gilbert M. Smith, *Marine Algae of the Monterey Peninsula,* Stanford University Press: 7–4; 9–2, *B–C;* 9–11; 10–2, *F–G;* 10–14, *C–D;* 10–19.

The following figures are reprinted from W. R. Taylor, *Marine Algae of the Eastern Tropical and Subtropical Coasts of the Americas,* University of Michigan Press: 8–10; 8–14; 10–10; 12–2; 12–4; 15–4.

Thanks also are due to the Office of Naval Research, Biology Branch, for the use of various illustrations prepared for other purposes during past contractual research programs.

The drawings were prepared for the most part by the writer, by Rosalie Baker, and by Jean Colton.

E.Y.D.

Washington, D.C.
January 1966

Contents

1

The Marine Environment
and Its Plants

The sea *is* everywhere around us. Literally, one can now cross it between meals, and the three oceanic shores of the United States can all be visited in a day's time. The astronauts see the world in a new perspective, as a watery planet with but minor patches of land. Indeed, the oceans are really all one, divided more or less into five regions by the great continental islands. We call these oceans by separate names — the Pacific, the Atlantic, the Indian, the Arctic, and the Antarctic. Yet they are a continuous 71 percent of the surface of the earth and there is more to them than meets the eye, for they are mostly deep and dark.

FACTORS AFFECTING MARINE LIFE

The oceans have an incredible average depth of more than 3 miles. We know from wide exploration and sampling by oceanographic expeditions that living things are present throughout all of them, to the greatest depths of over 10,000 meters; but we also know that, except for a minute surface fraction, the whole of the enormous marine environment is utterly dark and cold. The creatures that make it their home never know sunlight nor temperatures much above freezing. This preponderant darkness has a profound effect on the life of the ocean, for in the absence of light, plants, except for obscure fungi and bacteria, are essentially lacking, and the vast, dark spaces of the sea are almost the exclusive realm of animals.

Sunlight falling upon the sea surface penetrates the water to varying depths, depending upon the intensity and angle of radiation, the amount of surface reflection, and the transparency of the water. The sea has exceptional light-absorbing capacity, so that even in quite clear water only some 35 to 38 percent of the sunlight that enters the water reaches a depth of 1 meter. With increasing depth the light quickly fades, and only a fraction of one percent remains below 50 meters. In coastal waters, in which sediment or plankton produce a turbid condition of low transparency, 99.5 percent of the light may be absorbed in the first 10 meters.

Light is not only rapidly but selectively absorbed, so that the longer red, violet, orange, and yellow wavelengths are removed first, leaving only the shorter blue and green for deeper penetration. Thus, color below the surface is not in our familiar pattern, and the underwater observer must learn a new set of values in order effectively to interpret what he sees (Figure 1-1).

FIGURE 1-1. The author, fully clothed against coral scratches, collects calcareous algae at Isla Caño, Costa Rica (photo by Don Ollis).

Some years ago, I had opportunity to enter this strange narrow-color world as a member of an "aqua-lung" team studying the floor of Eniwetok Lagoon in the Marshall Islands. The lagoon waters are characteristically clear in such a tropical central Pacific region so that work at 160 feet can be carried out satisfactorily under normal daytime conditions. We went down a fixed line after setting our decompression stage at a 12-foot depth. A moving mosaic of light from the flexing surface played upon us at the stage, but in looking down we saw only the anchor line disappear in a gray-green mist far below. We descended slowly, adjusting pressure at intervals, until at 90 feet we could no longer see the hull of our boat, the stage, nor any distinct surface light. At that depth we seemed to be suspended in an apparently endless gray-green cosmos. At 120 feet, the sandy bottom came dimly into view, with its coral heads and giant clams, but all seemed a lifeless, dull gray. The brilliant colors of the clam mantle were not there; the blades of red algae, striking in the sunlight, were here so obscure and dull as to be almost invisible. It was as if all the colorful scenes of a tropical coral sea were being projected from a low-contrast black-and-white film.

The essential results of this selective light-absorbing property of seawater are these: that no photosynthetic plants can live and grow except in the uppermost 3 percent of the sea's mean depth; that only a small part of this thin surface layer has sufficient light for more than minimal growth; that below a few meters only those autotrophic plants with pigments capable of utilizing the available short wavelengths of blue and green light can survive.

Thus, it is clear that the animal life of the vast reaches of the oceans is dependent upon photosynthetic production by plants in an exceedingly limited upper portion of the medium. Nevertheless, such production is highly effective in providing enormous food supplies; but it is by no means uniform throughout the sea.

As already intimated, the transparency of the water largely determines the thickness of the productive surface layer, especially along the more fertile shore. One can determine, by refined techniques, the maximum depth of effective photosynthesis at a given time, by finding that depth at which the carbon dioxide consumed by a plant equals the oxygen produced. This point of equilibrium is called the compensation point, but under any given circumstance it varies with light and with temperature.

A number of other factors affect the growth of marine plants above their respective compensation points and, consequently, the abundance of animal life they support. The most widely influential of these is temperature.

The effect of temperature on marine plants is partly direct and partly indirect (see Chapter 13). Directly, temperature influences the rate of photosynthetic and respiratory processes. Indirectly, the solubility of oxygen is so affected that a higher temperature is associated with a decrease in the amount of dissolved oxygen available for dark-hour respiration. Unlike the terrestrial situation, in which the available amount of carbon dioxide is usually limiting to photosynthesis, the dissociation of carbonates in the sea generally provides adequate supplies of CO_2 for photosynthesis (although this is not always the case). On the other hand, and again unlike the atmospheric environment, seawater may be widely deficient in dissolved oxygen available for respiration, especially at night. In this respect, temperature may limit effective growth by restricting the solubility of O_2 in the water medium. Thus, in whatever of several ways it may have its effect, temperature controls the geographic distribution of a majority of marine plants, and many species tolerate only a narrow range. Lower temperatures generally favor the richer development of sea plants, as witness the abundance of vegetation on cool-temperate shores compared with tropical ones.

Some 40 years ago William A. Setchell made some of the first critical examinations of the temperature relations of seaweeds. He first divided the surface waters of the oceans into zones according to isotheres of 5°C and showed that a majority of species are confined to one of these 5-degree zones, that some extend over two of them, but that only a small number extend over three or more zones. He recognized further that although many species are normal in only one of these zones, in those regions of their occurrence in which the temperature rises above or descends below the normal range, the plants may undergo a condition of quiescence, or "rigor."

He especially studied the eel grass, *Zostera marina,* a species of wide geographic distribution and wide temperature tolerance. He presented evidence that through much of its American range, at temperatures below 10°C, the plants are dormant, that vegetative growth proceeds between 10 and 15° and flowering sets in at about 15°. Although temperature amplitudes differ markedly through the range of eel grass, as for example on the Atlantic coast of America, Setchell showed that from Carolina to Maine eel-grass flowering could be traced through essentially the same temperature range, even though this occurred at very different times of year. Thus, for instance, flowering takes place in North Carolina in March and April and in Maine in July and August.

The perennial brown alga, *Ascophyllum nodosum,* which ranges from Greenland to New Jersey, shows a similar response to temperature in that it fruits in Greenland in summer but in Long Island Sound in late winter or early spring. The red alga, *Pterocladia capillacea,* in the northern part of its Atlantic European range in Britain, never develops beyond the vegetative phase, while in southwest France, where the necessary higher temperatures obtain, reproduction regularly occurs. In both cases the effective reproduction is accomplished within narrower limits than vegetative development. Many instances of temperature influences of other kinds could be cited.

Although temperature commonly controls the distribution of marine plants by its several effects, the distribution of temperatures in the surface waters of the sea is in turn the result of the combined effects of a number of variables. The primary pattern of low Antarctic-Arctic temperatures and high tropical ones is, of course, provided by latitudinal differences in insolation. Upon this, however, are superimposed several profoundly modifying influences, the most pronounced of which is the circulation pattern of surface currents of the oceans.

The most conspicuous feature of the surface currents in the two major ocean basins, the Pacific and the Atlantic, is that both show clockwise circulation in the northern hemisphere and counterclockwise circulation in the southern. This has the effect of bringing widespreading warm water, and concurrently a warm tropical climate, to much of their western shores. At the same time, cold-water influences along the eastern sides provide more extensive temperate marine climates. An influence that further differentiates the two is brought about by the prevailing winds that tend to parallel the cool currents along the continental west coasts. These winds cause a coastal upwelling of subsurface waters that helps to maintain the cooling effects far into the tropics. Thus, we find a temperate ocean climate along Peru, which lies at the same latitude as steaming New Guinea and the Great Barrier Reef. In Peru's cool waters abound the plant life that feeds its multitudes of invertebrates and fish, of birds and sea lions and whales (Figure 1-2). Along cool Baja California grow enormous seaweed forests now harvested for a hundred uses, while opposite it, to the west along Okinawa, is a little-productive warm sea.

The physical configuration of the shore and the depth of the coastal waters provide for temperature modifications through eddying, confinement, and upwelling. The topographic features of the land affect weather patterns that in turn influence the amount of insolation reaching the sea surface. Accordingly, very different temperature conditions may occur in close proximity, especially along continental shores, and these support distinctive floras. A temperate coast, for example, with intermittent bays and headlands, flanked by seaward islands on the one side and by broken mountains and plains on the other, will surely display a varied marine flora replete with species of discontinuous distribution. Such is the case along the two Californias of the Pacific.

FIGURE 1-2. The cool fertile sea of southern Peru supports a rich biota of kelp beds, sea lions, and guano birds (photo courtesy Allan Hancock Foundation).

Although low seawater temperatures generally favor rich marine plant growth, those so low as to cause the formation of ice are extremely unfavorable. Not only does the presence of ice markedly reduce the penetration of light to the shallow sea floor during the already dimly lighted season, but its eroding and scouring effects on intertidal shores severely limit the development and persistence of plants. Perennial marine vegetation is all but absent from shores characterized by winter ice, and the intertidal floras generally are reduced and monotonous. At a little depth, where abrasion is not significant, however, quite luxuriant, perennial seaweed beds may occur.

The presence of favorable temperatures is not alone sufficient, for, despite these, macroscopic plants in the sea cannot ordinarily survive the agitation of surf and the movement of currents and surge without secure attachment to the substrate. Accordingly, one finds, except in the calmest situations, marine vegetation confined to permanent rocky outcrops and absent from shores of shifting sand, gravel, and cobbles. Inasmuch as sandy shores are by far the most extensive throughout the world, the marine botanist must often seek out favorable rocky habitats in order adequately to study the vegetation, even though a cast of driftweed from subtidal areas may litter the beach (Figure 1-3). In quiet bays and surfless shoals where erosion is minor, a sand or mud flora, often of marine flowering plants such as eel grass or turtle grass, may abundantly occur, but such is the exception rather than the rule. On the other hand, at depths below the effect of surf and surge, a rich vegetation may

FIGURE 1–3. A rocky outcrop on the Pacific shore of El Salvador provides materials in a study of the antibiotic properties of benthic algae, some of which are being dried here on top of the jeep.

be found even along the most exposed shores — limited mainly by the penetra
tion of light.

Free-floating seaweeds are usually but detached and dying fragments se
adrift by storm or by the natural breakup of overmature plants. A few un
attached forms live in salt marshes in the north Atlantic region and in New
Zealand, but only in the Sargasso Sea and in the Gulf of Thailand does one
encounter colonies of unattached seaweeds drifting more or less permanently in
oceanic eddies.

Apart from the aspects of temperature and substrate in the marine en
vironment, some features of the chemistry of the water medium are of far
reaching influence on the plants. The most obvious of these is salinity, which
has a general range of between $33\%_{oo}$ (parts per thousand) and $37\%_{oo}$, but
which may vary between wide extremes. In areas of high rainfall or extensive
runoff, such as the Baltic Sea, the dilution may be so great as to permit brown
algae and buttercups to grow within centimeters of each other. Conversely
the confinement and high-surface evaporation of the Red Sea provide for un
usually high open-sea salinities of $40\%_{oo}$. Such a shallow marine enclosure
as Laguna Madre, Texas, may have $100\%_{oo}$ of salt after a long dry period
Some seaweeds are sensitive to salinity changes and tolerate little deviation
from "normal" seawater, while others are adaptable to extreme and rapid
variations. One of the latter is the green alga *Enteromorpha,* some species of
which live successfully on the hulls of ferry boats traveling daily from open
sea harbors to the fresh water of river ports.

At least 44 chemical elements exclusive of gases occur in solution in
seawater (Table 1). For the most part, these are in unvarying proportional
concentrations so that, unlike terrestrial plants, marine vegetation is immersed
in a dilute but relatively constant nutritive medium. A few of the essential
elements, however, occur in variable amounts, and these concentrations may be
limiting to the growth of sea plants. Most attention has been focused on
the element phosphorus, partly from ease of analysis, but also because its
occurrence in the form of phosphates, according to some oceanographers, is
frequently a limiting factor in the sea's productivity.

The occurrence of nitrogen, too, in the form of nitrite, nitrate, and ammonia, profoundly affects the development of vegetation in the sea, either by
shortage or by overabundance. High concentrations in the vicinity of metro-
politan sewage outfalls may distinctly inhibit the growth of particular marine
plants. The significance of other chemical factors, such as the availability of
silicates, of Vitamin B_{12} and other substances will be discussed in Chapters
5 and 13.

An important consideration in interpreting the occurrence and abundance
of algal vegetation is the physical stratification of the water medium. In the
absence of continuous mixing, high surface temperatures may create a thermocline, resulting in water-density layers that effectively lock nutrients in the
lower, poorly-lighted waters and limit growth of plants above them. On the
other hand, under the influence of upwelling, rich supplies of nutrients are

TABLE 1
Elements Other Than Gases Present in Solution in Sea Water

Element	mg-atoms per Liter at Clorinity 19.00°/₀₀	Element	mg-atoms per Liter at Clorinity 19.00°/₀₀
proportionally unvarying			
Chlorine	548.30	Silver	0.000003
Sodium	470.15	Vanadium	0.000006
Magnesium	53.57	Lanthanum	0.000002
Sulphur	28.24	Yttrium	0.000003
Calcium	10.24	Nickel	0.000002
Potassium	9.96	Scandium	0.0000009
Bromine	0.83	Mercury	0.0000001
Carbon	2.34	Gold	0.00000002
Strontium	0.15	Radium	$0.8\text{--}12 \times 10^{-13}$
Boron	0.43	Cadmium	
Fluorine	0.07	Chromium	
Aluminum	0.02	Cobalt	
Rubidium	0.002	Tin	
Lithium	0.014		
Barium	0.0004		
Iodine	0.0004		
Zinc	0.00008	*Proportionally varying*	
Lead	0.00002		
Selenium	0.00005	Silicon	0.0007 —0.14
Cesium	0.00002	Nitrogen (comp.)	0.001 —0.05
Uranium	0.00001	Phosphorus	0.00003 —0.003
Molybdenum	0.000005	Arsenic	0.00015 —0.0003
Thorium	<0.000002	Iron	0.00003 —0.0003
Cerium	0.000003	Manganese	0.00002 —0.0002
		Copper	0.00002 —0.0002

brought from the sea floor and intermediate depths to the illuminated surface.

A great and omnipresent controller of vegetation is the animal life it supports, for plants are constantly being eaten by vegetarian vertebrates and by invertebrates. Drifted seaweeds on a beach may often be completely consumed overnight by amphipods and isopods that swarm over them. Much the same thing occurs on a submerged reef where, under the constant grazing, some plants succeed poorly and others succeed not at all. Observations in seaweed beds in which grazing is temporarily suspended by artificial destruction of most of the animal life have revealed a veritable tangled jungle resulting from the consequent luxuriant, unrestrained plant growth.

A vegetation-control factor only lately being recognized is the destructive effects of fungi. These, toward the end of a growing season, may sometimes be responsible for the breakdown and sloughing away of considerable portions of the benthic plants.

We have noted that, from the standpoint of vegetation, the habitable part of the sea is the photic zone, limited essentially to depths of 30 meters or less along most turbid mainland shores, and to 120 to 175 meters in clearest open water. Within this relatively thin layer of salt water, we may recognize four major environments of dissimilar character. The oceanic province includes the water of the open sea beyond the continental shelf. The neritic province is the water medium over the continental shelf. In both of these the freely floating phytoplankton flourish, but macroscopic seaweeds are rare (such as those that fasten themselves to fish). The benthic province is the sea floor habitat of the attached forms of vegetation with which, for practical purposes, we are more extensively concerned here. It contains two unlike environments, namely, the intertidal and the infratidal, or sublittoral. The former is in part an atmospheric environment in which intertidal organisms, except for those permanently submerged in tide pools, are subject at intervals to desiccation and direct solar heat, to rain, snow, and fresh-water runoff, to wind, and to frost. The sublittoral environment is strictly aquatic and more uniform, but has, nevertheless, marked variables of substrate, of temperature and light, of salinity and nutrient.

From the highest reach of the tide or the spray of the surf to the deepest penetration of light, the numerous interacting limiting factors of the environment provide a marvelous array of diverse habitats whose restrictions on life are met in interesting ways by the algae. Some of the interrelationships are treated in Chapter 15 on ecology, and throughout other parts of this book adaptations for survival will be pointed out in discussions of morphology, anatomy, cytology, and physiology.

These have been but a few notes on the characteristics of the marine environment that provide the framework for our interpretation of the lives of its plants. By and large, it is a far more uniform environment than that of the land, because of the all-pervading nature of the water medium and its modifying influence on the temperature extremes that daily and seasonally affect the land. Whereas the availability of water and carbon dioxide are the most widely limiting factors to plant growth on land, in the sea neither of these is ordinarily critical. Instead, two factors infrequently restricting on land are widely and severely limiting in the sea, namely, light and dissolved oxygen. Accordingly, one must orient himself to a new set of ecological values in studying marine botany and in interpreting the structure, the physiology, and the reproductive mechanisms of sea plants.

KINDS OF MARINE PLANTS

The fundamental contrasts in the terrestrial and marine environments are no less marked than are the differences in the vegetation. Whereas the vastly dominant and successful plants of the land are the seed bearers, of these the angiosperms are scantily present in the sea and the gymnosperms are totally absent. Instead, the oceans have seen long and complex development of a

TABLE 2
Kinds of Plants in the Marine Environment

Phylum or Division*	Approx. No. Living Species	Proportion Marine	Predominant Size	Marine Occurrence
Algae				
CHLOROPHYTA				
Green algae	7000	13%	microscopic to massive	benthos
CHAROPHYTA				
Stoneworts	76	(13%)	macroscopic	(brackish benthic)
EUGLENOPHYTA				
Euglenoids	400	3%	microscopic unicellular	benthos: mud and shallows
CHRYSOPHYTA				
Golden-brown algae	650	± 20%	microscopic unicellular	plankton
Coccolithophorids	200	96%	microscopic unicellular	plankton
Diatoms	6000–10,000	30–50%	microscopic unicellular	plankton; benthos
XANTHOPHYTA				
Vaucheria	60	15%	filamentous macroscopic	benthos: mud
PYRROPHYTA				
Dinoflagellates	1100 +	93%	microscopic unicellular	plankton
PHAEOPHYTA				
Brown algae	1500	99.7%	microscopic to massive	benthos
RHODOPHYTA				
Red algae	4000	98%	microscopic to massive	benthos
CYANOPHYTA				
Blue-green algae	7500 described taxa; probably < 200 autonomous species	± 75%	microscopic to macroscopic	benthos (marine to brackish and fresh water)
SCHIZOMYCOPHYTA				
Bacteria	1500	12%	microscopic	ubiquitous
MYXOMYCOPHYTA				
Slime molds	450	0	[± microscopic]	– – – – –
MYCOPHYTA				
Fungi	75,000	0.4%	microscopic	benthos
Lichens	16,000	0.1%	essentially microscopic	high intertidal
BRYOPHYTA				
Liverworts and mosses	25,000	0	[macroscopic]	– – – – –
TRACHEOPHYTA				
Psilopsida, club-mosses, horsetails, ferns, cycads, conifers	10,000	0	[macroscopic to massive]	– – – – –
Flowering plants	250,000	0.018	macroscopic to massive	benthos

*Some of the smaller, more obscure, or disputed groups are omitted.

lowlier assemblage, the algae, now enormously diversified in unconnected major groups. In this age the algae are altogether dominant in the marine environment. On the land the algae are scantily present as aerial organisms and are for the most part confined to specialized aquatic situations and to soil.

Two major groups of spore plants widely successful on land, the ferns and the bryophytes, are completely absent from the sea, even though in some tropical seashore areas the two environments are separated precisely by only a few centimeters.

The study of marine bacteriology only a few decades ago began to reveal a diverse and important occurrence of bacterial organisms in virtually every habitat, while marine mycologists, developing their field even more recently, are now discovering marine fungi in far greater numbers than had been anticipated only a few years ago. The marine fungi, however ubiquitous, are all of small and obscure forms, and one does not find in the sea anything comparable to our terrestrial mushrooms.

As shown in Table 2, the conspicuous and macroscopic components of the marine vegetation are all members of but five divisions (or phyla) of the "Plant Kingdom"; other divisions are represented only by microscopic organisms of principal occurrence in the plankton.

Marine Flowering Plants

Few as are the kinds of angiosperms in the marine environment, they are, nevertheless, often dominantly conspicuous. The eel grass, *Zostera marina*, is a common inhabitant of bays and estuaries on both coasts of the United States (Figure 1-4), while the receding tide on rocky shores of the north Pacific re-

FIGURE 1–4. A narrow ship's channel into the harbor of San Quintin, Baja California, is outlined by dark beds of *Zostera marina* occupying the silty shallows.

veals the emerald green masses of surf grass, *Phyllospadix*. The Gulf Coast, too, abounds in marine seed plants such as turtle grass, *Thalassia testudinum*, and manatee grass, *Syringodium filiforme*, which bed the sandy and silty shallows that formerly supported large populations of those grazing marine animals for which they are named.

Some 45 species of sea grasses are known. Although they occur widely on North American shores, they are not uniformly distributed. They are generally inhabitants of tropical and temperate waters, and only a few species extend into high latitudes. For reasons unknown they are virtually absent from the shores of South America. Their major centers of occurrence are the temperate north Pacific and north Atlantic, the Caribbean Sea, east Africa, and the tropical western Pacific.

Marine Algae

Four major groups of macroscopic algae make up most of the benthic flora: the Cyanophyta (blue-green algae), the Chlorophyta (green algae), the Phaeophyta (brown algae), and the Rhodophyta (red algae). These are all of world-wide distribution, but their numbers and proportions vary in different climates. Thus, the blue-green algae on temperate shores are mostly represented by slippery, dark films on intertidal rocks or by minute epiphytes on other larger algae, but in warmer situations and in tropical seas they form conspicuous filamentous skeins *(Lyngbya)* or spongy tufts *(Symploca)* that may be of marked abundance. Marine blue-greens, however, are of lesser significance in the marine flora than are their counterparts in the terrestrial flora.

Green algae along the open sea are of relatively minor occurrence compared with their overwhelming dominance in fresh waters. This is especially true in colder marine regions where only a few different kinds may be found in a given locality. On the other hand, species of the cosmopolitan *Ulva* and *Enteromorpha* may occur in abundance and overshadow the fact of small diversity. Marine members of the Chlorophyta show their best evolutionary development in the tropics, especially in the western Pacific, the Indian Ocean and the Caribbean region, where prominent and diversified assemblages of forms occur, many of them calcareous and of extraordinary morphology.

To most people, the brown algae are the familiar seaweeds. Not only are many of them among the largest of all the algae, but their exceeding abundance in cold northern waters has made them obvious to nearly every seashore visitor. Members of the Phaeophyta are almost exclusively marine, and wherever good algal habitats are found it is usually the "browns" that are most conspicuous, whether they be giant bladder kelps in the north Pacific, oarweeds of Scotland, or cystophoras of South Australia. Tropical regions, on the other hand, have few species, even though some of them, such as *Sargassum*, may appear as dominants.

The largest and most diversified assemblage of marine plants make up the division Rhodophyta, which numbers some 4000 members. Although red algae may now and then be encountered in fresh waters, on the seashore they are everywhere. They are the dominant, macroscopic rock-covering algae in numbers, if not always in size, in virtually all parts of the world. Except for a unique, free-floating *Antithamnion* in Australia, they are exclusively benthic, attached organisms and occupy not only all latitudes, but the entire range of depths inhabitable by autotrophic plants. The compensation point for some species, such as *Halymenia balearica* or *Fauchea repens*, may in rare instances be reached at depths as great as 175 meters, while others live far above sea level on cliffs wet only by spray from breakers or blow holes.

REFERENCES AND READING

Carson, Rachel L. 1951. *The Sea Around Us.* New York: Oxford. 230 pp.

Dawson, E. Y. 1951. A further study of upwelling and associated vegetation along Pacific Baja California, Mexico. *J. Marine Res.,* 10: 39–58.

———— 1952. Circulation within Bahia Vizcaino, Baja California, and its effects on the marine vegetation. *Am. J. Botany,* 39: 425–432.

Setchell, W. A. 1929. Morphological and phenological notes on *Zostera marina* L. *Univ. Calif. Publ. Botany,* 14: 389–452.

Sverdrup, H. U., M. W. Johnson, and R. H. Fleming. 1942. *The Oceans: Their Physics, Chemistry and General Biology.* Englewood Cliffs, N.J.: Prentice-Hall. 1087 pp.

2

Bacteria

Until 50 years ago, there was virtually no recognition that bacteria were either of wide occurrence or of significance in the sea. As late as 1939, only about 6 percent of the total number of known species of bacteria had been isolated from ocean waters or marine materials. The first monograph was Issatchenko's *Investigations on Bacteria of the Glacial Arctic Ocean* in 1914.

With Benecke's treatise on the bacteriology of the sea in 1933, the field rapidly expanded. After some 14 years of work at Scripps Institution of Oceanography, La Jolla, California, Zobell published in 1946 his *Marine Microbiology,* which has served as the principal monograph in the English language to date.

It is now recognized that bacteria are widely distributed in the sea. The inhabitable area for marine species is enormously greater than for terrestrial ones, and throughout the vast diversity of marine habitats, in the free water mass, in living organisms, and in the sediments, there may ultimately prove to be just as many species as on land. The influence of marine bacteria on chemical, geological, and biological phenomena in the sea is of major importance. They are the liberators of mineral nutrients for plants by their decomposition of marine plant and animal residues. They contribute to the regeneration of phosphate in that most important marine cycle; they transform sulfur compounds, oxidize ammonia to nitrate, and in various other ways affect the chemical composition of seawater and bottom deposits. The bacteria themselves are important food for numerous kinds of small marine animals. The distribution of oxygen in the sea is to a considerable extent influenced by their enormous consumption of this gas, probably equal to or greater than that of all other organisms combined. They are significant in the geological changes that they effect in sediments after deposition.

Notwithstanding the abundance of marine bacteria, there are few species known to be pathogenic in marine animals, and none has given evidence of causing disease in man. On the other hand, they do contribute to marine fouling and to decomposition of structural materials of organic origin submerged in the sea.

DISTRIBUTION

Marine bacteria are found everywhere in oceans and estuaries, but their frequencies vary with certain conditions. The largest populations ordinarily occur in waters along or near the shore, regardless of the temperature or the depth. Thus, shore waters may support 50,000 to 400,000 bacteria per milliliter, while open ocean waters may contain on the average about 40 bacteria per ml. as compared with 2000 per ml. in areas from 3 to 120 miles from land. The large numbers in nearshore waters are usually related to nutrients introduced by comparatively heavy runoff from the land, for along arid coasts the populations differ little from near shore to open sea. Below a depth of 200 meters, the bacterial populations become increasingly sparse until one reaches the sea floor, where vast numbers again occur in the muds at all water depths. As many as 160,000 viable bacteria per ml. have been taken from sea-floor muds in the West Indies, and these bottom dwellers are not confined to the surface sediments. Numerous bacteria have been obtained from portions of geological cores taken at depths of more than 5 meters below the surface.

Historically, some of the earliest described marine bacteria were photogenic species isolated from luminous fish, lobsters, and other materials. Later, various species were found associated with rotting kelp, oysters, various marine crustacea, and even ambergris.

The study of fish spoilage has resulted in isolation of a number of fish-decomposing species. Fish spoilage is a matter of considerable economic significance, since many of the organisms concerned are active at ordinary refrigeration temperature even in the presence of a high salt concentration. *Bacterium halophilum,* indeed, was first isolated from sea salt, and a number of species are known from the Dead Sea which reaches 10 times ocean salinities (that is, up to 35 percent).

CHARACTERISTICS

Marine bacteria have several physical characteristics that are notable. They are generally smaller than nonmarine forms. A large proportion (nearly 95 percent) are Gram-negative rods, and most of these are actively motile, flagellated forms. Cocci are infrequently encountered. Many seawater bacteria are of sedentary habit and attach themselves tenaciously to solid surfaces by means of a mucilaginous holdfast. It is possible that they find more nutrients adsorbed on solid surfaces than in free solution.

A striking characteristic of most marine bacteria that have been cultured is their color. Nearly 70 percent are pigment producers. Over 30 percent are yellow or orange; brownish, pink, and green pigments occur in lesser frequencies. A considerable number show fluorescence, usually of a greenish hue.

Marine bacteria have a wide temperature tolerance, but are generally much more sensitive to high temperatures than are most fresh-water or terrestrial forms. Most of those obtained from deep-bottom deposits in which the temperature normally never reaches above 5°C are killed in ten minutes by temperatures between 30° and 40°C. Some are quickly injured even by brief warming at 35°C, although some spores survive boiling for three hours.

The optimum temperatures for a large proportion of marine bacteria thus far cultured range between 18° and 22°C, but most remain active and may even grow slowly at 0° to 4°C. Some can multiply at temperatures as low as —11°C if the freezing point is depressed with suitable nontoxic solutes.

A high proportion of bacteria from seawater or marine muds are facultative anaerobes, but most of them apparently lose their ability to grow anaerobically after prolonged culture under aerobic conditions. Very few obligate anaerobes or obligate aerobes have been obtained from such habitats.

Some of the various kinds of marine bacteria may be mentioned as regards their special physiological properties. One of the first of these properties to be discovered was that of agar digestion by *Pseudomonas gelatica* in 1902. Many other digesters of agar have since been isolated, especially from marine algae (for example, *Flavobacterium polysiphoniae*). Other seaweed-associated species are capable of decomposing alginic acid (*Bacterium alginium*). A chitin-digesting *Bacillus* was discovered in 1905, and Zobell and Rittenberg subsequently isolated 31 of these chitinoclastic bacteria from a wide variety of marine materials.

Only a relatively few marine bacteria are able to decompose cellulose, but these are generally present in most samples of seawater and especially in bottom deposits. Zobell found only 1000 cellulose digesters per gram of sea-bottom mud in contrast with 10,000 bacteria capable of starch hydrolysis and 100,000 glucose fermenters.

Many species of marine denitrifiers are now described, and some of these may also indirectly promote the precipitation of calcium carbonate in seawater. Despite the widespread occurrence of denitrifiers in the sea, especially in bottom deposits, however, there is seldom sufficient organic matter in the environment to provide for much activity in this respect. Only a few species are capable of reducing nitrate to free nitrogen, even in the presence of abundant organic matter.

The role of bacteria in nitrification in the sea is still not well understood. The occurrence in the oceans of species of *Nitrosomas,* capable of oxidizing ammonia to nitrite, has been reported by many investigators, but it is suspected that some of these may have been terrestrial nitrifying species that had become acclimatized to the marine environment. Specifically marine species of nitrifiers are little-known, though they appear to be abundant in muds. Several hetero-trophic, fish-spoiling bacteria have been shown to produce nitrite from hydroxylamine.

The occurrence of marine nitrogen-fixing bacteria has long been suggested, but was not conclusively demonstrated until Sisler and Zobell showed in 1951 that certain hydrogenase-producing varieties of *Desulfovibrio,* widely distributed in the sea, can fix nitrogen.

Numerous autotrophic sulfur-oxidizing bacteria have been isolated from the sea since 1904, and it is reported that some of the brightly colored ones, such as *Rhodothece pendens,* may occur in such abundance in the North Sea as to give the water a milky rose-red color.

Desulfovibrio is a well-studied marine, obligate anaerobe that reduces sulfate to hydrogen sulfide and requires seawater or a comparable solution of salt for its growth. Sulfate-reducing bacteria of this genus are known particularly be-cause they are the only living things on the bottom of the Black Sea, where they are responsible for exceedingly high concentrations of hydrogen sulfide. Such sulfate reduction by anaerobic marine bacteria results in sulfur deposition, and it is generally believed that the great sulfur deposits of Sicily, Texas, and Louisiana resulted from bacterial reduction of sulfates in ancient shallow seas under conditions resembling those today in the Black Sea.

One of the aspects of marine bacteriology of wide interest has been the ability of sulfate reducers, almost universally present in marine bottom de-posits, to produce and transform hydrocarbons. For this and other reasons, these organisms are now considered to have been significant in the formation and accumulation of crude oil deposits.

Terrestrial species of bacteria commonly occur in inshore marine waters which they reach by runoff from the land and by precipitation from con-tinental air masses. Some of these species can become adapted to seawater conditions, but by and large the terrestrial forms cannot compete with marine bacteria in seawater and do not survive very long. It has long been known that seawater has marked inhibitory or even toxic effects on a variety of terrestrial microorganisms, but the nature of the bactericidal principles has not been entirely determined. Coliform bacteria introduced by sewage outfalls are not present in the ocean more than a few miles from the point of dis-charge, although they may survive for several weeks in the alimentary tracts of animals that feed in polluted waters.

SAMPLING AND CULTURE

The problems of collecting bacteriological samples at sea, particularly water samples, have led to the use of more than a hundred different devices, most of which are suitable only for collecting at the surface or in shallow water. Various kinds of metal bottles have been shown to be bactericidal. Zobell perfected in 1941 the J-Z bacteriological water sampler, which can be used with glass bottles to 200 meters, and with rubber bottles to any depth (Figure 2-1). It can be connected seriately to a standard hydrographic wire for collections concurrently at different depths. An important feature is a file-

FIGURE 2–1. Front and back view of the J–Z bacteriological sampler (after Zobell).

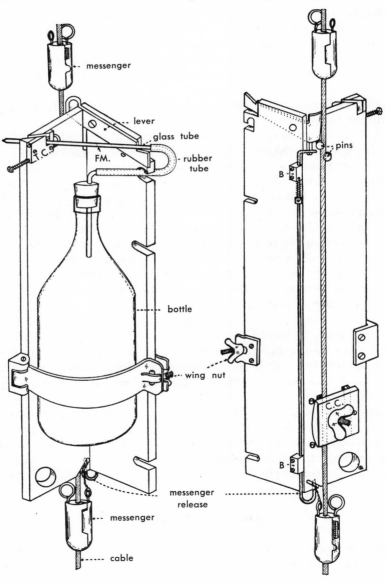

marked glass tube connected to the bottle by a bent rubber tube. When a lever, activated by the messenger, breaks the glass tube, the rubber straightens out and allows the sample to be taken at a distance sufficient to prevent it from contamination by the carrier or the cable.

Collection of mud samples presents fewer problems, for the bottom samples always contain hundreds to thousands of times as many bacteria as occur in the overlying water, and also minimize any aspects of contamination. Samples of bottom deposits may be collected with standard geological coring tubes, some of which can obtain cores 5 or more meters long.

Some kinds of marine bacteria may be collected by the simple method of submerging ordinary glass microscope slides. These may be examined by phase-contrast microscopy or by ordinary microscopy after direct staining. Special fixation methods are not always necessary. Bacteria from such slide collections may also be isolated by plating on nutrient agar.

Various kinds of nutrient media have been used for isolating marine bacteria. Ordinarily, these are prepared with seawater, for most forms grow preferentially or exclusively in seawater media. Most media successfully culture less than 1 percent of the bacteria present in a sample. The following formula developed by Zobell allows the cultivation of many marine aerobic hetero-trophs:

Bacto-peptone	5.0 grams	Bacto-agar	15 grams
Ferric phosphate	0.1 grams	Aged seawater	1000 grams

Zobell recommends that the seawater be aged in glass for several months to allow bacteria time to decompose most of the dissolved organic matter. He has found that neither artificial seawater nor isotonic salt solutions are as suitable for growing marine bacteria as natural seawater.

Some workers have reported that, after they are cultured in seawater media for several weeks or months, a considerable number of marine bacteria develop an ability to grow in fresh-water media, although attempts to acclimatize them by gradual dilution of seawater are usually unsuccessful. Generally, how-ever, they are fastidious in their salt requirements and tolerate neither increases nor decreases. Except for the specialized forms associated with salted fish or salterns, almost no marine bacteria will grow in seawater saturated with sodium chlorine.

REFERENCES AND READING

There are presently 4 key reference works in the field of marine bacteriology, as follows:

Brisou, J. 1955. *La Microbiologie du Milieu Marin.* Coll. Inst. Pasteur. Paris: Flammarion. 271 pp.

Kriss, A. E. 1963. *Marine Microbiology (Deep Sea).* New York: Interscience (Wiley). (English translation by Shewan and Kabata). 536 pp.

Oppenheimer, C. H. 1963. *Symposium on Marine Microbiology.* Springfield, Ill.: Charles C. Thomas. 769 pp.

Zobell, C. E. 1946. *Marine Microbiology.* Waltham, Mass.: Chronica Botanica Co. (Ronald). 240 pp.

3

Fungi

Although the science of marine mycology is somewhat more than 100 years old, a major part of the recorded studies of these plants have been made during the past 20 years. During the nineteenth century marine fungi were occasionally described incidentally as occurring in marine animals and in marine algae, but it was not until Petersen's 1903 work on marine phycomycetes that any significant effort was made to collect fungi in the oceans. Later, in 1934, Sparrow again focused attention on the marine phycomycetes and has continued his work to the present day. The extensive field of lignicolous marine fungi was scarcely touched until Barghoorn and Linder in 1944 reported their pioneering work. More recently, a considerable number of students have entered the field and a rapidly increasing volume of literature is accumulating. The entire subject of *Fungi in Oceans and Estuaries* has recently been summarized in a book by Johnson and Sparrow (1961).

The total number of known species of marine fungi (about 300) is but a small fraction of the known terrestrial forms (some 75,000). The occurrence of the various groups, also, is disproportionate, and the conspicuous large basidiomycetes of the land are absent. Johnson and Sparrow have given the following key characteristics of the major marine assemblages. (Various special groups such as yeasts, Actinomyces, and Ecerinids are excluded.)

KEY CHARACTERISTICS

1. Hyphae almost always present and septate; when present, the cells reproducing by budding; spores not motile 2
1. Hyphae, if present, nonseptate, except to delimit reproductive cells; but if absent, the thallus generally one-celled and holocarpic, or eucarpic with an assimilative rhizoidal system and reproductive cells; spores motile . . . . *Phycomycetes*
    2. Sexually formed spores present 3
    2. Sexually formed spores absent; reproduction usually by exogenously produced conidia . . . . *Fungi imperfecti* (Figure 3-1,*A*)
        3. Spores, usually 8 in number, produced in an ascus, and often within a conspicuous, multicellular fruiting body or ascocarp . . . *Ascomycetes*
(Figure 3-1,*B–F*)
        3. Spores produced exogenously on a short, slender filament, the basidium, or on a small cell (the single marine representative is a smut on *Ruppia*) . . . . *Basidiomycetes*

HABITATS

Marine fungi are known mainly from intertidal and shallow coastal waters where the most evident forms are the lignicolous ascomycetes. Although even these are inconspicuous and must be sought with care, they may be encountered commonly on driftwood, pilings, sunken timbers, cordage, and in the culms of marine phanerogams. Somewhat less evident during most of the year, but at certain seasons exceedingly abundant, are the phycomycetous fungi of thalloid algae. These may be partly responsible for the decline of many littoral algae at the end of a growing season, and it has been suggested that parasitic phycomycetes of diatoms may govern in part the rhythmic "blooms" of phytoplankton. Numerous species are now being found as pathogens or commensals in marine animals, and soil cores from both sandy and peaty shorelines are revealing fungal complements.

The general prevalence of fungi, especially of phycomycetes, is markedly influenced by salinity, for one finds an increasing number as his collecting progresses from higher to lower salt concentrations. A majority of species occur in salinities of 5°/∘∘ or less.

The first deep-water fungus, sampled from 200 meters, was detected in 1937. Since 1956 a number of forms have been cultured from water samples as deep as 4610 meters and from sediment samples from depths up to 3425 meters.

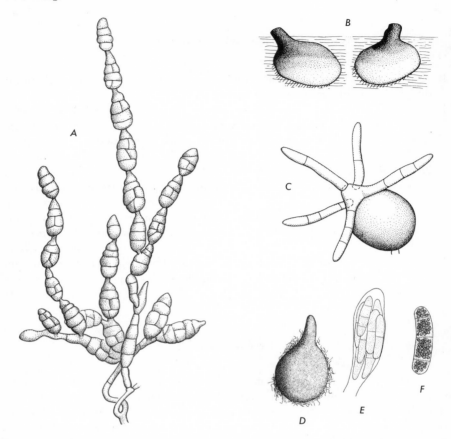

FIGURE 3–1. Reproductive structures of marine fungi. *A*, branching chains of conidia in *Alternaria maritima*, one of the fungi imperfecti. *B*, Perithecia of *Halosphaeria appendiculata* buried in a piece of wood. *C*, a conidium of *Orbimyces spectabilis* with appendages. *D–F*, *Sphaerulina codicola*, a parasite of *Codium*: *D*, perithecium; *E*, an ascus with young ascospores; *F*, a mature 3-septate ascospore. (*A–C* after Barghoorn & Linder.)

FUNGI ASSOCIATED WITH MARINE ALGAE

Although the occurrence of many fungi in marine algae may be associated with the death and decomposition of the thallus or parts of it, there is now considerable evidence that various phycomycetes are active pathogens in seaweeds. Observations of fungal infestations of such algae as *Ectocarpus*, *Striaria*, *Ceramium*, and *Seirospora* in several north-Atlantic areas have indicated that whole populations may be reduced markedly or even wiped out by fungus parasitism. In Japan these fungi have become economic pests, for destructive infection of intensively cultivated *Porphyra tenera* by a marine *Pythium* has posed a threat to the industry.

Ascomycetes and fungi imperfecti are known to occur in a number of marine algae, and in some cases appear to be parasites. *Guignardia gloiopeltidis,* which causes the "black dots disease" of economic *Gloiopeltis* in Japan, is one of these. *Sphaerulina codicola* in southern California sometimes produces an abundance of tiny, black perithecia between the utricles in *Codium* (Figure 3-1), but does not seem to affect seriously the life of the host.

Some of the most interesting and little-understood marine-plant relationships are those of algae and fungi that form "composites" such as are found in *Ulva, Prasiola,* and *Cladophora.*

In the *Ulva* composite, the fungus *Guignardia* produces perithecia in numerous, dark, wart-like eruptions in a wrinkled, thickened host thallus. The fungus develops a medullary mycelium layer and a mycelial network around algal cells and cell groups, but there is no intracellular penetration. In *Prasiola* a similar composite organization obtains, but instead of the normal division of the host cells in two planes, divisions are stimulated in three planes, so that a distinctively thickened frond results. In both cases, a symbiotic, lichenlike relationship is suggested.

The most curious of these composites is that described by Harvey in 1858 as an alga, *Blodgettia confervoides.* It has recently been shown that this is an instance of a fungus (*Blodgettiomyces*) showing constant association with an alga (*Cladophora fuliginosa*) in a manner of a lichen, even though neither thallus form nor reproduction is lichenoid (Figure 3-2).

FIGURE 3–2. *"Blodgettia confervoides,"* a fungus-alga composite: *A*, part of a plant of *Cladophora fuliginosa; B*, tip of a branch of *Cladophora fuliginosa* showing outer layers of cell wall dissected away to reveal filamentous growth of *Blodgettiomyces* within the substance of the inner wall; *C*, detail of the *Blodgettiomyces* hyphal network in the *Cladophora* wall and showing chains of spores (redrawn from Harvey).

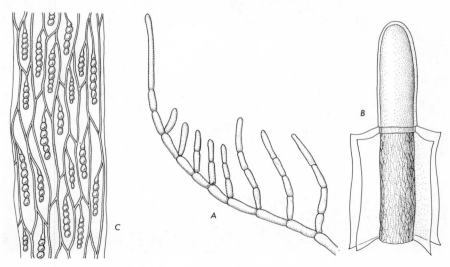

An association between *Pelvetia* and *Mycosphaerella* has also been considered as a lichen. The fungus penetrates the alga's receptacle and both fungus spores and algal eggs are discharged simultaneously.

True marine lichens also remain among the very poorly known marine plants, even though they may be the dominant vegetation at very high intertidal levels (Figure 3-3). They are predominantly saxicolous and occur for the most part in the supralittoral fringe, although some are found in midlittoral surfy regions. They are not present on all shorelines, but where they do occur, they show by their blackish covering of high rocks a most conspicuous feature of zonation. The genera *Verrucaria*, *Lichena*, and *Caloplaca* are the most widely reported.

FIGURE 3–3. Intertidal zonation in an area of consistent calm. The smooth rock slope behind the bay shows a sharp dark line of marine lichens at the highest reach of high tides (note the stranded driftwood). Below the lichens is a lighter band occupied mainly by small barnacles. This is followed by a broad, dark zone of *Fucus*. San Juan Islands, Washington.

LIGNICOLOUS FUNGI

Until the last two decades not only was the involvement of fungi in the degradation of organic material in the sea seriously doubted, but the very existence of saprobic marine fungi was questioned. In 1944 Barghoorn first suggested that some fungi are capable of enzymatic hydrolysis of lignin. This has been confirmed experimentally by Johnson, who demonstrated the penetration of wood cells by fungi and their destructive cellulolytic activity in the absence of any contaminating organisms such as bacteria. These evidences have led to the investigation of the contributions of fungi to the decomposition of cordage in the sea, and, in India, to studies of the fungus damage of catamarans and small boats, apart from the effects of marine borers. Nevertheless, the role of fungi in the decomposition of organic material in the ocean remains a neglected field of investigation largely limited to studies of wood decomposition. Even these measurements of cellulolytic activity in laboratory pure culture provide limited information on the decomposing abilities of fungi under the competitive conditions that prevail in the sea.

Lignicolous fungi are the forms most likely to be encountered by students who have limited time to seek out these obscure organisms. They are sufficiently abundant on pieces of sea-soaked wood, so that a careful examination with the dissecting microscope will often reveal the definitive, dark, superficial perithecia (Figure 3-1). These may be removed to a slide and crushed out to show the ascospores, whose septation, size, and shape are such important characters in taxonomy.

FUNGI AND MARINE ANIMALS

Because of their economic significance, the infectious fungi of several marine animals have attracted considerable study. *Ichthyosporidium* is pathogenic in herring, mackerel, and flounder, among others, forming cysts in various parts of the body and discharging spores into the blood and lymph. Mortality is sometimes very high, as evidenced by markedly depressed catches during epidemic seasons, and up to 70 percent infection is sometimes reported.

Dermocystidium marinum of oysters is another notable pathogen of commercial importance. Almost all tissues of the oyster are susceptible to invasion by this fungus, which, in advanced cases, causes the adductor muscles to lose their ability to maintain shell closure. High mortality occurs in the resulting "gapers."

The wasting disease of commercial sponges, which became epidemic in 1938–1939 throughout much of the Caribbean, is supposedly caused by the fungus known as *Spongiophaga*, but proof of pathogenicity has not yet been adequately provided.

A number of other fungi are found predominantly in invertebrates. *Lagenidium* is a virulent pathogen in the ova of blue crabs. The intestinal tracts of the sand crab, *Emerita,* are often packed with an extensive flora of fungi, and there are many hindgut commensals in marine arthropods.

YEASTS

Many yeasts and yeast-like fungi have been reported from the marine environment, but a majority of these are now considered to be nonmarine species. Others have been identified only for genus or color group. True marine yeasts, however, have been recovered from various commercial sea foods (shrimp, oysters, clams) as well as from deep-sea water and benthic sediments.

LABYRINTHULA

One of the most widely known of the marine microbes is one that cannot satisfactorily be assigned to any of the known classes of fungi. The Labyrinthulae include organisms of exceedingly rudimentary organization, consisting only of uninucleate, amoeboid "spindle cells" which glide along delicate, net-like slime ways. *Labyrinthula* has been studied widely in connection with its supposed cause of wasting disease of eel grass.

Wasting disease was first noted on the East Coast of the United States in 1930 and in France in 1931. The disease expressed itself as brown streaks in the leaves, followed by the death of the plant. *Labyrinthula* was named as the causal agent in 1936 when it was shown that infected leaves fastened to sound ones for 48 hours produced 100 percent new infection. Some workers subsequently have claimed, however, that other fungi and bacteria are the primary causal agents, and that *Labyrinthula* is a secondary invader of weakened plants. The problem is still not completely resolved. *Labyrinthula,* however, is apparently abundant and widespread, for it may often be obtained from apparently healthy *Zostera* plants simply by laying a portion of a leaf on a seawater agar plate and waiting overnight for the characteristic slimeways to appear.

REFERENCES

Barghoorn, E. S., and D. H. Linder. 1944. Marine fungi: their taxonomy and biology. *Farlowia,* 1: 395–467.

Johnson, T. W., and F. K. Sparrow. 1961. *Fungi in Oceans and Estuaries.* Weinheim: J. Cramer. 668 pp.

4

Benthic Diatoms;
Vaucheria

DIATOMS

The most ubiquitous of all the benthic marine plants are the diatoms. One will encounter no problems of tidal timing nor any of finding favorable rocky shore habitats in seeking members of this group. This is because species of attached, littoral diatoms can be found epiphytic on a great majority of drift-weed fragments and may be scraped from almost any intertidal rocky surface, as well as from pilings, floating wood, buoys, mud flats, mollusk shells, and so forth, and even from the belly of the sulphur-bottom whale! Many species have their frustules arranged in filaments so that prominent, macroscopic tufts and skeins are formed and sometimes dominate the life of the shore, covering everything with a soft, brown, filamentous growth.

The number of species that may be encountered in an intertidal locality is overwhelming. Hustedt recognized 369 species in two small mud samples from Beaufort, North Carolina, but most of our coasts have not been sampled, and there remains much exploration to be done among these abundant organisms.

Since the diversity of diatoms is so great, only a few representative types can be mentioned in this brief treatment. They are usually classified as one (Bacillariophyceae) of the three classes of the phylum (or division) Chrysophyta, although they are sometimes treated as a separate phylum (Bacillariophyta). Two major groups, namely, the Centrales and the Pennales, are recognized, distinguished by their fundamental centric or bilateral morphology. Since representatives of both groups are widely present both in fresh and in marine waters, their general study can be conducted anywhere (Figure 4-1). The Pennales show a typical elliptical outline (but include sigmoid, crescent-shaped, wedge-shaped, or nearly circular forms) and have the characteristic puncta of the silicified cell wall (frustule), arranged in series of longitudinal rows on either side of a median line. This median line sometimes includes slit-like openings through the frustule which constitute the raphe. The Centrales have, typically, a circular frustule (but include triangular and ellipsoidal forms) with the puncta and striae arranged about a central point rather than about a median line.

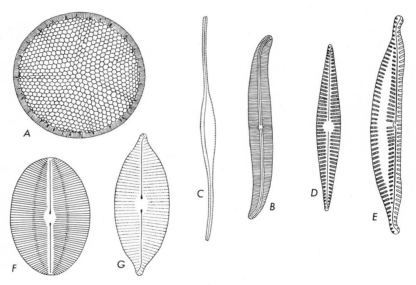

FIGURE 4–1. Varied forms of centric and pennate benthic diatoms: *A, Coscinodiscus excentricus; B, Gyrosigma beaufortianum; C, Nitzschia closterium; D, Navicula abunda; E, Amphora elegantula; F, Cocconeis latestriata; G, Achnanthes curvirostrum.*

The diatom frustule has the structure of a pillbox with a lid, consisting, thus, of two major parts. One of these parts, the epitheca, slightly overlaps the other, the hypotheca. Each of these frustule parts is composed of two or more pieces. Those corresponding to the bottom of the box and the top of the lid are called valves, while the band-like side pieces are the connecting bands which overlay to constitute the girdle (Figure 4-2). Thus, dorsal and ventral views of a diatom frustule are called valve views, and lateral views are called girdle views.

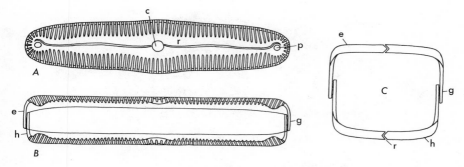

FIGURE 4-2. Valve (*A*), girdle (*B*), and cross-sectional (*C*) views of a diatom frustule (a: epitheca; h: hypotheca; r: raphe; p: polar nodule; c: central nodule; g: girdle with connecting bands).

Diatom valves are usually highly ornamented with fine lines composed of series of closely spaced puncta. These are actually minute perforations whose structure is shown by the electron microscope to be amazingly complex (Figure 4-3). *Isthmia nervosa* has been investigated by Desikachary and shown to have particularly complex pore structure. The minute puncta, which have been shown to be open pores permitting communication through the silicious frusture to the outside, are not merely perforations, but are thrice-compound areolae. Each areola consists of a primary pore subtended by a plate-like diaphragm provided with secondary pores; these, in turn, are sieve-like in containing up to eight smaller pores. A classification of the sieve-membrane structure of the areolae has included some two dozen different types among a relatively small number of species thus far investigated.

In *Isthmia,* the acute corner of a cell has a group of very small areolae through which mucilage is secreted. This mucilage pad serves to join daughter cells together after division, so that chains of many frustules may occur (Figure 4-4). Such mucilage secretion in some colonial benthic forms results in the formation of simple or compound mucilage stalks by which these forms are attached to the substrate. Sometimes the stalks are so richly branched as to form erect, bushy, macroscopic colonies. The mucilage in other forms may be more general so that large numbers of frustules embed themselves, by repeated division and continuous secretion, in branched mucilage strands that may have a morphology suggestive of a macroscopic, fleshy alga. In many of these the individual moves freely within the colonial matrix (*Schizonema*).

The cell contents of diatoms have been comparatively little studied because the characters used in identification are mostly those of the silicious frustule. Specimens to be identified are usually boiled in acid to remove internal structures thay may obscure the distinctive fine-structural features of the frustules. (Cleaned frustules of *Amphipleura* and *Pleurosigma* are employed for testing the efficiency of microscope lenses.) Nevertheless, a considerable diversity of internal structure is present in the cell, particularly in the form, position, and size of chromatophores, which range from band-shaped or stellate-lobed

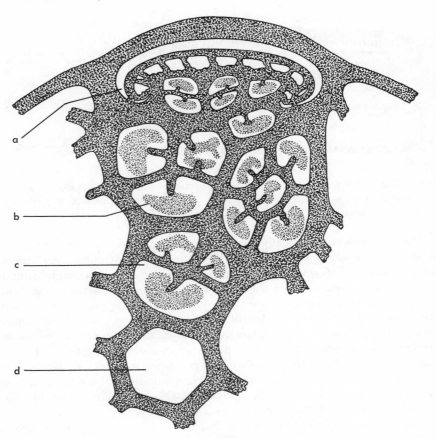

FIGURE 4–3. A single areola of *Isthmia nervosa* as reconstructed from an electron micrograph by Desikachary (a: frill-like structure of marginal secondary areola; b: kidney-shaped growth within tertiary areola; c: tertiary areola; d: secondary areola).

parietal structures to minute granules. The color of chromatophores depends in part upon the intensity of illumination and varies from brown to olive-green or yellow. Chromatophores may be studied readily by staining with 1 percent aqueous aniline blue.

One of the conspicuous internal features of the cell is the accumulation of large droplets of oil, which, as in other members of the Chrysophyta, is the usual form in which the products of photosynthesis occur. Starch granules are absent in the diatom.

The nucleus, which contains one to several nucleoli, may readily be observed by staining with weak methylene-blue solution.

The method of multiplication of diatoms is usually by cell division, in which each of the resulting cells retains one of the thecas of the parent cell and produces a new theca whose connecting band is overlapped by that of the

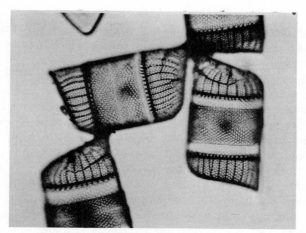

FIGURE 4–4. Several frustules of *Isthmia* joined by mucilage pads, showing comparison of 2 cell shapes, the rhombohedron and the trapezohedron, × 155 (courtesy Richard L. Steele).

parent theca. Thus, normally, although one of the progeny remains exactly the same size as the parent, the other is slightly smaller, by an amount equal to double the thickness of the connecting band. The result of this difference is the progressive decrease in size of some frustules until a critical survival size is reached. Within a certain size range above this critical limit, the diatom cell is capable of compensating for this diminution by production of what have long been called auxospores. An auxospore is produced by the emergence of the protoplast from the frustule and its expansion to the characteristic size of the species. When fully formed, the auxospore is bounded by a silicified membrane, the perizonium, within which the protoplast secretes the epitheca and hypotheca of a new vegetative cell (Figure 4-5).

FIGURE 4–5. A mature auxospore of *Isthmia* beginning to divide by shedding the perizonium, × 155 (courtesy Richard L. Steele).

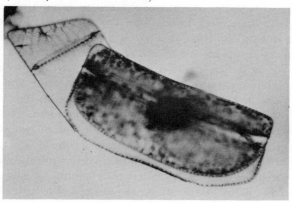

Until 1907 the auxospore was considered to be solely an asexual means of reestablishing the normal vegetative cell size. In recent decades it has been shown that auxospores result from a sexual process which may be autogamous, isogamous, anisogamous, or oögamous.

In autogamy, two nuclei formed within one mother cell fuse to initiate auxospore formation. In isogamy, one or two gametes are produced and freed from each mother cell. These fuse in pairs to form an auxospore. In anisogamy (applied in this special sense in the diatoms, in which it is apparently the most frequent condition in pennate forms), one gamete is amoeboid while the other is nonmotile. The amoeboid gamete (male) travels through a mucilage matrix, or a fusion tube, toward the female.

Within the last decade oögamy has been shown to be frequent among centric diatoms, but is reported in only one pennate diatom. The process is somewhat varied, but involves the production of either one or two eggs in an oögonium (auxospore mother cell) and from 2 to 32 sperm in a spermatocyte. One of the most recent studies of this process conducted by Steele (unpublished), serves here as an example of oögamous sexual reproduction in diatoms.

Isthmia nervosa is of widespread intertidal north-temperate occurrence in Europe and America and is one of the largest diatoms. Cells range upwards from a minimum of 61 microns (μ) to as great a length as 460 μ. The cells are usually observed in girdle view, which is the longer dimension, and two cell shapes are characteristic: a rhombohedral form and a trapezohedral form, determined by the angle of wall formation in vegetative cell division (Figure 4-4). Such division is completed in about 26 hours.

The critical survival size after vegetative division is somewhat below that for sexual reproduction (auxospore formation), for male cells are produced during size diminution from 122 to 81 μ, while female cells are produced from 132 to 114 μ. Sexual reproduction is seasonal and shows a peak in early summer, with negligible occurrences from October through May.

The sequence of events in sexual reproduction in *Isthmia* is reported by Steele as follows: The auxospore mother cell (female cell) is first recognizable when its nucleus moves to one end of the cell to leave a clear space in the cell center. Three intercalary bands then develop from the vegetative connecting band, and on the third of these a pair of large "fertilization pores" 5 to 6 μ in diameter appear, one on either broad side of the cell (Figure 4-6). This is followed by a first division of the nucleus into two nuclei, one of which aborts. The remaining nucleus divides into two, and one of these aborts to leave one large nucleus and two degenerated nuclei. These latter remain in the cytoplasm throughout auxospore development. The entire process to this point occupies about 26 hours. Meanwhile, the microspore mother cell (male cell) undergoes division and formation of a central wall separating two spermatocytes within each of which further divisions produce four seemingly uniflagellate sperm (Figure 4-7). A central spindle is observable during metaphase and anaphase. Fertilization has not been observed, but when auxospore mother cells and microspore mother cells were placed in the same culture dishes, 92 percent of the auxospore mother cells produced auxospores.

FIGURE 4–6. Part of a female cell of *Isthmia nervosa* showing the "fertilization pore" and the dovetail form of the structure around it, × 1550 (courtesy Richard L. Steele).

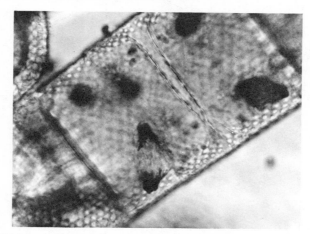

FIGURE 4–7. Division stages of the microspore mother cell in *Isthmia nervosa*, showing late anaphase or early telophase figures in the third divisions of spermatogenesis, × 625 (courtesy Richard L. Steele).

VAUCHERIA

The genus *Vaucheria* is one of the best-known filamentous algae by virtue of its long use in general botany courses as a ready example of a "green alga" with oögamous sexual reproduction. In recent years it has been demonstrated on morphological and biochemical grounds that *Vaucheria* belongs not to the Chlorophyta, but to the Xanthophyta. Accordingly, we treat it here well apart from the group with which it has traditionally been associated.

Although the plant has been widely known in the fresh-water environment, few marine occurrences were recognized until recent decades, and identifications have been handicapped by the infrequency of fertile plants. Several American workers have now reported sexual material from diverse mud-flat habitats in marine and brackish waters, and it is evident that marine vaucherias are more abundant than earlier supposed. The most detailed studies of American marine species have been conducted by Taylor and Bernatowicz on five kinds of *Vaucheria* in Bermuda. The plants occur commonly there on quiet, sandy bay bottoms, but usually are scantily in fruit. It was found that abundant fruiting could be induced by keeping them for some time in running seawater on outdoor aquarium tables. The reproductive structures show many variations on the well-known classical theme. The distinctiveness of shape, size, pedicellation, and relative position of oögonia and antheridia in two of these species is seen in Figure 4-8.

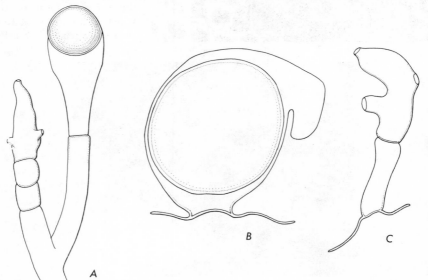

FIGURE 4–8. Mature antheridia and oögonia in *Vaucheria: A, Vaucheria bermudensis; B–C, Vaucheria nasuta* (after Taylor & Bernatowicz).

REFERENCES

Ferguson Wood, E. J. 1963. A study of the diatom flora of fresh sediments of the south Texas bays and adjacent waters. *Publ. Inst. Marine Sci.*, University of Texas, 9: 237–310.

Hustedt, F. 1955. Marine littoral diatoms of Beaufort, North Carolina. *Duke Univ. Marine Station Bull.*, (6): 1–67.

Taylor, W. R., and A. J. Bernatowicz. 1952a. Bermudan marine vaucherias of the section Piloboloideae. *Papers Michigan Acad. Sci., Arts and Letters*, 37: 75–85.

——————— 1952b. Marine species of *Vaucheria* at Bermuda. *Bull. Marine Sci. Gulf and Carib.*, 2: 405–413.

5

Phytoplankton

The term "plankton," coined by Hensen in 1887, does not refer to any definitive group of organisms, but denotes collectively all freely floating and suspended bodies, both plant and animal, living and dead, that essentially move passively in a body of water. The size of the body of water is not significant, for plankton organisms occur in rain puddles, in seashore splash pools, in streams and rivers, in lakes and inland seas, and in the oceans. Individually, the bodies are plankters or planktonts. The plant components are known as phytoplankton and, with a few fresh-water exceptions, all are algae of several different phyla (see Table 2 in Chapter 1). They are almost exclusively microscopic forms and, except for instances of heavy blooms causing water discoloration or nighttime luminescence, are ordinarily not conspicuous to the naked eye.

The great significance of phytoplankton organisms to the world's organic economy lies in their occurrence in the sea, where their minute size belies their importance. Compared with less than a mere 1 percent of sea-surface area suitable for attachment of the conspicuous benthic plants, are the vast "meadows of the oceans." These constitute some two-thirds of the surface of the earth; throughout them the minute photosynthetic phytoplankters are making enormous contributions to the world's supply of organic matter.

SAMPLING

The small size of phytoplankton cells has always presented special problems in the collection of samples. The plankton net, the primary item of standard equipment, is made of fine silk bolting cloth (number 20 or 25) with mesh openings of 0.040–0.076 millimeters. A small vial is attached to the end of the net. This allows the algal cells to be collected by a little sloshing of a concentration within the net obtained by drawing it through the water. This method provides only the grossest qualitative collections, however, as it has been shown to be ineffective for obtaining many of the smaller cells, and even with the most careful use may succeed in retaining only 1 to 10 percent of the phytoplankters of a given sample of water. One improvement to the simple net is the Clarke and Bumpus plankton sampler, which provides a measurement of the volume of water strained through the net.

More complete and quantitative samples must be obtained by settling, by centrifuging, or by filtering. A method of obtaining virtually complete collections from a known volume of water without damage to the smallest living cells was devised recently by Allen. It uses a pair of telescoping plastic cylinders, filter paper, and a siphon (Figure 5-1).

Preservation of most plankton samples for ordinary examination may be accomplished by adding 10 to 15 parts of commercial formalin per 100 parts of seawater sample. For cytological purposes, the Gran and Angst preservative may be used, consisting of a solution of 5 milliliters of formalin, 5 ml of glacial acetic acid, and 40 ml of seawater diluted to 100 ml by the plankton sample. No universal fixative satisfactory for all types of plankton has yet been devised, however, and many forms are lost in the preservative.

Plankton samples may also be provided with nutrient media and maintained in living culture. Allen's formula consists of

NaCl	0.5 M	$CaCl_2$	0.01 M
$MgSO_4$	0.05 M	$NaNO_3$	0.02 M
KCl	0.01 M	Agar	1.5 percent (if desired)

micronutrient mix 2 ml/l, in which 2 ml contains Fe 4.0 mg; Mn 0.5 mg;
    Zn 0.05 mg; Cu 0.02 mg; B 0.5 mg; Mo 0.01 mg; V 0.01 mg.
K_2HPO_4 0.001 M (autoclaved separately)
soil extract 50 ml/l (obtained by autoclaving and filtering an equal
    mixture of water and fertile loam)

Although representatives of Chlorophyta, Cyanophyta, and Euglenophyta may occur in marine phytoplankton, the principal components are members of the Chrysophyta and Pyrrophyta. Of these, the diatoms and dinoflagellates, respectively, are ordinarily by far the most conspicuous, although often they are outnumbered by other kinds of nannoplankton (see below). They illustrate two of the principal modes of coping with the pelagic environment and of maintaining a position in the euphotic zone. The diatoms have succeeded

FIGURE 5–1. The Allen live-plankton filter in operation on shipboard. The large plastic cylinder is provided with seawater dipped by bucket from the collecting area. An inner plastic ring is fitted with filter paper and weighted with a lead wire. This slowly sinks as the water is filtered upwards and the plankton concentrated undamaged at the bottom. The filtrate is siphoned off with a rubber tube (photo by Don Ollis).

through various developments of both morphological and physiological modifications for flotation. The dinoflagellates also may possess morphological flotation devices, but they are in most instances capable of sufficient flagellar motility to maintain themselves within the surface waters.

The term nannoplankton has come into general use to designate members of any of diverse groups which are so small as to pass through ordinary phytoplankton-collecting nets. Some of the nannoplankton consists of small dinoflagellates and diatoms, but coccolithophorids are often abundant, and various microflagellates occur, some of them only 1 to 3 μ in diameter (*Micromonas pusilla*, Figure 7-21). Despite their minute size, these nannoplankton organisms may occur in such vast numbers as to be of major importance in the productivity of the sea. One investigation in the Coral Sea revealed that 90 percent of the producers were nannoplankton.

THE RED-WATER OR RED-TIDE PHENOMENON

The most striking evidence of the abundance of microorganisms in the sea is provided by those occasions on which the numbers of phytoplankters become so great as to discolor the water to a reddish, brownish, or yellowish hue. The daytime coloration is commonly coupled at night with brilliant luminescence. Such occurrences are the result of an exceptional "bloom" of diatoms or dinoflagellates whereby concentrations reach 500,000 to 2 million cells per liter. In some regions the phenomenon occurs fairly frequently and is known as red tide. Other regions may have rare occurrences accompanied by devastating mass mortality of marine organisms. Such mass mortality of fishes, crustacea, mollusks, and other invertebrates has called sharp attention to these occurrences in several regions: the southwest coast of India, southwest Africa, southern California, Florida, Peru, and Japan. In the 1947 red-tide disaster in Florida, the number of dead fish was estimated at a half-billion.

Red-water mortality is usually caused by dinoflagellates of the genera *Gymnodinium* and *Gonyaulax,* which produce a water-soluble toxin that acts specifically upon the nervous system. The principal occurrences are in regions where a high concentration of nutrients is combined, at least temporarily, with a sufficiently high temperature. Brongersma-Saunders in 1948 tabulated a great many records of this phenomenon and showed that the occurrences are in the high-production areas of low and moderate latitudes, especially in regions of upwelling. She concluded that the heavy deposition of organic materials in upwelling areas, particularly from incidents of mass mortality, have contributed to the formation of petroleum.

PLANKTON DIATOMS

Plankton diatoms are mainly pelagic species that live and reproduce normally near the surface of the ocean. Occasionally, attached, benthic diatoms may be dislodged and appear by chance in plankton samples, but with very few exceptions they do not reproduce there. Among the pelagic species are those neritic ones that occur regularly in coastal waters, while those of open ocean situations are called oceanic. Neritic species often go through a resting spore stage in which they sink to the bottom or into deeper water and remain for several months until conditions are favorable for their germination and transport to the surface.

Structurally, the plankton diatoms have the same, bivalvulate frustule as the benthic ones mentioned in Chapter 4, but their cells are modified in a number of ways favorable to flotation and to absorption of nutrients. In *Fragilaria,* a flattening of the frustule increases the surface-volume ratio, and an adherence of cells in long, ribbon-like colonies provides a kind of flotation advantage, especially during periods of vertical mixing. In *Rhizosolenia* the individual cells are exceedingly attenuated, hair-like structures with a high surface-volume ratio favorable to nutrient absorption. They often have curved or beveled tips that serve to provide horizontal orientation in flotation. A more elaborate flotation modification is seen in *Chaetoceros,* in which four long, hair-like appendages are produced from each cell and the cells in turn are organized in chains (Figure 5-4,*A*).

Physiological adaptations for flotation of diatoms may be recognized in the storage of oil droplets, in the production of gases, in the secretion of mucus, and in the extrusion of protoplasmic threads from the frustule. In *Ethmodiscus,* in which the cell wall and protoplast are but thin membranes around a relatively large cavity filled with fluid of nearly the same specific gravity as seawater, it has been shown that a reduction in the ionic content of the cell sap provides a buoyance mechanism. Other experiments indicate that the physiological condition of the cell during spring, when nutrients are abundant and growth is rapid, produces a lower sinking rate. On the other hand, with depletion of nutrients and aging of the surface bloom, settling increases until a level is reached at which nutrient supply is sufficient to retard further sinking and to maintain the plants until vertical mixing again carries them up to the surface waters.

Cupp's work (1943) on the "Marine Plankton Diatoms of the West Coast of North America" provides abundant illustrations of the diverse forms of these organisms and is one of the few handbooks for identification. Since oceanic phytoplankton does not seem to differ greatly from region to region, the work may also serve well in the north Atlantic.

OTHER PLANKTONIC CHRYSOPHYTA

Other than the diatoms (Bacillariophyceae), three assemblages of organisms in the Chrysophyta occur in the marine phytoplankton: Chrysophyceae, Coccolithophorineae, and Silicoflagellatophycidae. All of these microflagellates are taxonomically in a state of flux, for they have remained little known until recent years of electron microscopy, which is now rapidly elucidating their obscure characters. The systematics is already becoming so refined that it is now necessary to employ an electron microscope to identify many of these minute plants to the species. All of these groups are important in the nannoplankton, and it is becoming evident that their combined biomass is so much greater than was earlier supposed, that of all marine organisms the Chrysophytes may prove to be the most important in the oceanic economy. The Coccolithophorids alone have been shown to make up 45 percent of the total phytoplankton in middle latitudes in the south Atlantic.

The Chrysophyceae were traditionally classified by the number and length of flagella, but current studies by Parke and associates at Plymouth are providing refinements based upon submicroscopic structure and biochemical composition. The presence of various kinds of scales on the cell body and on the flagella has been revealed. Differences in the type of flagellar structure are now observable, and the presence of vestigial flagella not previously known permit recognition of evolutionary series.

It was recognized only a few years ago that many Chrysophyta have life histories that include both motile and nonmotile phases, but that some of these organisms can be kept indefinitely in either their motile or nonmotile phase, depending upon external conditions. The phase assumed is apparently not genetically controlled. Such remarkable discoveries have pointed up numerous inadequacies in the system of classification of these plants and are now calling for widespread taxonomic reappraisal.

The marine chrysophyte genus most intensively studied in recent years is *Chrysochromulina*. Numerous species have been described from the sea off Plymouth, England, by the team of Parke, Manton, and Clarke. The living morphologies of these have been studied in detail with the light microscope, and their ultrastructure has been examined with the electron microscope. Figures 5-2 and 5-3 show some of the structural details this team of scientists has worked out in *Chrysochromulina pringsheimii.*

The Coccolithophorineae have an interesting history, for the coccoliths were originally described as minute carbonate discs in cretaceous deposits and thought to be of inorganic origin. Later they were found in sea-bottom oozes brought up for the first Atlantic Cable survey in 1858. Their algal nature was not recognized until 1898.

It is now known that the coccoliths, which range from 1 to 35 μ in diameter, are really calcium carbonate plates produced by biflagellate algae with pigments relating them to the Chrysophyta (Figure 5-4,*E–F*). Two different categories of coccoliths have been recognized, depending upon their crystalline structure, and a system of classification is based upon them. *Coccolithus pelagicus* bears up to 30 of these plates of one kind on a mature cell, and in some species two different forms of coccoliths may occur on a single cell. In 1960, however, Parke and Adams discovered that the life history of a single species of coccolithophorid includes a motile phase with one kind of coccolith and a nonmotile phase with the other. This has called again for a revision of the classification of the group. Some of the recently successful cultures of these organisms have come from bottom samples in very deep water, suggesting the occurrence of resting stages resistant to conditions in the deep sea.

Another group of marine nannoplankton first recognized from cretaceous strata, and still represented to a large extent by fossil specimens, is the Silicoflagellatophycidae. Skeletons of these silicoflagellates occur frequently in diatomaceous-earth deposits of southern California. They were early considered to be diatoms, but are now known to be flagellated plants with an internal silicious skeleton and with brown plastids relating them to the Chrysophyta (Figure 5-4,*G*).

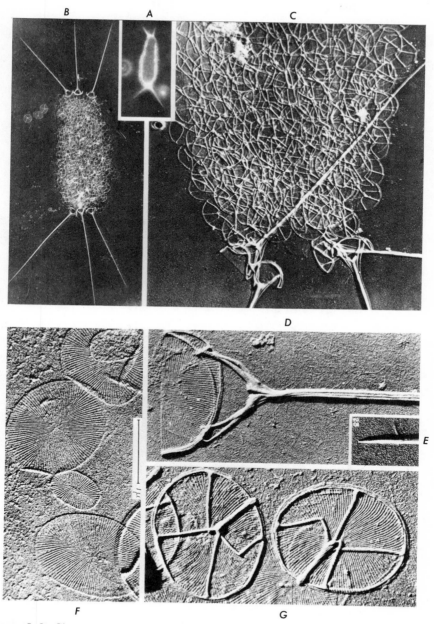

FIGURE 5–2. *Chrysochromulina pringsheimii:* A, an empty case seen in a liquid mount under dark-ground illumination with the light microscope, × 1000; B, a dried empty case as revealed by the electron microscope, × 2000; C, one end of the same, × 7000; D–E, a large spine with folded base plate, × 30,000; F, a group of plate scales showing the 2 sizes, × 30,000; G, two of the smaller spined scales, × 30,000 (courtesy of Mary Parke and Irene Manton).

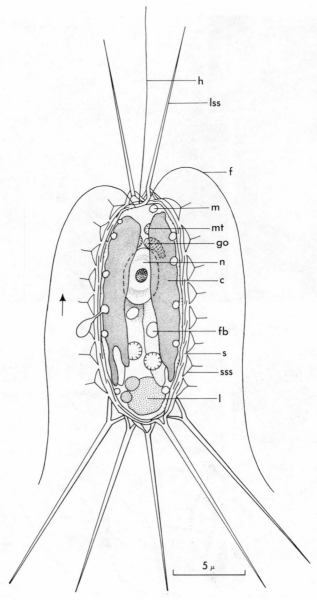

FIGURE 5–3. *Chrysochromulina pringsheimii* as reconstructed from electron micrographs (h: haptonema; lss: long-spined scale; f: flagellum; m: muciferous body; mt: mitochondrion; go: golgi; n: nucleus; c: chromatophore; fb: lipid globule; s: plate scale; sss: small-spined scale; l: chrysose (leucosin) (after Parke & Manton).

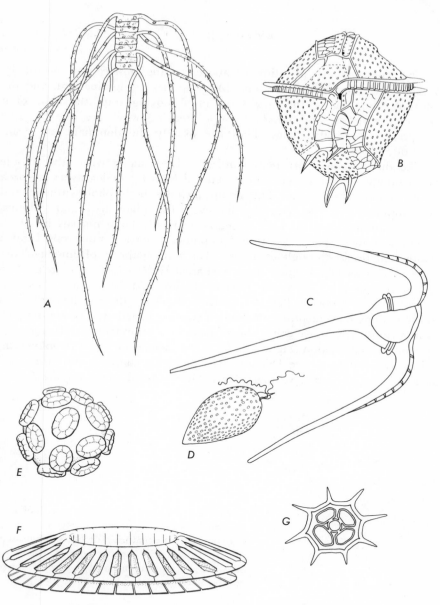

FIGURE 5-4. Various kinds of phytoplankton organisms: *A,* the diatom *Chaetoceras tetrastichon,* showing a chain of 3 frustules, each with long setae (after Cupp); *B,* the armored dinoflagellate *Ceratocorys aulti,* in ventral view (after Graham); *C,* the armored dinoflagellate, *Ceratium horridum; D,* the naked dinoflagellate, *Prorocentrum micans; E,* a coccolithophorid, *Pontosphaera huxleyi,* showing arrangement of coccoliths; *F,* model of a single coccolith of *Pontosphaera huxleyi* based upon investigations with the electron microscope (after Braarud et al.); *G,* a silicoflagellate, *Distephanus crux* var. *octacanthus.*

PYRROPHYTA

The dinoflagellates, as intimated above, are the most conspicuous of the plankton organisms for two reasons. Many species are luminescent, and the nighttime sparkling of the bow wave of a moving ship, the glow of a swimming porpoise, and the flash of a breaking wave are due to large populations of dinoflagellates. They are usually the dominant organisms in red-tide blooms.

The dinoflagellates are motile unicells. They, along with other motile photosynthetic organisms, have been claimed both by zoologists as protozoa and by botanists as algae. The group includes both photosynthetic and heterotrophic forms. Structurally, however, the pigmented and colorless forms are similar, and all have a characteristically large nucleus in which the chromosomes appear as if in "prophase," showing numerous beaded threads that persist throughout mitosis. The great majority of dinoflagellates (those classed as Dinokontae) have a characteristic organization related to the insertion of the two ventral flagella (Figure 5-5). The longer flagellum emerges from a groove called the sulcus and pushes the cell forward by a kind of sculling movement from behind. The other flagellum is ribbon-shaped, lies in a transverse groove called the girdle (which encircles the cell), and provides for rotating motion (Figure 5-4,*B*). A few members of the Pyrrophyta, including *Prorocentrum* in the Desmokontae, lack this characteristic girdle and sulcus orientation and have their flagella inserted anteriorly (Figure 5-4,*D*).

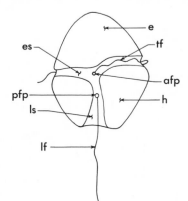

FIGURE 5–5. Diagram of a generalized dinoflagellate cell (*Gymnodinium*) in ventral view (e: epicone; h: hypocone; es: equatorial sulcus; ls: longitudial sulcus; afp: anterior flagellar pore; tf: transverse flagellum; pfp: posterior flagellar pore; lf: longitudinal flagellum).

In some dinoflagellates the cells are naked and so fragile that many species are known only from drawings made during the fading life of the organism that disintegrated on the study slide at death. Most, however, have their protoplast enclosed by a heavy cellulose wall which is often composed of a number of plate-like parts, some of which may be elaborated into projecting spines or wings (Figure 5-4,*C*). The number, arrangement, and form of the plates are commonly used in classification.

The photosynthetic species are of extraordinarily varied colors, although most are yellow-brown or yellow-green. The pigments may be dissolved in the cytoplasm, in definite vacuoles (called pursules), or they may occur in chromatophores variously shaped as discs, rods, or stars. Storage products are starch or oils. The latter may form brightly colored droplets of red or yellow.

Some of the heterotrophic species are holozoic and may feed upon other dinoflagellates. Some have nematocysts resembling those of coelenterates.

Reproduction is ordinarily by cell division in which the fission line always passes through the point of insertion of the flagella. In some cases the fission divides the cellulose wall into two halves. These are retained by the daughter cells that regenerate the missing part. In others, such as *Peridinium*, the old cell develops a break along the girdle from which the protoplast emerges as a naked cell before dividing into two daughter cells, each of which develops a complete new wall. A reproductive peculiarity currently being studied is the striking resemblance of the emergent naked cell to free-living, nonarmored dinoflagellate genera such as *Gymnodinium*. The improvement of culture methods has made possible the study of morphological types that can be changed from one "species" to another and are necessitating revision of the classical taxonomy.

Sexual reproduction is almost unknown in the group, having been established for only two of the thousand-odd species, and there are many questions to be answered here.

PLANKTONIC CYANOPHYTA

The occurrence of blue-green algae in the phytoplankton is generally inconspicuous, although a number of species are reported, especially in coastal waters. Some of these seem to be bottom-dwelling, filamentous plants that are periodically brought into the upper water layers where they sometimes flourish to produce prominent blooms. Such abundance of the red *Trichodesmium erythraeum* is responsible for the name of the Red Sea. Other kinds of *Trichodesmium* (and *Katagnymene*) occur in tropical oceanic waters very low in dissolved nitrogen compounds, and some, such as *T. thiebautii*, from the Sargasso Sea, seem to be able to fix molecular nitrogen.

PLANKTONIC CHLOROPHYTA

Unlike the situation in fresh waters, in which a great variety of motile and nonmotile Volvocales, Chlorococcales, and Desmidiaceae occur in the plankton, marine planktonic green algae are generally uncommon, especially in the open ocean. A number of flagellated, unicellular forms are, however, abundant in certain inshore habitats such as high, warm tidepools, especially those polluted by sea-bird droppings or seal excrement. In such places *Platymonas* and *Stephanoptera* may form a greenish soup. A conspicuous one is *Dunaliella salina,* which is widespread in high, briny tidepools and on salt flats where it imparts a bright red color to the ponds. Species of *Dunaliella,* and other of these flagellate, unicellular green algae widely tolerant of temperature, salinity, and nutrient changes, are being employed as experimental culture organisms in aerospace laboratories.

FACTORS CONTROLLING PHYTOPLANKTON POPULATIONS

It has already been pointed out that only a relatively thin surface layer of ocean water is in the euphotic zone. At varying depths, down to a maximum of 100 meters, sufficient light may penetrate to sustain photosynthetic plants. At such depths the light is reduced to about 1 percent of the surface intensity. Within this euphotic zone the life of the phytoplankter cell is dependent upon the light-absorptive capacity of its pigments. Absorption spectra have been obtained for natural phytoplankton populations in the water off Woods Hole, Massachusetts. These and action spectra of photosynthesis for some cultures of marine phytoplankton organisms, together with data on the penetration of light in seawater, have led to estimation of the action spectra at different depths. Thus, the absorption of red light by chlorophyll is limited to the upper 10 meters, while its blue-light absorption is effective down to 50 meters. Below 50 meters, carotenoid pigments are the principal absorbers. The plankter's utilization of light, however, depends upon the light intensity, which fluctuates seasonally and geographically, and which varies with the turbidity and the amount of plankton contained in the water. At the same time, the plankters are capable of adaptation to ambient light intensities by developing "sun" characteristics and "shade" characteristics affecting their photosynthetic capacities.

Although most chemical elements needed by plants are overabundant in the sea, others may be reduced by phytoplankton blooms in the surface waters to the point that plant production is limited. Thus, the supply of essential nitrate or phosphate, normally present in small amounts, may become limiting as a result of organic combination. Replenishment of the supply occurs from decomposition of organic matter and the redistribution of the nutrients to surface water by means of upwelling or other vertical circulation. Although it was once supposed that the decomposition occurred in bottom deposits, it is now recognized that such organic breakdown takes place throughout the water column, releasing phosphate, nitrite, nitrate, and ammonia, all of which may be used as nutrient sources by phytoplankton. They also may use animal excretions of urea, uric acid, and amino acids as nitrogen sources in the marine nitrogen cycle.

The recycling of nutrients by phytoplankton is sometimes very rapid. It has been determined that phosphate may be recycled as many as 16 times within a period of only two months.

A few other substances may be limiting to the growth of phytoplankton. Silicon, which in the form of silicate is a requirement for diatoms, may limit growth as well as the thickness of the cell wall. Iron is essential to all organisms containing cytochrome, and manganese is needed under certain circumstances. Vitamin B^{12} is known to be required by many.

The very nature of the planktonic existence, in which water movements control the position of the organism in the medium, implies the primary importance of circulation in the phenomenon. Thus, horizontal transport by surface currents carries plankton from one region to another with the result that more favorable or less favorable temperature or nutrient conditions are encountered for various species and lead to consequent changes in the composition of the moving flora. Of particular importance to the plankton populations of different regions, however, are the several kinds of vertical currents that provide replenishment of nutrients. The most prominent of these are the upwelling movements that result in the open sea from divergence of surface currents and in coastal waters from offshore surface currents produced by prevailing winds. In both cases, cooler, nutrient-rich water is brought to the surface. Such regions have long been recognized for the richness of their floras and consequent faunas. In other areas, in which upwelling is not a factor, turbulence may serve to maintain supplies of nutrients in the surface waters, but, on the other hand, may also transport plants below the compensation depth and effectively limit phytoplankton populations. In the absence of upwelling or of appreciable turbulence, insolation may create temperature layering of the water in which the thermocline forms an effective barrier to renewal of nutrient supplies.

A further factor of importance to phytoplankton populations is the grazing pressure of zooplankton. It was earlier observed that large concentrations of phytoplankton and zooplankton are seldom encountered at the same time, and this was explained by saying that the zooplankters reduce the plants by grazing, or that they avoid heavy phytoplankton populations. The rapidity with which a phytoplankton bloom can develop within a few days, however, and the fact that relatively light grazing may profoundly affect the resulting population after a few cell divisions, provides a complex picture in which the peaks of abundance need not be expected to coincide. Thus, an initial population of 100 plants would produce 6400 individuals in six divisions if there were no grazing, while if only 20 percent were consumed at each division by zooplankton, the net result would be only 1692 individuals.

The extent of grazing may commonly be limited by the size and shape of a phytoplankter cell in relation to the esophagus of the animal feeding upon it. Many diatoms, for example, are too large or unsuitably constructed to be eaten by the prevalent zooplankton.

PRODUCTIVITY OF THE SEA

The interaction of the several factors mentioned above results in the "productivity" of the marine environment. This term, however, has varied meanings. *Primary productivity* best denotes the rate of organic synthesis by the phytoplankton, while *gross primary production* is the resulting quantity of the yield. In addition, there is production throughout the food chain, whether related to zooplankton, fish, or whales (Figure 5-6).

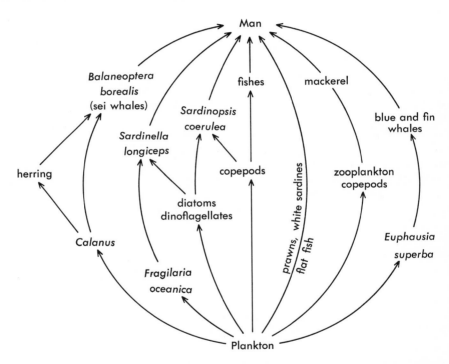

FIGURE 5–6. Diagram of some of the numerous food chains extending from the plankton base to man (after Desikachary).

In earlier studies of the magnitude of plant production in the sea, three indirect considerations were traditionally involved in making determinations: 1) the size of the standing crop, which is the momentary census of individuals in a given area; 2) the fact that certain ingredients in the water, such as phosphorus or nitrogen, show a correlation with the amount of activity of the phytoplankton; and 3) the fact that a difference between the oxygen evolved from the photosynthesis of a population and the oxygen consumed by its respiration is a measure of the gross production.

Primary production has been determined more recently by direct measurement of photosynthesis of the phytoplankton. The so-called "light and dark bottle oxygen method," in which photosynthesis is deduced from the amount of oxygen produced by phytoplankton during a given time, has been most extensively employed. A more sensitive method of measuring photosynthesis, and one now widely used, was developed by Steeman-Nielsen on the Galathea Expedition (1950–1952) exploring the oceans of the world. This is known as the carbon-14 method, in which a water sample, after the addition of a definite amount of Carbon 14 in the form of carbonate, is exposed to light for a given time. After exposure, the water sample is filtered, and the amount of Carbon 14 fixed in the phytoplankton cells is determined as a measure of photosynthesis.

Another important kind of production measurement is that of the amount of chlorophyll in the ocean water. This gives a measure of the standing crop of phytoplankton. Refinements in both the chlorophyll and the Carbon-14 techniques, especially the incorporation of corrections for various ecological factors, are together bringing advancement in the study of primary production in the sea.

Although it was long supposed that tropical oceans are generally areas of low production, it is now evident that this is not so, and that there is no great latitudinal difference. Whereas there are marked seasonal differences in the production in high latitudes and greater summer concentrations in surface waters, the compensation depth is greater in the tropics, and the total annual production in the entire water column may be just as great.

Comparisons of the organic production in the sea and on land have generally well substantiated the sea as the preponderant producer of the earth. When values for organic production are converted to tons of dry plankton per acre, one obtains figures of up to 10 tons, with about 3.2 tons as an average yield in many nearshore areas. These compare more than favorably with terrestrial agricultural yields in which fresh weight production of grain, corn, or sugar-beet crops are between 2 and 13 tons per acre. Notwithstanding this favorably large marine production, man gains proportionally little from it, for he harvests only a fraction of 1 percent of the production from even the most intensively fished areas and takes nothing at all from many vast areas of open water.

Although the "pioneer" era of productivity studies of the last half-century is over, we still know remarkably little about the chemical composition of phytoplankton or of their nutritive value. In other words, we have yet to answer the question: How well and by what organisms are the plant cells being utilized in the food chain? Further, there is a severe shortage of knowledge of the nutritional requirements of marine zooplankters, of their grazing habits and filtering rates. Another little-pursued line of investigation is the contribution of algae to the presence of detritus in seawater and, especially, of dissolved organic matter. This may prove to be the most important contribution as a source of essential growth factors to supplement the solid diets of zooplankters. All of these matters have an important bearing on the whole marine food cycle of this planet and call for a great deal of research from many approaches.

We must admit that the oceans are still a wild habitat, which man has only begun to utilize and to cultivate. Accordingly, they contribute relatively little as yet to the support of the world's population. We have changed the nature of the land by control and cultivation, while our use of the sea is still primarily limited to the pursuit of wild game. Marine biology and oceanography, however, are rapidly pushing back the frontiers, and we are entering now upon a phase of development and conservation of marine resources that will vastly increase their usefulness to man. Much of that development will be derived from studies of the phytoplankton, which forms 99.9 percent of the photosynthetic base of the food pyramid in the sea.

REFERENCES

Brongersma-Sanders, Margaretha. 1948. The importance of upwelling water to vertebrate paleontology and oil geology. *Kon. Ned. Ak. Wet., Verh. Afd. Nat.* (Tweede Sectie), 45 (4): 1–112.

Cupp, Easter E. 1943. Marine plankton diatoms of the west coast of North America. *Bull. Scripps Inst. Oceanogr.,* University of California, La Jolla, 5: 1–238.

Desikachary, T. V. 1962. Biology of phytoplankton. Darjeeling: *Proc. Summer School of Botany,* 1960: 69–76.

Doty, M.S. (Ed.) 1962. Proceedings of the conference on primary productivity measurement, marine and fresh-water, held at University of Hawaii Aug. 21–Sept. 6, 1961. *U.S. Atomic Energy Comm.,* Div. Tech. Inform., Dept. Commerce, Washington. ix + 237 pp.

Graham, H. W. 1942. Studies in the morphology, taxonomy and ecology of the Peridiniales. *Carnegie Inst. Wash. Publ.* (542): v + 129 pp.

Hasle, Grethe R. 1959. A quantitative study of phytoplankton from the equatorial Pacific. *Deep-Sea Res.,* 6: 38–59.

Kofoid, C. A., and O. Swezy. 1921. The free-living unarmored dinoflagellata. *Mem. Univ. Calif.,* 5: 1–538.

Parke, Mary. 1961. Some remarks concerning the class Chrysophyceae. *British Phyc. Bull.,* 2: 47–55.

Parke, Mary, and Irene Adams. 1960. The motile *Crystallolithus hyalinus*. . . and non-motile phases in the life history of *Coccolithus pelagicus*. . . *J. Marine Biol. Assoc. U. K.,* 39: 263–274.

Parke, Mary, and Irene Manton. 1962. Studies on marine flagellates VI. . . . *J. Marine Biol. Assoc. U. K.,* 42: 391–404.

6

Blue-green Algae (Cyanophyta)

CHARACTERISTICS

Although the most prevalent occurrences of the blue-green algae are in fresh-water, terrestrial, and aerial habitats, these plants are ubiquitous and widely adapted to diverse brackish and strictly marine environments. They are usually inconspicuous in the marine benthos compared with the larger and more abundant green, brown, and red algae, but they are sufficiently abundant that almost any collection from a marine area will contain some of them. The total number of autonomous marine species is estimated at more than double that of strictly terrestrial ones.

Whereas the other benthic algal groups contain a great range of forms, from very simple unicells or filaments to highly complex thalli, the marine blue-greens are clearly circumscribed by their low state of cell differentiation and thallus organization. Nothing more complex than a branched, uniseriate filament occurs, and there is a general absence of clearly differentiated reproductive organs. All the plants are individually microscopic. The simpler members are unicellular, but are usually aggregated in mucilaginous, palmelloid colonies. Most of the species occur as simple, uniseriate filaments, commonly within a stratified and colored mucilaginous or gelatinous sheath. The cells are usually provided with bluish-green pigments, although purplish and reddish forms are not rare. Nuclear differentiation is of a very low order, and no certain evidence of sexual reproduction has been obtained. There are no flagellated reproductive elements in the group.

The blue-green algae give the impression of being an archaic assemblage of plants, and although there are few, if any, certain records of fossil examples (for lack of hard parts readily preserved), there are widespread evidences of their occurrence in some of the oldest proterozoic strata. These take the form of calcareous and silicious deposits of tufa, marl, and sinter that evidently represent mineral precipitates by ancient filamentous colonies similar to those well-known today in hot-springs environments.

There are no indications of close relationships of Cyanophyta with any other group of plants. The blue-green algae resemble bacteria in lacking organized nuclei and in the manner of cell division by constriction or by centripetal membrane formation through the protoplast. The bluish pigment, c-phycocyanin, sets them chemically apart from most other plant groups, although the occurrence of slightly different r-phycocyanin in red algae suggests, together with other characters, a remote evolutionary connection.

Apart from any possible phylogenetic relationship, there are a number of instances of parallel morphological development between the primitive cyanophytes and the green algae. Some examples of these are seen in *Lyngbya* and *Hormidium*, *Chroococcus* and *Pleurococcus*, *Stigonema* and *Wittrockiella*.

The methods of reproduction in blue-green algae are generally simple and very largely vegetative, although endospores and akinetes occur in a number of genera. In addition to simple cell division, a more specialized kind of vegetative multiplication occurs in some of the filamentous groups in which hormogonia are formed. These are short lengths of trichomes with rounded ends and without cellular differentiation. They characteristically show a gliding motion which may be as fast as 2 to 5 μ per second. The hormogonium, upon coming to rest, grows directly into a new trichome. Hormogonia are formed in some genera by fragmentation of the trichomes between intercalary heterocysts (enlarged cells with thickened end walls) (Figure 6-4,*A*). In other instances, occasional cells become modified and moribund to form points of separation, or the hormogonia may break off terminally.

Heterocysts of other kinds and positions than those that function in hormogonium formation occur in filamentous forms, but their functions are not yet understood despite numerous hypotheses.

A more specialized reproductive method in various filamentous forms is through resting spores (akinetes). These oblong, cylindrical, or spherical cells, with thickened walls and with crowded food reserves, may be solitary or in series, often in close association with a heterocyst. Although akinetes may be capable of germinating soon after being formed, they are commonly very resistant to desiccation and temperature extremes, and may germinate only after a resting period. The extraordinary capacity for survival is indicated by the rejuvenation of a specimen of *Nostoc* after 87 years on an herbarium shelf.

Another method of spore reproduction in cyanophyte groups is by non-resistant endospores. These usually arise within a somewhat enlarged or differentiated cell by successive division of the protoplast in three planes. The endospores serve for direct propagation, are usually spherical and naked at time of liberation, and do not undergo a resting period.

The taxonomy of blue-green algae has been extraordinarily complicated by the remarkably wide geographic ranges of these plants, their extreme adaptability, and their morphological variability. Some investigators have been inclined to describe as distinct species numerous variations of a single plant, in evident disbelief in its ability to exist in different forms in widely separated and diverse geographic areas. The plant known as *Microcoleus vaginatus* (Vauch.) Gom., for example, occurs in wet soil or in fresh or brackish water from northern Greenland to Antarctica, and from the floor of Death Valley to the top of Pikes Peak. Clearly, this plant name has many synonyms resulting from description of numerous variations throughout the world range. Not so clear until recently (Drouet, 1962) has been the extent of morphological variation in such a cosmopolitan species. Drouet studied the cyanophyte flora of the rigorous and changing environment of the desert at Tucson, Arizona. Critical studies of *M. vaginatus* in desert pools as they gradually dried up revealed that the single species was behaving in a variety of ways, and under these changing conditions modifying its form so diversely that it passed across the morphological boundaries not only of several different species, but into the circumscriptions of species recognized in several different genera. Similar results have been obtained in a study of *Schizothrix calcicola*. These have revealed how artificial are some of the characters upon which species and genera of blue-green algae have been described, and point up Drouet's contention that despite the presence of some 7500 named entities in the literature, there are probably fewer than 200 autonomous species in nature.

CLASSIFICATION

The Cyanophyta (also known as Myxophyceae, or Schizophyceae) have been variously classified in recent decades, and there has been little agreement. Some authors have employed large numbers of orders and families. Geitler (1932) and Fritsch (1945) recognized 5 orders, and 17 and 19 families, respectively. Papenfuss (1955) uses 3 orders and 22 families. Drouet (1964) prefers to treat Cyanophyta in a single order with 8 families. Inasmuch as in 36 years Drouet has examined more specimens of blue-green algae than has any other botanist, I am inclined to follow his simplified taxonomy in this introductory presentation.

> Chroococcales
>> Chroococcaceae
>> Chamaesiphonaceae
>> Clastidiaceae (fresh water only)

Oscillatoriaceae
Nostocaceae
Rivulariaceae
Scytonemataceae
Stigonemataceae

The morphological characteristics of these groups will be taken up in turn.

Chroococcaceae

The family Chroococcaceae consists of plants with spherical (coccoid), ovoid, or cylindrical cells which become separated from one another by gelatinous sheath material after each division (Figure 6-1). Generic distinctions are largely based upon a combination of cell shape and planes of division. Thus, *Johannesbaptistia* has discoid cells dividing in one plane and remaining in a linear series within a gelatinous matrix. *Gomphosphaeria* has spherical cells that divide in two planes perpendicular to each other and commonly become irregularly disposed in the matrix. *Anacystis* has spherical cells that divide successively in three perpendicular planes.

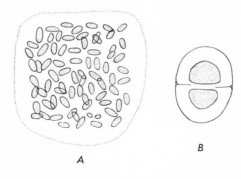

FIGURE 6–1. *A,* A colony of *Coccochloris stagnina,* showing coccoid cells scattered in the gelatinous matrix. *B, Anacystis dimidiata,* showing angular shape of cells after division.

A common marine form is *Anacystis aeruginosa,* present in quiet, brackish, or strictly marine waters throughout much of the temperate and tropical world, and usually forming macroscopic gelatinous masses on rocks, wood, seaweed, and sessile animals. Its cells are 6 to 12 μ in diameter and become spherical soon after division, in contrast to *A. dimidiata,* also partly of marine occurrence, in which the cells remain angular for a time after division (Figure 6-1,*B*).

Chamaesiphonaceae

The family Chamaesiphonaceae, sometimes treated as an order with 7 or more families, has undergone extraordinary reduction by Drouet and Daily (1956). They recognize a single extremely polymorphic genus *(Entophysalis).* In some forms the plants may consist only of a sessile, solitary cell. In others the initial cell may divide into daughter cells of equal size, which become separated by sheath material, and by successive equal and unequal divisions develop into cushions. Sometimes branching chains of cells (trichomes) grow down into penetrable substrates. Reproduction is by endospores which arise by enlargement and division of a solitary cell or of any cell of the group.

Entophysalis plants, consisting of solitary cells or of small groups of cells, are commonly noted as epiphytes on a variety of algae and have traditionally been known as species of *Dermocarpa, Hyella, Xenococcus,* and other genera. According to Drouet and Daily, however, plants previously assigned to these various genera are only phases in the development of *Entophysalis.* For example, smaller growth forms live epiphytically on short-lived benthic host algae (Figure 6-2,*A–B*), while more massive growth forms occur on perennial hosts. On tide-pool algae a great variety of shapes of unicellular and few-celled *"Dermocarpa"* growth forms occur and produce endosporangia (Figure 6-2,*C*). On larger, perennial algae and barnacles, well-developed penetrating filaments and macroscopic cushions of the fully-formed *Entophysalis* type more commonly occur (Figure 6-2,*D*).

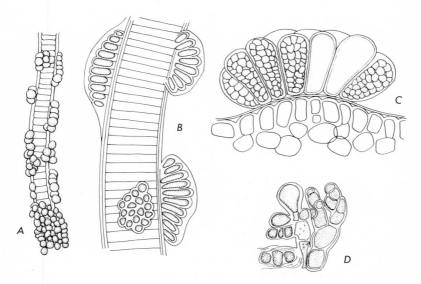

FIGURE 6–2. *A–B,* Groups of epiphytic plants of two of the smaller growth forms of *Entophysalis* (*Xenococcus* forms) growing on other blue-green algae. *C,* A colony of the *Dermocarpa* growth form of *Entophysalis,* showing production of endosporangia. *D, Entophysalis deusta,* showing the filamentous *Hyella* growth form (after Tilden).

Clastidiaceae

The Clastidiaceae is a small group of fresh-water forms characterized by basally attached, short trichomes.

Oscillatoriaceae

The Oscillatoriaceae is by far the largest family in the blue-green algae and includes all the relatively simple forms in which the trichomes are unbranched and develop neither heterocysts nor hairs. Although in some genera, such as *Oscillatoria*, the trichomes appear to be naked, a diffluent mucilage envelope formed during movement is probably present even though it is often indiscernible. Under favorable conditions, the sheath material is secreted copiously, sometimes in a well-hydrolyzed, sometimes in a solidified state. The most popular system of classification has been that of Gomont, which is based in large part on the structure of the sheath. Thus, in *Lyngbya* the sheath is discrete and contains a single trichome. *Symploca* is similar, but the filaments adhere in fascicles at the surface of the colony (Figure 6-3,*B*). In *Phormidium* the sheaths are commonly coalesced. *Hydrocoleum* has several trichomes within a single sheath; *Microcoleus* has filaments containing a single bundle of many trichomes. *Sirocoleum* has several such trichome bundles within a common sheath. Drouet's recent work on ecophenes, however, has shown that a single species may, under certain changing environmental conditions, modify its sheath characteristics to resemble species of *Oscillatoria, Lyngbya, Phormidium, Hydrocoleum,* and *Microcoleus*.

Trichome characters are also used in classification. *Spirulina* is distinguished by spirally coiled trichomes. In *Crinalium* the trichomes are flattened. Various species, especially of *Oscillatoria* and *Lyngbya,* are distinguished by characteristics of the terminal portion of mature trichomes. These may be attenuated or have a thickened hood, or calyptra (Figure 6-3,*C–D*).

In *Oscillatoria* and *Lyngbya,* hormogonia are liberated soon after formation, while in *Hydrocoleum* and *Microcoleus* they germinate *in situ* to produce the numerous trichomes within a sheath (Figure 6-3,*G–H*).

False branching of filaments (Figure 6-3,*I*) results in *Hydrocoleum* and *Schizothrix* from trichomes tending to grow out laterally and to continue to secrete a sheath as they extend.

Nostocaceae

The Nostocaceae resemble the Oscillatoriaceae in their diffuse growth and the unbranched structure of the trichomes, but are distinguished by the prevalent production of heterocysts and frequent reproduction by akinetes. The sheaths are well hydrolyzed and do not function to restrict growth. The cells are uniseriate and generally ellipsoidal. Division may occur in all the vegetative cells of a trichome at the same time.

Hormothamnion is a common marine form of warm seas. It has filaments resembling *Anabaena,* with subspherical vegetative cells and many heterocysts with discrete, cylindrical sheaths (Figure 6-4,*B*). It does not, however, produce spores. The sheaths are agglutinated to form superficial wefts on the substrate, and from these, *Symploca*-like erect tufts may later arise.

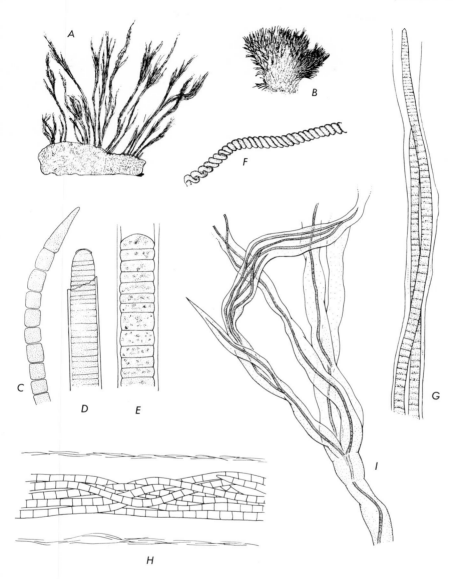

Figure 6–3. *A*, A colony of *Phormidium penicillatum*. *B*, A colony of *Symploca muscorum*. *C*, Attenuated trichome of *Microcoleus chthonoplastes*. *D–E*, Ensheathed trichomes of species of *Lyngbya* with and without calyptrum. *F*, Spirally coiled trichome of *Spirulina subsalsa*. *G*, *Hydrocoleum*, showing 2 trichomes in a single sheath. *H*, A filament of *Microcoleus* with its bundle of many trichomes. *I*, False branching in *Schizothrix*.

Rivulariaceae

The Rivulariaceae is a well-circumscribed family including many marine forms that occur as gelatinous strata or hemispherical masses on rocks, plants, and marsh soil. The trichomes are unbranched and are oriented in their relation to the substrate to show a heterocyst terminating the basal end and a colorless hair terminating the distal (Figure 6-4,*C–D*). The cells are uniseriate, and transverse division occurs mainly in the region just above the heterocyst. The development of the marked difference between the base and apex of the trichome is secondary. Reproduction is commonly by hormogonia produced from portions of the trichome beneath the terminal hair. As the hormogonia germinate and grow, they become tapered at either extremity and ultimately break to form two or more trichomes, each with a basal heterocyst.

In the marine genus *Isactis* the filaments are erect and parallel, with their sheaths coalesced to form densely gelatinous colonies. *Calothrix*, which includes a number of species characteristic of the marine littoral, always has a single trichome in a sheath (Figure 13-6). *Gardnerula* has many trichomes packed inside a thin sheath.

Scytonemataceae

The Scytonemataceae are characterized by cylindrical, untapered, un-branched filaments of uniseriate cells, but with characteristic false branching of the firmly sheathed filaments. Heterocysts occur here and there, tending by their shape to hold the trichome in the sheath and to favor apical growth. In the areas between heterocysts, however, cell division may occur and tends to cause pressures that burst the sheath. This allows one or both broken ends to protrude and to continue growth as a single branch or as twin branches (Figure 6-4,*E*).

Many of the Scytonemataceae suggest derivation from *Lyngbya*-like types by the acquisition of heterocysts and false branching. Reproduction may be by simple fragmentation of the trichomes or filaments, or by production of hormogonia.

The manner of branching is used in some generic separations. In *Scytonema* branching takes place well removed from heterocysts, so that twin branches are prevalent. In *Tolypothrix* the growth break occurs at the heterocyst and results in a solitary branch (Figure 6-4,*F*).

Stigonemataceae

Some of the largest and most elaborately organized blue-green algae are included in the Stigonemataceae. The plants are characterized not only by trichomes exhibiting true branching, but there is in many a strong tendency to multiseriate construction and heterotrichy. Heterocysts are formed here and there as the filaments elongate by transverse division of the cells at their tips.

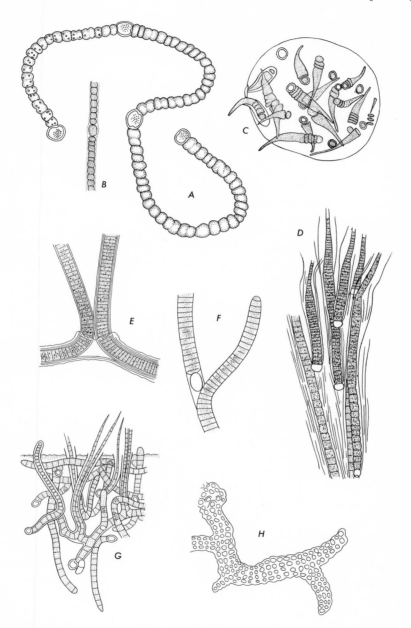

FIGURE 6–4. *A Nostoc caeruleum,* showing intercalary heterocysts. *B, Hormothamnium solutum,* showing sheath and heterocyst. *C, Rivularia polyotis,* showing tapered trichome and basal heterocyst. *D, Rivularia atra,* showing short trichomes in a gelatinous matrix. *E,* Twin false branches of *Plectonema. F,* Solitary false branch of *Tolypothrix* at a heterocyst. *G, Mastigocoleus testarum* growing in a shell, showing heterocysts and hair attenuations. *H,* Multiseriate construction of the fresh-water *Stigonema.*

Cell division may occur in planes parallel with the axis, resulting in increased thickness and production of branches. Reproduction is accomplished mainly by simple fragmentation, but hormogonia are sometimes produced by erect filaments and akinetes by the prostrate ones.

Mastigocoleus testarum is a common marine species inhabiting molluscan shells and other calcareous substrates. It has prominent terminal heterocysts, and some of the laterals are attenuated to hairs (Figure 6-4,*G*).

The most complex thallus structure among the Cyanophyta occurs in the fresh-water *Stigonema* (Figure 6-4,*H*).

NONPIGMENTED GROUPS

In addition to these variously pigmented cyanophytes, some authors are now inclined to place the colorless Beggiatoaceae and Thiotrichaceae with the blue-green algae instead of with the bacteria.

DISTRIBUTION

Blue-green algae may be encountered almost anywhere in the world where water and light are present. They have extreme temperature tolerances that permit them to grow in holes in the Greenland ice cap as well as in hot springs at 82.2°C. They live in all parts of the lighted marine environment and in the exceedingly saline waters of the Dead Sea. They survive extreme desiccation for years in the driest deserts and may be dredged from the sea floor at depths of over 36 meters under conditions of very dim illumination. Planktonic forms sometimes cause brilliant water blooms such as those of the Red Sea and of the Vermilion Sea (Gulf of California).

Of the aquatic forms of Cyanophyta, most seem to be confined either to marine or fresh-water habitats, although some are remarkably tolerant of salinity changes. Numerous narrowly endemic species have been described, but careful study is proving that these in many cases are but variations of more widely distributed forms. A few species are commonly encountered in all latitudes and in a great variety of habitats. More species, however, are characteristic either of temperate or of tropical environments. In many tropical areas the marine blue-greens are relatively conspicuous on intertidal reefs where species of *Symploca, Calothrix,* and, especially, *Lyngbya* may be dominant in local situations. *Lyngbya majuscula,* in varied color phases, often is a conspicuous macroscopic plant forming soft, reddish or purplish skeins up to a meter in length. Occasionally it occurs in abundance, notably in disturbed shallow waters in the tropics. In Hawaii it has been responsible for a severe toxic reaction of the skin known as "swimmers' itch." *Lyngbya* and other blue-green algae are the prime suspects in the chemical toxicity chain in ciguatera fish poisoning in certain tropical Pacific areas.

The cyanophytes are often especially prominent elements of the higher littoral vegetation in temperate and subtemperate areas. They commonly form conspicuous zones at upper intertidal levels and have attracted the attention of numerous investigators. Mud surfaces in salt marshes almost invariably show colonies of *Chroococcus, Microcoleus, Phormidium, Lyngbya,* and so forth.

The Cyanophyta contains a higher proportion of endolithic forms than any of the other algal groups. Lime-boring blue-greens occur in a great diversity of structures from limestone and dolomitic sea cliffs to dead corals, mollusks, and living and dead coralline algae. In these lime-dissolving activities (suspected to be accomplished by secretion of oxalic acid), they are important geological agents of erosion. Whereas solution of calcium carbonate is widespread among marine forms, deposition of lime is mainly confined to fresh-water ones, especially thermal cyanophytes.

A large number of symbiotic relationships of blue-green algae have been reported. Many endophytes occur in terrestrial plants (liverworts, cycads, ferns, and phanerogams). Various species commonly known as *Gloeocapsa, Scytonema, Nostoc,* and *Stigonema* combine with fungi to form lichens. Numerous reports have appeared of nonpigmented flagellates occupied by symbiotic blue-green algae. Many interesting nutritive relationships are involved, such as the production of food substances by the dual organisms that cannot be produced by either partner individually. An unusual case is that of *Richelia intercellularis,* inhabiting various marine diatoms *(Rhizosolenia)* that themselves possess chromatophores (Figure 6-5).

FIGURE 6–5. *Richelia intercellularis* inhabiting the diatom, *Rhizosolenia* (after Karsten).

REFERENCES

Desikachary, T. V. 1959. Cyanophyta. New Delhi: *Indian Council of Agri. Res.* x + 686 pp.

Drouet, F. 1962. Gomont's ecophenes of the blue-green alga, *Microcoleus vaginatus* (Oscillatoriaceae). Philadelphia: *Proc. Acad. Nat. Sci.,* 114: 191–205.

_____ 1963. Ecophenes of *Schizothrix calcicola* (Oscillatoriaceae). Philadelphia: *Proc. Acad. Nat. Sci.,* 115: 261–281.

Drouet, F., and W. A. Daily. 1956. Revision of the coccoid Myxophyceae. *Butler Univ. Bot. Stud.,* 12: 1–218.

Geitler, L. 1932. Cyanophyceae. In: L. Rabenhorst, *Kryptogamen-Flora von Europa,* 14: 1–1196.

Papenfuss, G. F. 1955. Classification of the algae. In: *A Century of Progress in the Natural Sciences, 1853–1953.* Calif. Acad. Sci., San Francisco. pp. 115–224.

Tilden, Josephine E. 1910. Myxophyceae of North America and adjacent regions (cover title: *Minnesota Algae,* vol.1). University of Minnesota Press. iv + 319 pp.

7

The Seaweeds: Structure, Development, Reproduction

Most traditional floristic accounts of the marine algae have treated the three groups of macroscopic, benthic forms: the red algae, the brown algae, and the green algae. These constitute most of what we recognize generally as the seaweeds, and, since these are the marine plants most widely noted and of interest, a large part of this book is devoted to them. For purposes of orientation, a number of general features, comparable among all of these seaweeds, are taken up in this chapter before consideration is given to the various systematic groups.

The seaweeds are primarily attached plants, fixed to the substrate by some kind of holdfast. The holdfast may sometimes resemble roots of higher plants, but both its structure and its functions are distinctly different. It is essentially an attachment organ, although not always exclusively so. Above the holdfast, the thallus may consist of a simple filament, a branched filament, a hollow tube or bladder, a bushy tuft of cylindrical or flattened branches, or of a simple or compound blade, sometimes called a lamina. For recognition of these principal parts we may first consider a plant such as *Laminaria*, in which they are well defined (Figure 7-1,*A*).

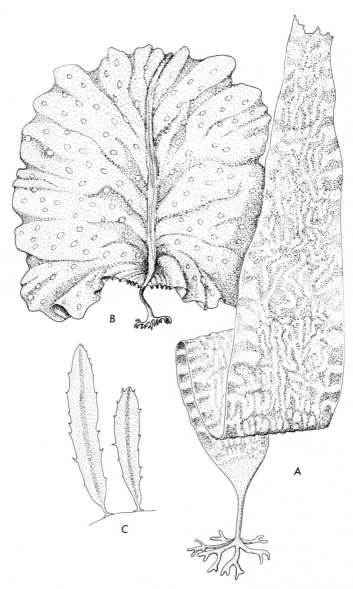

FIGURE 7–1. Examples of the simple blade and stipe: *A, Laminaria* (entire and bullate), *B, Agarum* (perforate, undulate, and ruffled), *C, Erythroglossum* (dentate). Attachments by haptera and by a discoid holdfast are shown. A distinct apophysis is evident in each, and *B* and *C* show a coarse midrib.

Laminaria, commonly called an oar weed, is attached by a small group of branched haptera. Above the holdfast is a cylindrical or compressed stemlike portion known as the stipe. At the top of the stipe is a region of growth and of more or less abrupt expansion into the blade (the apophysis). Comparison of the basic thallus characters in *Laminaria* may be made with other genera of comparable form in which the blade may be simple (unbranched), or divided, or branched into segments. It may be complete and entire (smooth-margined) as in the red alga, *Iridaea,* or it may be perforated and ruffled as in *Agarum cribrosum,* or it may have dentate margins as in *Erythroglossum californicum* (Figure 7-1). It may be smooth-surfaced, or undulate and bullate. Some blades are attached directly by a small disc or by a group of haptera without a stipe; these are called sessile *(Hedophyllum)*. Almost as great a range of form occurs in the blades of algae as in the leaves of flowering plants: in such features as their size, shape, dissection, venation, apices, margins, surface, and orientation. Furthermore, the whole thallus may assume the photosynthetic function. Some of the remarkably diverse forms of these thalli are shown in Figure 7-2.

THE HOLDFAST AND STIPE

Since the benthic environment is to a large extent one of moving water in which the survival of larger plants depends upon the effectiveness of their attachment, the holdfast is an organ of primary structural importance to most marine algae. The diversity of its form attests to multiple evolutionary adaptations to different substrates and to varied degrees of shock, of lash, and of tension. Whereas the severe agitation of a surf-swept shore provides constant buffeting of its vegetation, the regular tidal currents of quiet bays exert on seaweeds a gentler but still appreciable force, sufficient to dislodge those not securely fastened to immobile substrates. Even in deep waters below the effects of normal surge and surf, the periodic violence of storms causes agitation to considerable depths that loosens and casts up those plants adhering only to small pebbles or shells.

A very few of a diversified array of specialized kinds of holdfasts may be mentioned. In sand and mud habitats such successful seaweeds as *Penicillus* and *Avrainvillea* (Figure 8-14) possess an elaborate system of deeply penetrating, root-like filaments that surround and attach to sediment particles to form an anchor within the loose substrate (Figure 7-3,*A*). Such sand dwellers are not always small forms of algae, for some plants of *Macrocystis* similarly are able to survive on sandy, pebbly, or shelly bottoms in depths of 40 to 60 feet. After initial development on a well-fixed worm tube or shell, they produce spreading masses of haptera that penetrate the bottom material, and surround and hold a sufficient amount of it to serve as a weighty anchor for the massive canopy of floating blades.

The peculiar, vesicular *Halicystis* fastens to wave-dashed crustose coralline algae by means of a peg-like, somewhat tuberous rhizoid deeply embedded in

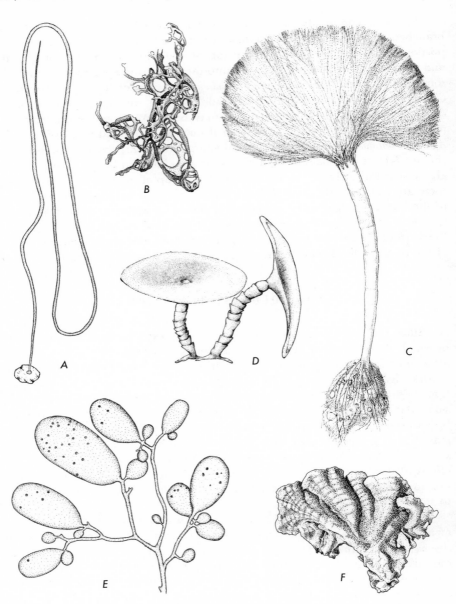

FIGURE 7–2. Diversity of form among the benthic algae: *A, Chorda; B, Hydroclathrus; C, Penicillus; D, Maripelta; E, Botryocladia; F, Ralfsia.*

the calcareous crusts (Figure 7-3,*B*). Other small algae may be more intimately associated with a living algal substrate and produce penetrating rhizoidal processes that firmly unite them as partial endophytes or parasites to a host

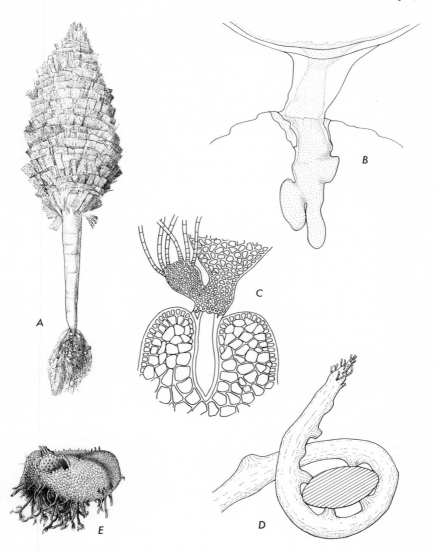

FIGURE 7–3. Some specialized kinds of holdfasts: *A,* root-like filaments of the mud-dwelling *Rhipocephalus; B,* multinucleate rhizoid of the vesicular *Halicystis* penetrating a crustose coralline alga (after Hollenberg); *C,* endophytic rhizoidal process of *Erythrocystis,* hemiparasitic on *Laurencia; D,* accessory holdfasts of the twining *Chondria californica* attached to *Phyllospadix; E,* multinucleate attachment protuberances of *Dictyosphaeria.*

plant. In most endophytes the penetrating parts possess chromatophores and merely traverse more or less gelatinous cell walls of the host without actually penetrating the cells (various Ectocarpales, Sphacelariales, and

Polysiphonia fastigiata). The hemiparasitic *Erythrocystis*, inhabiting the apical pit of *Laurencia*, is exemplary of those that form penetrating processes that develop an intimate relationship with the host cells (Figure 7-3; 15-5).

Some benthic algae that are provided with ordinary discoid or rhizoidal holdfasts in younger stages may in age break loose and float off to continue growth after becoming entangled among other plants and forming secondary rhizoidal attachments to them. A few have evolved special hook-shaped branchlets that aid in this mode of life *(Hypnea musciformis, Acrosorium uncinatum)*, while others *(Chondria californica, Laurencia subopposita)* develop tendril-like entwining branchlets that provide numerous accessory holdfasts long after the plant has broken away from its initial attachment and drifted off among other seaweeds (Figure 7-3,*D*).

Because of these diverse and often special forms, holdfast characters are important to the diagonosis of genera and species. Accordingly, one should note the value of obtaining in field collections entire specimens representing whole plants complete with holdfasts.

Whereas the holdfast provides for stable attachment of the thallus, the stem-like stipe between holdfast and blade provides for flexibility and resilience in meeting the varying forces of water movement. Sometimes, by its lengthening, it serves to support the blades in suitably illuminated positions. Because of its intermediate position and the gradations that exist between lower and upper portions of the thallus, the stipe is commonly not sharply defined. In many narrow, many-branched, or filamentous types no definitive stipe is recognizable, and all parts are equally adapted for flexibility and assimilation. A prominent number of conspicuous seaweeds, especially the large brown kelps, however, exhibit distinctly stipitate blades, and several of these may be considered for features they especially exemplify.

The most prominent stipe with respect to blade size, and that exhibiting the most remarkable adaptation for resilience following shock, is seen in the sea palm, *Postelsia palmaeformis*. This plant grows in the most exposed rocky situations under conditions of extremely violent surf. It consists of a thick stipe securely fastened by massive haptera and supporting a terminal hank of drooping blades. Not only is the stipe of resilient, rubbery texture, but it is hollow and responds to the most violent lashing of waves like a stiff rubber tube (Figure 7-4).

Whereas *Postelsia* seems to be a short-lived annual whose stipe has the soft texture of vigorously growing young tissues, many other kelps are perennial and support an increasing number and size of blades on stipes that become coarse and leathery. *Pterygophora* is one in which the stipe in age becomes stiff and provides erect support of its broad, pinnate blades which, unlike *Postelsia*, are not subject to severe agitation, but stream out in the gentler currents of deep water or of sheltered bays.

The most remarkably extensive simple stipes are those of *Nereocystis* and *Pelagophycus* which live in water depths usually of about 15 to 30 meters and in a single season's growth float their blades to the surface by exceedingly rapid

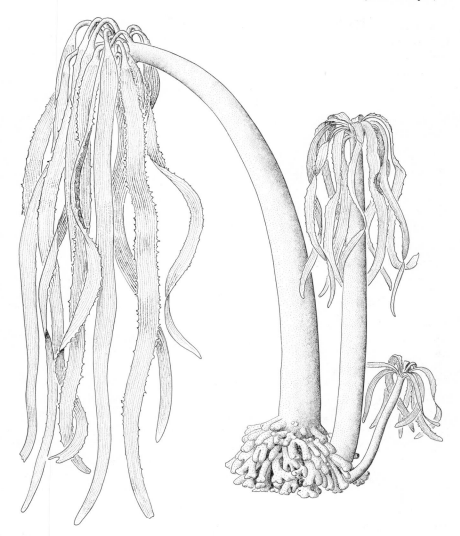

Figure 7-4. *Postelsia palmaeformis,* showing hapteroid holdfast, flexible heavy stipe and drooping photosynthetic blades (after Smith, reprinted by permission of Stanford University Press).

elongation of the stipe with its terminal pneumatocyst (Figure 7-6). The multiple stipes of *Macrocystis* reach even greater lengths and achieve higher growth rates.

Growth in thickness or diameter of the stipes of kelps is accomplished primarily by a surface layer, the meristoderm, that remains actively meriste-matic during initial elongation and enlargement. In *Macrocystis* the meristoderm continues to serve this function throughout the life of the structure, but in

Laminaria, Pterygophora, and others, the meristematic activity is transferred to a cortical layer a little below the surface. Perennial activity of this secondary meristem results in concentric zones of growth recalling the annual rings of higher plants (Figure 7-5).

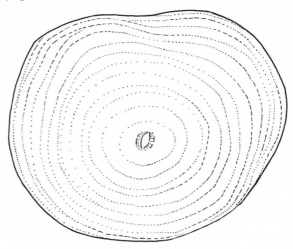

FIGURE 7–5. Transection of an old stipe of *Pterygophora* showing concentric rings representing approximately 17 seasons' growth (after MacMillan).

Despite the diversity of stipe form and branching among the kelps from *Postelsia* to *Macrocystis,* all these plants show juvenile stages of the fundamental *Laminaria* type. Thus, kelps of such distinct genera as *Egregia, Agarum,* and *Pelagophycus* show a common youthful stage consisting of a simple cylindrical stipe attached by haptera and supporting a simple, entire, foliar blade (Figures 7-6; 7-7). One will commonly encounter intertidally along the Pacific Coast numerous plants that resemble a small species of *Laminaria.* Upon close comparison, however, these prove to be juvenile examples of, for example, *Egregia, Eisenia, Macrocystis,* or *Pterygophora,* for which distinctive developmental series can be assembled.

Although many stipitate algae are annual and the past-mature plant breaks away at the holdfast or degenerates *in situ,* some are perennial and show regeneration from the stipe. *Laminaria* produces for two or more years an annual renewal of the blade from the top of the stipe, often before the previous season's blade has eroded away, so that the old remains as a tattered appendage on the tip of the new. *Eisenia* develops new blades progressively in a series on either side of the apex of the stipe (actually the basal margins of the eroded primary blade) and produces a falsely forked stipe by this progressive incrementation

FIGURE 7–6. *Pelagophycus porra,* showing small hapteroid holdfast and long stipe terminating in a large pneumatocyst supporting the system of blades. A juvenile plant to larger scale appears at the right.

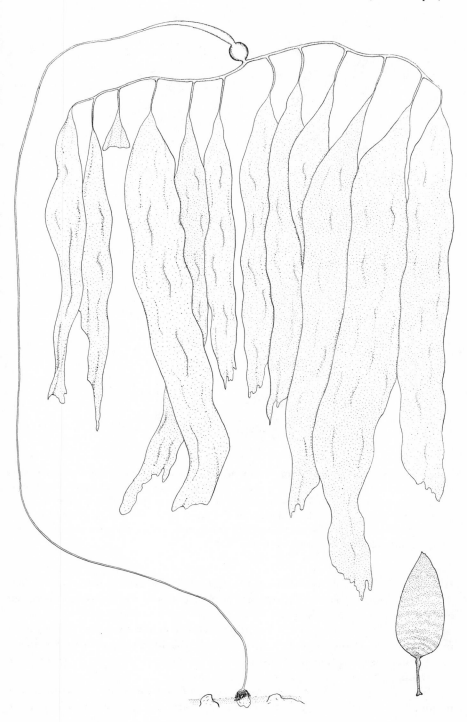

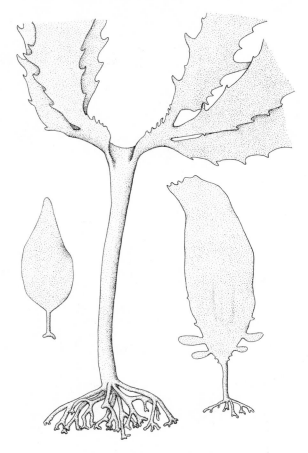

FIGURE 7–7. Intercalary meristem development in *Eisenia*. The juvenile thallus consists of a small blade much resembling a tiny *Laminaria*. While this enlarges, the tip begins to erode away and the intercalary meristem at the base of the primary blade produces initials of a series of secondary blades. In the adult plant the primary blade is completely gone and the meristem has become marginal, giving rise successively to new lateral blades as older ones are worn and lost.

(Figure 7-7). The peltate red alga, *Constantinea*, has a broad, rotate blade that is annually deciduous. At maturity the stipe projects upward through its center as a short prong, and when the blade breaks away to leave only an annulate scar, the short prolongation of the stipe forms a new rotate blade at its apex and continues its own elongation to provide the following year's stipe increment. Such regeneration may continue for ten years or more in *C. rosa-marina,* or for up to 17 years in *C. simplex* (Figure 7-8).

This brings us to a brief consideration of the longevity of seaweeds. A majority of species, especially the small ones, are annuals, and may complete

FIGURE 7–8. *Constantinea rosa-marina* with rotate blades largely removed, showing many annual stipe increments separated by scars of deciduous blades.

their growth and reproduction in a few months. Others persist through all or the greater part of the year. *Nereocystis* reaches great size in the span of a single season and dies. Some strains of gigantic *Macrocystis* may live only 2 or 3 years. Various species of *Sargassum* and many other algae decline to a perennial holdfast from which regeneration occurs repeatedly for several years. Many quite small plants may persist year after year by regeneration from the stipe, as in *Constantinea*. *Phyllophora brodiaei* is one of these; the branching stipes show distinct secondary thickenings (resulting from periclinal divisions of the superficial cells) that represent growth periods usually of annual cycle. These stipe thickenings may be concentric, but more often they are asymmetrical or patchy. In some dredged specimens from the North Sea an estimated age of 7 years has been obtained by study of these thickenings and of successive branch increments. Stipe rings and blade scars of *Pterygophora* provide a close estimate of age up to 24 years (Figure 7-5).

Holdfasts generally do not serve the absorptive and conducting functions of terrestrial plant roots, although the chemical nature of the substrate does seem to provide favorable or unfavorable conditions for the growth of various algae. On the other hand, a conductive function of the central tissues of stipes and main axes of some algae has long been assumed. This is especially so for certain forms with extensive stipes and blades remote from basal parts that display conspicuous accumulations of starch or other products. Anatomical study of the tissues has supported this assumption, inasmuch as nonpigmented cells of markedly elongate form are noted inside layers of storage cells and of photosynthetic cells in such plants as *Plumaria, Chondria, Cystoclonium,* and *Asparagopsis* (Figure 7-9,*A*). Some workers have thought they observed with the light microscope fine cytoplasmic strands passing through perforations in transverse septa. The anatomy of the stipes of Laminariales have provided, however, the most striking suggestions of a conductive function. In various members, especially *Macrocystis* and *Nereocystis,* elongate cells are found in the inner cortex and medulla (Figure 7-10). These have transverse walls with numerous perforations through which the protoplasm is continuous. Some of these elements have been called sieve tubes or sieve filaments, and the function of conduction (translocation) has been attributed to them. The pits in their perforated end-walls are observed with the electron microscope sometimes to be closed by a delicate membrane. In other instances, however, they seem to be open. The sieve filaments run longitudinally in series in which the individual cell may be 5 millimeters in length *(Pelagophycus).* Other, more intertwined, of these elongate cells with pitted walls are much expanded at the septa and are called trumpet hyphae (Figure 7-9,*B*).

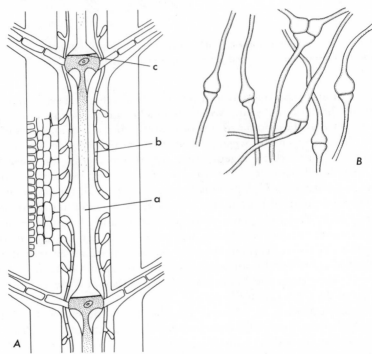

FIGURE 7-9. *A,* Diagram of the disposition of axial conductive cells in *Asparagopsis:* a, axial cell; b, collective filament; c, axial cell juncture (after Feldmann). *B,* Trumpet hyphae in *Laminaria.*

Only recently has experimental work employing radioactive tracers been conducted to test this conductive function. Parker (1963) collected a fully intact plant of *Macrocystis* to test in this manner. By using a laboratory aquarium system including a lighted reaction chamber containing a $NaHCO_3$ solution labeled with C^{14}, he found that organic products of photosynthesis are translocated from mature blades through the stipe either apically or basally. In one experiment he obtained a rate of about 60 centimeters per hour.

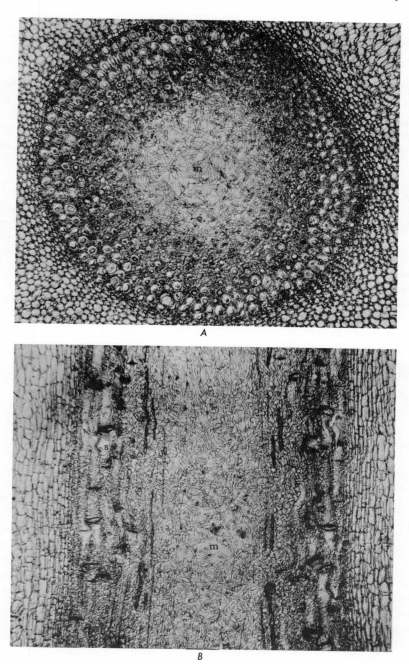

FIGURE 7–10. Transverse (*A*) and longitudinal (*B*) sections of a mature stipe of *Macrocystis pyrifera,* showing medullary filaments at m, and sieve tubes at s (photo by B.C. Parker).

THE BLADE AND ITS COUNTERPARTS

The conspicuous broad-bladed forms of marine algae, such as *Laminaria* and *Ulva,* are in a sense comparable to the terrestrial broadleaf trees, and they similarly represent only one of many ways in which the photosynthetic parts are adapted to meet effectively the limiting factors of the environment. Thus, the simple, laminar blade has many counterparts in the branched, divided, and sometimes intricately dissected forms of the foliar parts that serve the photosynthetic function.

Whereas in terrestrial flowering plants the leaf is predominantly photosynthetic, the stem parts are photosynthetic to a far lesser extent and the root portions only under special circumstances, in a majority of marine algae, under usual circumstances, all portions of the thallus are exposed to illumination and contain pigments active in photosynthesis. Accordingly, a great diversity of thallus morphology occurs in relation to varied conditions of light availability and to the numerous other environmental factors correlative to photosynthesis. Limitations on growth imposed by variations in temperature and salinity, available respiratory oxygen, and nutrients are reflected in particular morphological adaptations, while such physical conditions of the environment as tidal exposure, water movement, wave shock, and sand abrasion contribute further to the range of form assumed by the photosynthetic parts.

In its simplest form the entire attached plant is a single cell. In some motile, unicellular types the attached, sedentary form is assumed only temporarily as the swimming individual briefly comes to rest prior to division of the protoplast to form a new motile generation. In others, however, such as the *Dermocarpa* phase of *Entophysalis,* the sedentary coccoid habit is the permanent one, and the ovoid cells may be solitary or aggregated into colonies. Most solitary cells are microscopic, but some, such as *Halicystis,* reach macroscopic size of a centimeter or more (Figure 8-12,*H*).

Apart from the unicell, the most elementary thallus type is the filament, which in its simplest form consists of a single, uniseriate row of cells resulting from division in one plane. In such genera as *Ulothrix, Rhizoclonium,* and *Chaetomorpha* (Figures 8-2; 8-8) all but the basalmost of the cells may be similar and the filament may be essentially or wholly without branches. In other uniseriate forms the primary, simple filament may become more or less elaborately branched and septate in the same manner as the main thread *(Cladophora),* or it may consist of several distinctive cell types as well as specialized forms and orientations of branches *(Platythamnion,* Figure 7-11).

At this point, one should note some of the various branching types to be encountered among benthic algae (Figure 7-12). Fundamentally, these may be dichotomous, alternate, opposite, or secund (unilateral). The branches may be oriented bilaterally in one plane (distichous, or pinnate), in two opposed planes (tetrastichous), or in various planes (polystichous). In the latter case,

FIGURE 7–11. *Platythamnion reversum,* showing indeterminate and determinate branching. The determinate branches are tetrastichous, a longer opposite pair in one plane
and a short, spinous pair in the other (after Setchell & Gardner).

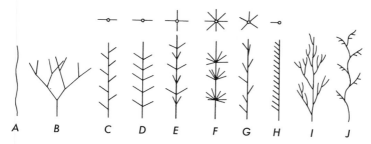

FIGURE 7–12. Some examples of diverse types of branching among the marine algae:
A, unbranched (simple); *B,* dichotomous; *C,* pinnate (alternate); *D,* pinnate (distichous,
opposite); *E,* tetrastichous; *F,* verticillate; *G,* polystichous; *H,* pectinate or secund;
I, monopodial; *J,* sympodial.

the branches may arise radially in spiral sequence. If opposite, the branches may be whorled (verticillate). Commonly the branches arise successively from a primary axis in monopodial manner. The branching is called sympodial if the primary axis is replaced each time it produces a branch by the branch assuming the position of the axis. As a result of growth according to one or a combination of these branch patterns, an alga consisting only of a uniseriate filament may develop into a complex and intricately elaborated thallus. Further differentiation is provided by various combinations of determinate and indeterminate branches. Thus, *Platythamnion* has an indeterminate main axis with opposite, pinnate lateral branches that are of uniformly limited growth (determinate). In the opposite plane are other pairs of even shorter determinate branchlets reduced to simple or branched spines (Figure 7-11).

In all of these thalli consisting of simple or branched, free, uniseriate filaments, the function of the foliose blade has been assumed by a slender, cylindrical structure provided with large surface in contact with the water medium in comparison with the total thallus volume. The diameters of such filaments commonly range from 30 to 500 μ, although in a few cases they may be somewhat larger or smaller.

A beginning of thallus differentiation toward larger, coarser plants is seen in *Antithamnium pseudocorticatum,* in which some of the lateral branchlets tend to enclasp the axis and to protect and thicken it (Figure 7-13,*A*). In *Wrangelia penicillata* secondary lateral filaments grow downward, appressed to the larger axis cell, their walls becoming united into a continuous layer of cells around the axis. The cortex in this instance is formed from the downward growing corticating filaments (Figure 7-13,*B–C*). Numerous variations of this kind of cortication of the axis occur, and they may produce some fairly massive axial tissues, such as in *Dasya* and *Pogonophorella.*

In other filamentous types the axial cell row undergoes division immediately back of the growing point to produce pluriseriate filaments, as in *Sphacelaria* (Figure 9-3), and polysiphonous filaments, as in *Polysiphonia,* in which regular tiers of pericentral cells surround a central axis (Figure 7-13,*G*; 10-22). Cortication around the outside of the pericentral cells may further elaborate this type of thallus, as is seen in a cross section of *Polysiphonia elongata* (Figure 7-13,*D*).

Another elaboration beyond the uniseriate filament, with its cell division essentially in one plane, is seen in such plants as *Monostroma* and *Porphyra.* In these, after an initial filamentous stage, septation occurs in two planes at right angles to form sheet-like expansions only one cell thick (monostromatic). In some instances one or a few cell divisions occur in a plane parallel to the surface of expansion and result in a distromatic *(Ulva)* or pluristromatic, parenchymatous thallus *(Dictyota).* It is evident that in such thalli of only one or two cell layers every cell is in contact with the water medium and its solutes, although to a lesser extent than in the case of the uniseriate filament. Similarly, light need pass through only a single cell wall in order to reach pigmented photosynthetic organelles (Figure 7-13,*F*).

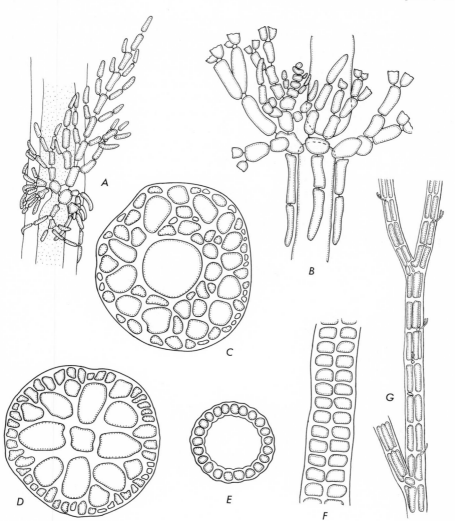

Figure 7–13. *A–C,* Thallus elaboration from the uniseriate filament. *A, Antithamnion pseudocorticatum,* showing a loose, axial cortication by enclasping lateral branchlets; *B–C, Wrangelia penicillata,* showing (*B*) appressed, downwardly-growing lateral filaments that in age coalesce to form the solid cortex seen in the transection. *D,* A transection of a corticated *Polysiphonia* showing the elaboration of tissue surrounding the central axial filament and the pericentral cells. *E–F,* The tubular thallus of *Enteromorpha* (*E*) could be interpreted as an inflated form of the bistratose thallus of *Ulva* (*F*). *G, Polysiphonia,* showing pericentral cells in regular tiers.

A distinctive tubular or vesicular form may sometimes result from extensive or limited separation of the cell layers composing the thallus (*Enteromorpha*) (Figure 7-13,*E*).

In contrast to erect, filamentous, or foliar habits are those of the prostrate disc, the crust, or the cushion. A few green algae and larger numbers of brown and red algae are dorsiventral and more or less completely adherent to the substrate. In some green algae, such as *Pringsheimiella* and *Entocladia,* the thallus consists of radiating, branched filaments forming a loose disc on or within the cell membranes of various larger algae and the chitinous stalks of bryozoa. Often the filaments coalesce to form a compact, monostromatic disc (Figure 7-14,*B*). Among brown and red algae the crustose or prostrate thalli are more often of quite complex structure. *Ralfsia* is a dark brown crust commonly spreading over intertidal rocks. It consists of an adherent basal cell layer from every cell of which an erect or ascending filament arises and coalesces with its neighbor into a dense, firm, pseudoparenchymatous tissue. Figure 7-14,*C* shows a similar red-algal form, *Cruoriella.* In other plants, such as *Petrocelis* and *Petrospongium,* the thallus structure is less firmly coalesced, and the erect filaments may be separated easily.

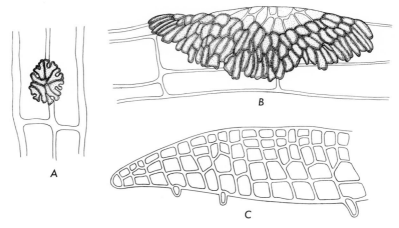

Figure 7–14. Two forms of crustose thalli. *A–B*, Young and adult thalli, respectively, of *Pringsheimia scutata,* growing on *Polysiphonia* (after Reinke). *C*, Vertical, radial section of the margin of a thallus of *Cruoriella dubyi* showing young rhizoids (after Kylin).

A great number of crustose red algae are calcified and so firmly adherent as almost to unite with the rocky substrate on which they live. These crustose forms are rarely epiphytized while living, and many of them so effectively cover an area by their perennial lateral and superficial growth as to exclude other plants that might overgrow and shade them. Thus, they remain recipients of all available light. They are also some of the deepest-growing algae and occur as the basal stratum in many submarine plant communities.

Coenocytic forms, especially among the siphonalean Chlorophyta, often show a remarkable enlargement of the thallus without the occurrence of septation (Figure 7-15). These plants of siphonous habit may develop branching photosynthetic systems that are nearly as elaborate as those of cellular, septate

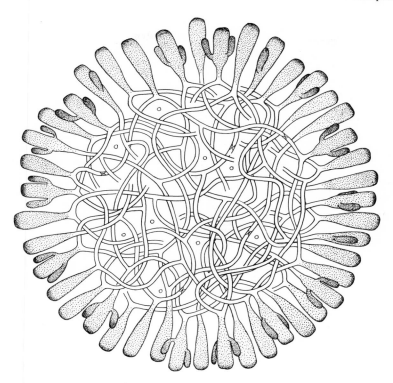

FIGURE 7–15. Idealized transection of a *Codium* thallus showing the branched and interlaced central mass of filaments and the peripheral layer of inflated utricles.

algae. Some of the most striking examples of morphological differentiation in aseptate, multinucleate thalli occur in the widespread genus *Caulerpa*, which may be found in almost all tropical or near-tropical waters (Figure 7-16). Some of them have a marked superficial resemblance to terrestrial plants, for they are often mud and sand dwellers of quiet waters and have prostrate rhizomes. The upright assimilatory shoots may be as much as 30 centimeters tall and exhibit a variety of shapes. In *C. prolifera* these are broad, green, entire, and complanate structures remarkably suggestive of higher plant leaves, yet they are aseptate (Figure 7-17). The central vacuole and the lining of cytoplasm with its chloroplasts and nuclei are continuous throughout the plant and traversed only by slender, strengthening trabecula of the walls (Figure 7-16,*F*).

Such broad, leafy axes of bilateral form seem to constitute advantageous assimilatory equipment, as evidenced by their ability to persist under dimly lighted conditions. *C. prolifera* and similar species may occur at depths of 15 to 50 meters or more, which for green algae is remarkable when one considers the exceedingly limited light of short wave length at those depths.

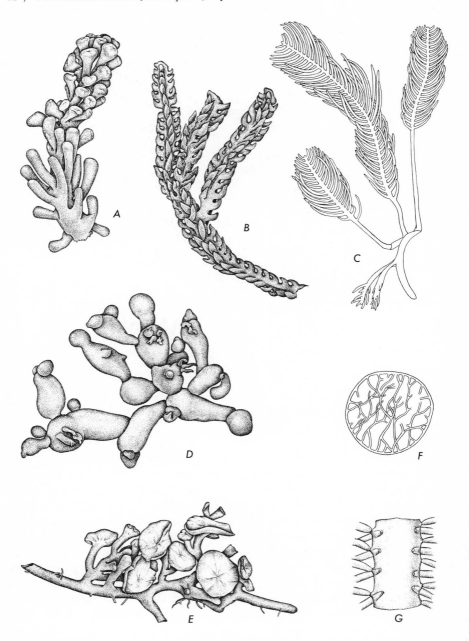

FIGURE 7–16. Diversity of form and branching among coenocytic algae: *A–C, E,* Species of *Caulerpa,* showing turbinate, falcate, plumose, and peltate branches. *D, Valonia utricularis,* showing septation of main branches. *F,* Transection of a branch of *Caulerpa,* showing bracework of trabecula. *G, Bryopsis indica,* with paired distichous pinnae, each with a basal septum, as seen in a small portion of a main axis.

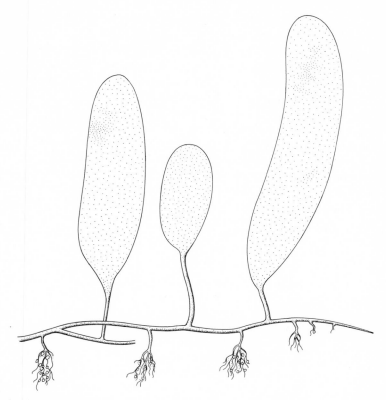

FIGURE 7–17. Habit of a portion of a plant of *Caulerpa prolifera* as an example of a multinucleate, aseptate form developing foliose parts.

Apart from the several relatively simple types of construction just reviewed (the uniseriate filament, the crustose thallus of compacted, prostrate, or erect filaments, and the branched, aseptate, multinucleate thallus), the great majority of benthic algae have evolved a more complex structure involving diverse tissue types derived from both primary and secondary meristematic activity. A discussion of these meristems will be given later in this chapter. A knowledge of the varied tissue and cell types in the structure of algal blades is, however, of more than academic interest. The phycologist discovers in practice that the complicated life histories of the marine algae, and the difficulties of obtaining certain reproductive phases or stages for examination in connection with identifications, makes it necessary to resort frequently to a study of the vegetative anatomy as a means of determining the identity or relationships of a plant. Accordingly, it is of utmost importance at the outset that one learns to prepare sections of both fresh and dry specimens, either mechanically or by hand. Directions for making these preparations are provided in Chapter 18, but their interpretation is achieved only as a result of the experience gained by patient examination and comparison with explanatory figures and descriptions. As an aid in this endeavor, a considerable number of illustrations of cross sections of various thalli are provided in this book.

Furthermore, it cannot be emphasized too strongly that one must recognize the rapidity with which secondary tissues are formed in many of the larger algae with consequent obscuring or virtual obliteration of primary thallus organization. Interpretation of the latter can often be accomplished only by examination of the youngest actively growing apices, for sections taken only a few millimeters from a tip may fail to show unmodified fundamental structure on account of age.

Whatever the structural composition of the blade or its counterpart, the primary functions are light reception and photosynthesis, which are accomplished by diverse positions or orientations of these principal photosynthetic parts with respect to available light. In shallow waters, where light is abundantly available, a diversity of blade forms occurs, and the plants compete there more for attachment space on the substrate than for light. Nevertheless, the density of growth often results in complete overshading of the substrate to the extent that delicate and small algae are deprived of a place in the sun. Instead, they have widely adapted to a life of attachment as epiphytes on larger algae. In deeper waters, too, such epiphytes may live at well-illumined upper levels, far above the dim sea floor, attached to the blades of large brown algae which are buoyed at or near the surface by their pneumatocysts.

Pneumatocysts of many sizes occur, from the massive float bulbs of *Nereocystis* and *Pelagophycus,* to the tiny vesicles of *Sargassum* and *Cystoseira* (Figure 7-18). *Pelagophycus* pneumatocysts contain up to 2.6 liters of gas and are large enough to buoy at the surface masses of enormous blades that hang down in the water like great brown curtains. *Macrocystis* has a pneumatocyst at the base of each blade, and a single plant may have thousands of them supporting long streamers flagged with the photosynthetic "leaves" that spread as a forest canopy over the sea floor 10 to 30 meters below. The upward growth of these long, blade-bearing shoots is one of the most remarkable phenomena in the plant kingdom, for in their phototropic growth they achieve what are evidently the fastest elongation rates of all plants. The most rapid elongation on record for land plants is 30 centimeters per day for bamboo, while *Macrocystis* fronds have been observed many times to elongate at rates of more than 30 centimeters in a day, and 25 meters of growth has been measured for a 120-day period. The pneumatocysts achieve their full development and buoyancy in 30 days in their contribution to the extraordinary rise of this photosynthetic column from the sea floor.

Some buoyant algae such as *Fucus* produce air bladders in the tips of their blades, while in *Ascophyllum* they occur as inflations of the main axis. In *Durvillea,* of subantarctic regions, the massive parenchymatous tissue of its blades (several centimeters thick) breaks down into chambers that become inflated with gaseous respiratory products. It is evident that not all of these adaptations are necessarily related to the display of photosynthetic tissue, but may be significant with respect to other life processes.

FIGURE 7–18. A colony of *Nereocystis leutkeana* in the Straits of Juan de Fuca, Washington, showing upper portion of hollow stipes with terminal pneumatocysts lying horizontally at the surface and supporting massive photosynthetic blades that hang down from the tips.

Whereas the majority of higher terrestrial plants have their leaves more or less fixedly oriented dorsiventrally with respect to the maximum incidence of illumination, the marine algae are more comparable to those terrestrial grasses in which the blade is flexible, essentially erect or drooping, and usually without pronounced dorsiventrality. In such blades the photosynthetic tissues are equal from side to side, and a transection shows symmetrical gradation toward the interior unlike the typical leaf transection with its adaxial palisade parenchyma and abaxial spongy parenchyma and vascular system (Figure 7-19). This symmetrical structure is prevalent in the larger algae. Transections usually will show a densely pigmented outer cortical layer of small, actively productive cells; and a medulla of colorless, larger, vacuolate, translucent cells, or of a translucent matrix traversed by filaments. If ribs, veins, or nerves are present, these are usually centrally and symmetrically located and apparently serve largely a strengthening rather than conductive function.

CYTOLOGY

The most conspicuous structural feature of the marine algal thallus is its cellular organization. Recognition of this leads us to a consideration of some

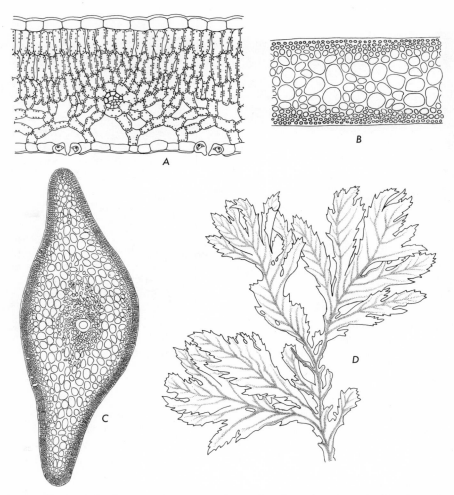

FIGURE 7-19. *A–C,* Comparative transections of a flowering-plant leaf and marine algal blades: *A,* A typical green leaf showing dorsi-ventral arrangement of tissues; *B,* *Rhodymenia,* showing bilateral symmetry of small-celled photosynthetic cortex and medulla of large, vacuolate cells; *C, Leptocladia,* showing denser cellular structure but similar symmetry and lack of dorsiventrality. *D,* Part of a plant of *Phycodrys,* showing a shape and venation similar to a flowering-plant leaf, but without dorsiventrality.

of the chief characteristics of algal cells as a background for the study of growth, which in most instances is fundamentally a multiplication and expansion of cells.

Apart from zoospores, gametes, and certain microscopic unicellular flagellated plants, the algal protoplast characteristically is surrounded by one or more layers of nonliving material known as cell wall. The composition of the wall is mainly of carbohydrates of two general categories: those that are soluble in boiling water and those that are not. The former are mucilage-like, soluble polysaccharides, some of which, on account of their gel-forming properties have become important articles of commerce, namely, agar, algin, and carrageenin from red and brown seaweeds. The water-soluble carbo-hydrates are mostly forms of cellulose, but such other substances as mannan and chitin have been reported, and recent studies indicate that cellulose in the strict sense is probably confined to certain green algae.

Phycologists have long noted under the light microscope that certain algal cell walls appear laminated. Only in recent years with the use of the electron microscope has it been possible to investigate these walls at ultra-structural level. Since the first work on *Valonia* in 1948, it has been shown that algal cell walls usually exhibit a layering of microfibrils in an amorphous matrix. The microfibrils are of diameters ranging from 30 to 250 Å, and may be arranged in various ways, from irregular felts and networks to distinctly crossed layers in which straight and parallel microfibrils of one layer are oriented at right angles to those of another (Figure 7-20). They always lie, how-ever, in the plane of the cell surface.

FIGURE 7–20. Electron micrograph of outer cell wall of *Chaetomorpha torta*, showing reticular layering of microfibrils and anastomosis of microfibrils to form fibrils, × 8000 (courtesy Clinton Dawes).

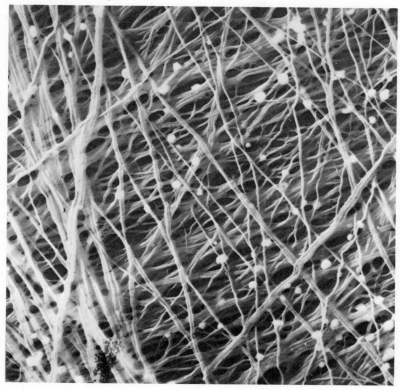

The new information on ultrastructure has given fresh interpretation of the manner of expansion of the algal cell wall which may enlarge several thousandfold during the course of maturity. During such expansion it not only is continuously yielding, but retains a firm texture. This is accomplished by the addition of mass to the inner wall surface through the deposition of microfibrils in the amorphous matrix. The rate and direction of cell-wall expansion appears to be controlled in some way by the orientation of the microfibrils. Dawes has shown that in the apical cells and their early derivative stages in *Dictyota* the microfibrils are in reticulate pattern, while in mature cells they are dominantly parallel.

Whereas the enlargement of algal thalli is due principally to the expansion of cell walls, there is in most cases a limit to the extent of such expansion and a need for multiplication of cells by the repeated partitioning of those capable of this meristematic activity. In such siphonous green algae as *Caulerpa* and *Codium*, however, lateral-wall expansion and extension may be continuous throughout the life of the plant, without the formation of transverse partitions, and unrelated to nuclear divisions. In such red algae as *Griffithsia*, multinucleate segments occur as a result of partial septation of the thallus into quite large cellular units.

In the algae, despite such frequent variations in the independence of mitosis and cytokinesis indicated above, the majority of vegetative cells and nearly all differentiated reproductive cells are uninucleate and in many ways comparable to the cells of higher plants.

More or less detailed observations of mitotic divisions have been reported for most of the larger groups of algae, and it is generally stated that nuclear division in the algae is essentially like that of higher plants and without significant differences in the origin and behavior of chromosomes. Some very recent work by Cole, however, partially unpublished, suggests that there may be some marked exceptions to such a statement and that nuclear division may occur in very different ways in some red algae such as *Antithamnion*. In that genus she observed a kind of division in which no spindle apparatus was visible. Nor did she see any sign of a metaphase plate of chromosomes, but only a simple pinching in two of the nucleus. Furthermore, in the gametophytes of Laminariales she has searched in vain for 6 years for a normal set of mitotic-division sequences. Clearly, there is much investigation to do, not only in examining new and different forms, but in reevaluating some of the older observations that seem to include details that could hardly have been detected with the equipment available at the time.

Cytologists working with algae, particularly marine ones, have long been handicapped by several unfavorable factors such as the gelatinous walls, the large vacuoles, the usually small nuclei, and an unfamiliarity with the physical conditions of life of the plants. New techniques, especially with the electron microscope, are now rapidly improving our knowledge of algal cytology, in which almost any organism that may be investigated represents an unexplored field. Even the most obscurely minute algae, such as *Micromonas pusilla*, which measures scarcely a micron in diameter, can now be examined in structural detail (Figure 7-21).

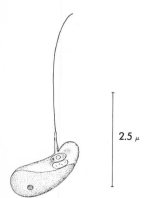

2.5 μ

FIGURE 7–21. Structure of *Micromonas pusilla,* one of the smallest marine flagellates, as reconstructed from electron micrographs, × 10,000 (after Manton & Parke).

Apart from the highly technical considerations of cellular fine structure, the algal student working with the light microscope should become familiar with some general and conspicuous characteristics of the cell contents.

The vacuoles are variable structures of considerable prominence in all of the algae except the Cyanophyta, in which they are small, obscure, and rarely discernible with the light microscope. Their principal fame is in their enormous size in some of the aseptate Chlorophyta such as *Caulerpa, Halicystis,* and especially *Valonia,* in which a single delimiting vacuolar membrane may enclose several cubic centimeters of cell sap. Some vacuoles may be of intricate shape and traversed by strands of cytoplasm. Others may be microscopic alveolae in the cytoplasm.

The vacuoles are commonly obscured by the parietal arrangement of plastids which are the most conspicuous elements of the cells. These chromatophores (chloroplasts, when containing predominantly chlorophyll) are of varied pigmentation and shape in different algal groups, and are sometimes employed morphologically as diagnostic characters in the recognition of genera and species. Chemically, the pigments provide the fundamental distinctions between the major algal divisions, or phyla.

The plastids may be small discoid or spindle-shaped structures, as in *Bryopsis,* or band-shaped and spirally oriented, as in *Stictyosiphon.* The chloroplasts of *Ulothrix* and other green algae are solitary, parietal, entire, sometimes cup-shaped structures, while those of *Cladophora* may be perforate or intricately reticulate (Figure 7-22). In some genera the chromatophore is not parietal but axial and often stellate. In its simpler forms the plastid is distinctly delimited, but in the more elaborate ones boundaries are difficult to establish. Electron microscopy is now rapidly extending our knowledge of the structure of the chloroplasts and their relationships to other intracellular organelles.

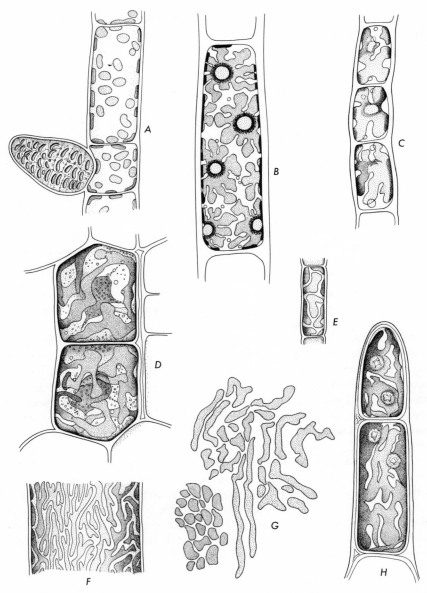

FIGURE 7–22. Various plastid types: *A*, small discoid plastids as seen in *Ectocarpus* (*Giffordia*) *ovatus*; *B*, a stellate form with central pyrenoid as seen in *Kylinia* (*Chromastrum*) *floridulum*; *C*, parietal, stellate to irregularly band-shaped forms in *Waerniella lucifuga*; *D*, parietal ribbon-shaped plastids of *Stictyosiphon tortilis*; *E–F*, progressive development of numerous, parietal, band-shaped plastids from juvenile to adult cells of *Antithamnion boreale*; *G*, plastid growth in *Aglaothamnion*, from small, angular juvenile forms to ligulate adult forms; *H*, reticulate form as seen in *Cladophora*. (*A, D–F, H*, after Reinke; *B–C*, after Kuckuck; *G*, after Feldmann-Mazoyer)

Evidently, in most cases the plastids are transmitted through cell division by segregation during cytokinesis. Likewise, in the formation of unicellular reproductive bodies the plastids are segregated so that daughter cells contain segments of the parental chromatophore. Transmission in the colorless spermatia of red algae is little known, but is presumed to be in a very reduced, leucoplast form.

The absence of any differentiated plastid in the cells of blue-green algae has long been puzzling to biologists and has led to a remarkable theory first expressed a half-century ago and recently revived as a result of electron-microscope studies of the ultrastructure of algal chloroplasts (Figure 7-23). These investigations have shown a striking similarity between the ultrastructure of a green algal chloroplast and that of a blue-green algal cell, sufficient to support the old hypothesis that chloroplasts may have evolved from endosymbiotic blue-green algae (such as occur today in several types of protozoa).

The pyrenoid is a colorless, usually spherical proteinaceous structure within the chromatophore. It has been studied especially in green algae, in which it is often prominent and sometimes so regular in numerical occurrence (*Enteromorpha* species) that the number may be used for specific identification of these plants. Pyrenoids may arise by division or *de novo*. They have an obscure function related to starch formation, and it is not clear to what extent the supposed pyrenoids of other groups of algae are like those of the Chlorophyta.

Starch formation, in any event, provides a conspicuous feature of many algal cells, for older thallus parts may have their cells so completely packed with starch grains that no other internal structures are evident. The pseudo-parenchymatous stipe cells of such plants as *Rhodymenia* and *Gracilaria* are commonly densely filled with floridean starch and afford a ready demonstration of this storage product.

One of the conspicuous intercellular features of many algae is the occurrence of pits or thin spots in the walls of adjoining cells that provide special transport of materials between them. These pits are especially conspicuous and large in many red algae and may be of two kinds: primary pits formed initially following cell division (Figures 7-32,*A*; 10-23,*A*), and secondary pits formed later either between cells that have remained in contact or between cells that achieve new contact by tissue invasion or displacement. There has long been uncertainty as to the actual occurrence of protoplasmic bridges or plasmodesmata through these pits (as has recently been demonstrated conclusively in higher plants by electron micrographs). Among Phaeophyta the extension of protoplasmic strands through the pits has been recognized only in the sieve plates of larger kelps such as *Macrocystis* (see end of section, "The Holdfast and Stipe"). Generally, the pits seem to be closed by a membrane. In the Florideophycidae, however, Dawes has recently recognized two major groups of pit connections: 1) in which the pit connection is an open channel between two cells, and 2) in which numerous plasmodesmata traverse a continuous, loose, microfibrillar wall.

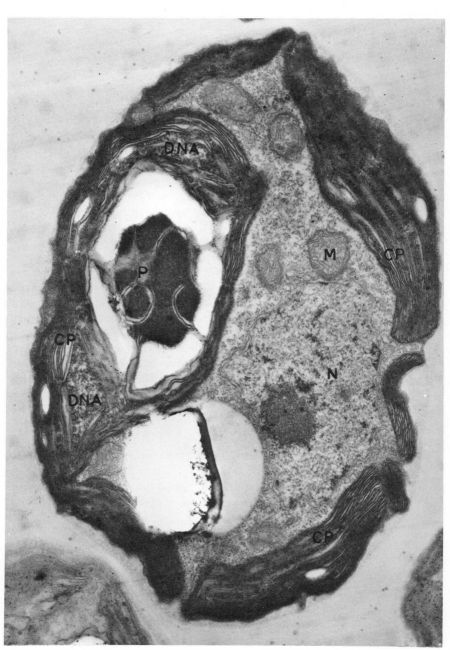

FIGURE 7–23. Electron micrograph of section of *Chlamydomonas moewusii*, showing fine structure of chloroplast (cp), mitochondria (m), nucleus (n), and pyrenoid (p), ×
21,000 (courtesy of Walter Plaut and Hans Ris).

ZYGOTES, SPORES, AND GERMLINGS

Early botanists recognized a fundamental difference between the higher and the lower plants in that the latter did not arise by germination of recognizable macroscopic seeds, but by obscure microscopic spores or invisible means. This led them to designate the entire vast assemblage as cryptogams. The gradual improvement of microscopic techniques has brought belated advance of the developmental morphology of cryptogams in which studies of the marine algae long lagged. Recent emphasis by numerous workers on perfection of marine culture methods is now rapidly adding new data on early growth-stages of seaweeds at marine stations throughout the world.

The vegetative algal thallus develops in numerous ways, but, with rare exception, only from a uninucleate, unicellular zygote or spore. The zygotes result from the fusion of several kinds of gametes (Figure 7-24). In the green and brown algae both gametes are motile (or at least the male gamete is), while

FIGURE 7–24. Various types of marine algal gametes: *A–C,* motile isogametes of scarcely distinguishable size and form as seen in *Enteromorpha,* showing copulation; *D,* motile anisogametes of *Cutleria; E,* motile male gametes and large, nonmotile egg of *Fucus; F,* nonmotile gametes (spermatia) of *Nemalion* at discharge and adhering to the female reproductive organ, the carpogonium.

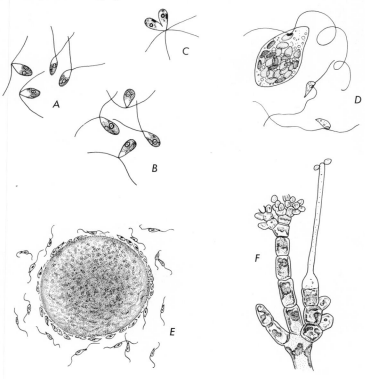

in the red algae both gametes are nonmotile. Fertilization by fusion of flagellated gametes of the same size and morphology is called isogamy, while that involving flagellated gametes of dissimilar size is called anisogamy. The fertilization of a nonmotile but free oösphere by a flagellated spermatozoid is oögamy. In the red algae, fertilization is accomplished by a passive, nonflagellated spermatium fusing with the protoplast of a female cell (carpogonium) that is never released from the female plant. This is followed by a unique series of postfertilization stages (see concluding portion of this chapter) that are designated by a special terminology.

Spores are of several kinds (Figure 7-25). In a large majority of brown and green algae they are motile, flagellated bodies called zoospores or swarmers. In most of the red algae and in some brown algae, nonmotile spores are

FIGURE 7–25. Various types of spores: *A*, motile, quadriflagellate zoöspores as in *Enteromorpha; B*, a tetrad of spores of *Dictyota; C*, zonately arranged tetraspores in a vertical section of the crustose thallus of *Haematocelis; D*, tetrasporangium of *Antithamnion*, showing 3 of the 4 spores; *E*, polysporangium of *Pleonosporium* (*B*, after Thuret).

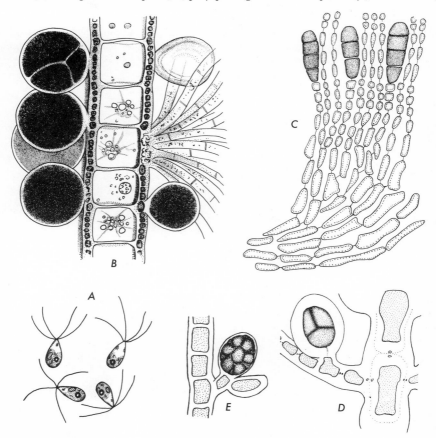

produced in groups of four (tetraspores), or, occasionally, sporangial contents may divide into numerous polyspores before they are released. In some instances a single spore (monospore, within its sporangial wall) is cut off from a bearing cell. Another kind of red algal spore, the carpospore, is produced in groups or dense masses in special structures on the female gametophyte plants (see conclusion of this chapter; Figure 10-15,*E*).

There are three principal methods of germination of the spore or of the free zygote to form initials of the photosynthetic blade and its holdfast: 1) it cuts off a basal cell which develops into a primary rhizoid; 2) it produces a protuberance into which the spore empties itself followed by division to form a creeping or prostrate filament system; or 3) it divides by diversely oriented walls to form a primary disc or cushion (Figure 7-26).

Laminaria and *Fucus* are examples of the first type, in which in the early germling stages the primary rhizoid and the erect blade develop simultaneously. The first rhizoid is soon supplemented by others that emanate from the lower cells of the germling so that a complex of unicellular rhizoids provides the initial holdfast and anchorage. Soon, however, cell division at the base of this rhizoidally attached stipe results in an expanding parenchymatous basal disc. From this a whorl of branched haptera extend and are progressively augmented by successive whorls of haptera from higher levels on the stipe base.

Essentially the same type of holdfast development obtains in many small filamentous algae *(Antithamnion)*, in which an initial rhizoidal attachment is later supplemented by the production of secondary anchoring stolons from the lower vegetative cells of the erect axes.

The second type of germling development is exemplified by *Nemalion*, which develops a spongy basal stratum of short, rounded cells bearing erect threads that develop as a group into the mature thallus. Epiphytic forms of *Acrochaetium* may also show this kind of attachment by a prostrate system of radiating filaments giving rise to erect axes (heterotrichous filament development).

The third type is found throughout most of the larger red algae and is exemplified by *Cystoclonium*, in which the spores divide irregularly to form a small, hemispherical, primary attachment disc anchored by short, unicellular rhizoids (Figure 7-26,*C*). The erect frond develops subsequently from this disc or cushion which expands with age, but which usually retains its essential discoid or cushion-like form. Supplemental attachment may be afforded by downwardly growing rhizoids or by spreading or penetrating stolons. The rhizoids may sometimes develop in great quantity to form a felted, spongy (stupose) holdfast, as in *Dictyopteris* and *Zonaria*. The stolons may emerge from the base of the stipe in a radiating, root-like tangle *(Rhodymenia)*, or from upper parts of a plant that has become decumbent or arched back to the substrate *(Coeloseira)*. Especially interesting examples of stoloniferous development are seen in *Laminaria sinclairii* and in *Sciadophycus* (Figure 7-27).

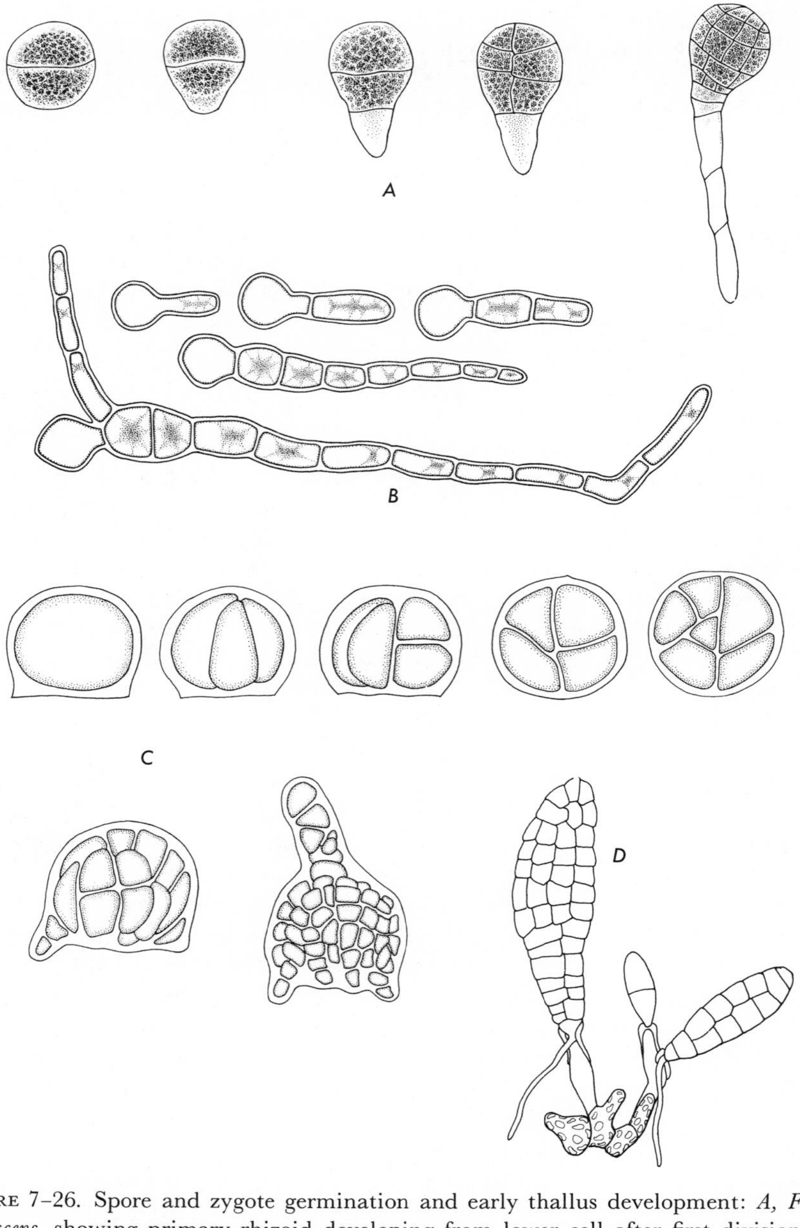

FIGURE 7–26. Spore and zygote germination and early thallus development: *A, Fucus evanescens,* showing primary rhizoid developing from lower cell after first division; *B, Nemalion multifidum,* showing protuberance into which spore contents move and are cut off followed by development of a prostrate filament system; *C, Cystoclonium purpurascens,* showing divisions to produce a primary disc from which the erect thallus arises; *D, Laminaria digitata,* showing a mature female gametophyte and 3 stages in germling development from zygotes (*A,* after Inoh; *B–C,* after Kylin).

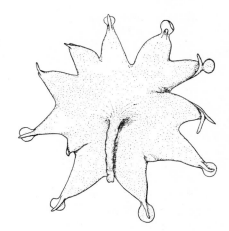

FIGURE 7–27. *Sciadophycus stellatus,* showing the parasol-like thallus and the development of secondary attachment stolons from the tip of each point of the star.

MERISTEMS

In the several kinds of germling plants mentioned above, the blade portions develop by means of three principal kinds of meristems, namely, diffuse, intercalary, and apical. A fourth kind (marginal) may be a modified intercalary or apical type, or may often be of secondary development. Growth from any of these may be augmented by localized secondary meristematic cells in various parts of the plant.

Diffuse Meristems

Diffuse growth may be studied in a filamentous plant, such as *Ectocarpus* or *Ulothrix;* in a foliose one, such as *Ulva, Punctaria,* or *Porphyra;* or in a fleshy form, such as *Colpomenia.* In heterotrichous *Ectocarpus* the prostrate system shows apical growth of its filaments, whereas the erect system shows cell divisions occurring irregularly throughout the uniseriate strands, seldom confined either to apical or intercalary regions (although special cases of the latter will be mentioned below). In *Porphyra* the sheet-like thallus begins as a simple filament and for a brief time may exhibit an apical cell. A broadening monostromatic or distromatic blade soon develops, however, as a result of numerous longitudinal divisions. It then undergoes diffuse expansion by divisions in all planes perpendicular to the surface. In species with marginal reproductive areas, successive inward maturity of these and subsequent erosion may for a considerable time keep pace with the vegetative growth so that the small intact plant shows little evidence of the growth it has achieved. On the other hand, in quiet pools detached forms of *Ulva* and *Porphyra* may be encountered in which vegetative expansion of the fragile sheet may continue without interruption to an extent of several meters.

Intercalary Meristems

Intercalary meristematic activity is widely present among brown algae and occurs in some red algae. It may be of massive or of trichothallic type. Trichothallic growth is encountered in various of the lower groups of brown algae and consists of growth from the base of one or more terminal hairs. In some species of *Ectocarpus* and other Ectocarpales, the uniseriate filament exhibits a distinct zone at which cells are cut off above and below. Those cut off on the upper side are usually fewer and narrower and are added to the length of the terminal hair which may have reduced pigmentation. Those cells cut off toward the base develop into ordinary photosynthetic cells themselves capable of producing branches.

In *Desmarestia* a uniseriate apical hair (Figure 9-8,*C*) initiates the development of an often massive blade. The hair exhibits at its base closely spaced transverse divisions representing the trichothallic meristem. This meristem adds cells to the hair, which continually erodes away, while those it cuts off below develop opposite, distichous, secondary lateral hairs with meristems at their bases. From these a corticating envelope rapidly encloses the axial filament and its derivatives.

Cutleria achieves trichothallic growth in a flat blade through a large number of terminal hairs arranged in a double row in one plane and constituting a terminal fringe (Figure 9-4). Each of these has a basal meristem which, on its lower side, cuts off cells that undergo several transverse and longitudinal septations as they fuse to form the compact blade tissue.

The Pacific brown alga, *Haplogloia* (Figure 9-8,*A*), exhibits trichothallic growth in a thallus of radial organization. Numerous other variations of intercalary growth occur in brown algae of primarily filamentous construction (Figure 7-28).

Massive intercalary meristems are best known in the kelps, of which *Laminaria* is a prime example. As in all Laminariales, the primary meristem of *Laminaria* is situated between stipe and blade in the transition zone. This zone consists of a compact, massive parenchymatous tissue many cells broad and thick. A series of specimens from small juveniles to adults shows clearly the two-way addition of tissue to the stipe and to the blade, but it is not easy to discern by observation the limits of the critical region of cell division. This can be determined in a marine laboratory by a simple experiment in which a series of juvenile plants several centimeters tall are grown on an illuminated seawater table. Small rectangles of tissue are cut out of the base of the blades at varying measured distances above the stipe, and the plants are affixed with silicone rubber to a convenient moveable substrate. After a few weeks the growth of the plants will reveal the effect of the cuts on the development of the blade. Cuts made above the meristem will simply enlarge as they are carried upward by cell expansion and secondary septation, while cuts inflicted on the meristem itself will result in a longitudinal slit that, with terminal erosion, splits the blade.

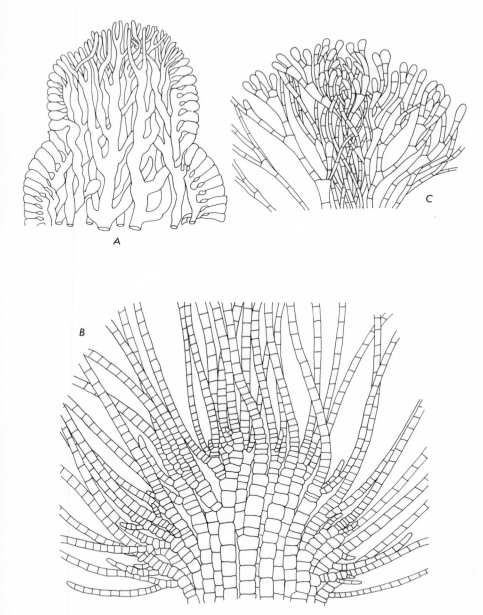

FIGURE 7–28. Examples of multiaxial construction as seen in (*A*) the siphonous green alga *Pseudocodium,* (*B*) the brown alga, *Myriogloia,* and (*C*) the red alga, *Dermonema* (after Weber van Bosse, Kuckuck, Børgesen, resp.).

Eisenia exhibits a particularly interesting meristem that demonstrates the changing gross morphology of many kelps with age. Juvenile plants are of the characteristic *Laminaria* type with simple stipe and blade. The blade is, however, determinate and shows early terminal erosion. As this erosion proceeds, the intercalary meristem, which at first produced the symmetrical primary blade, becomes confined to its two basal margins where initials of a series of lateral blades are formed. These secondary blades develop by means of secondary intercalary meristems at their bases, while the marginal remnants of the primary meristem continue to initiate new blades below them. By this time the old primary blade has eroded away, leaving a pseudo-forking which in age becomes stipe-like (Figure 7-7).

Apical Meristems

Apical meristems are those in which one or more apical cells cut off new cells, usually basally. They are conspicuous in members of the Fucales, Dictyotales, and Sphacelariales among brown algae, and provide for growth in a majority of the floridean red algae (Figure 7-29). In such brown algal forms as *Zonaria* and *Padina* the terminal meristem consists of a broad, marginal row of initials.

In some of the Ectocarpales, such as *Nemacystus,* it is evident from comparative morphology of adult axes that a trichothallic meristem has been replaced by a single apical cell through evolutionary loss of the terminal hair. The germling stages of *Fucus,* likewise show the origin of a definitive apical cell from the intercalary meristem of a hair. The zygote develops polarity by producing its first wall at right angles to the direction of incident light. A pear-shaped mass of cells develops from the upper cell and an attachment rhizoid from the lower (Figure 7-26). From among the cells occupying the apex of this germling, one cell divides and grows out into a first hair which elongates by means of an intercalary meristem at its base. Subsequently, other hairs develop from surrounding cells in the same way, while the first hair degenerates down to its basal cell, which then becomes the apical cell of the young plant (Figure 7-30). This apical cell has been observed in young stages of many Fucales as a three-sided cell in transverse section and more or less biconvex in longitudinal section. The three-sided form may persist through the life of the plant in some Fucales, or, as in *Fucus,* may develop early into a four-sided apical cell having the shape of a truncated pyramid.

In *Dictyota* the apical cell is of prominent lenticular form and affords the classical example of dichotomous branching, inasmuch as the longitudinal division of this large cell into two equal halves can be observed with ease (Figure 7-29,*A–B*).

Sphacelaria is a good example of the occurrence of a prominent apical cell in a filamentous brown alga, and illustrates a method of development of a multiseriate filament from a uniseriate one. The comparatively large apical cell cuts off segments parallel with its base, so that the end of a branch consists of

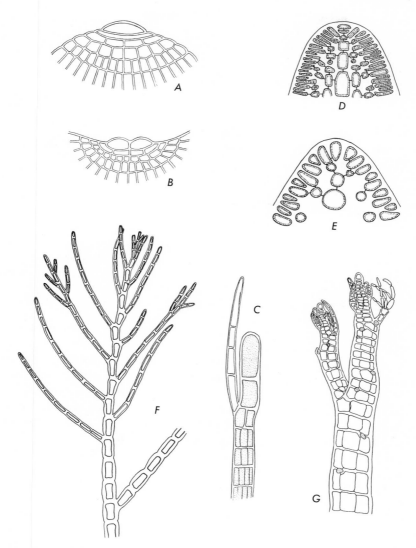

FIGURE 7–29. Various examples of apical cells: *A–B, Dictyota,* showing an undivided apex and a dichotomy; *C, Sphacelaria; D, Gelidium; E, Gracilaria; F, Callithamnion; G, Polysiphonia.*

a short series of these of the same diameter as the apical cell. Longitudinal (and sometimes also transverse) septations produce smaller and smaller cells from these segments, which exhibit no further enlargement (Figure 9-3,*A*). Thus, the diameter of the branches is essentially the same as that of the apical cell that produces the entire growth in length of a branch essentially without intercalary elongation or enlargement.

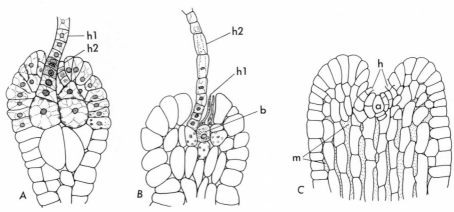

FIGURE 7–30. Early development of *Fucus*, showing origin of apical cell: *A*, development of first hair (h1) at apex of germling; *B*, degeneration of all cells of the first hair except the basal cell, which becomes the apical cell (b), and development of second hair (h2); *C*, advanced stage of functioning of apical cell (a) after degeneration of hairs (h). The cortex is seen forming from the meristoderm and the medullary cells show stretching and mucilage spaces (m). (*A* after Nienberg; *C* after Oltmanns).

Apical growth may be studied in greatest diversity among the floridean red algae whose fundamental structural characteristic is that of a system of branched filaments exhibiting growth by apical cells. There are two major types of this filamentous construction, the uniaxial and the multiaxial, in which the thallus is derived, respectively, from one or from several axial filaments. These structural types are of fundamental significance, for they are generally characteristic of the larger taxonomic units. Thus, all members of the order Ceramiales are strictly uniaxial, and all members of the Rhodymeniales are strictly multiaxial. In other instances family assemblages may be distinguished by these basic features. In uniaxial types an individual apical cell is recognizable, while in multiaxial types the number of apical cells may be so large as to make them indistinguishable. In either case the apical cells cut off segments that undergo little or no further division (except to cut off branch initials) so that enlargement of the thallus is effected mainly by continued apical growth of filaments rather than by intercalary division of derived cells. Several illustrative examples of the major types may be taken up in turn. Small and delicate forms are best chosen for ease of interpretation, inasmuch as the complexities of secondary tissue developments and those of compaction of the filamentous structure in many larger forms obscure the fundamental features. This may be so even when distinct apical cells are evident.

Uniaxial Types

Callithamnion represents a simplified, monopodial branching type in which the apical cell of a uniseriate filament basally cuts off segments that are added to the primary axial filament (Figure 7-29,*F*). These, in turn, (usually at a very early stage) cut off alternately or spirally from the distal end of each cell the initial of a lateral branch whose length becomes governed by the determinate or indeterminate potential of its apical cell. The cells of the axial filament undergo no further division involving septa, although they may emit rhizoidal corticating filaments. These filaments characteristically grow downward around the axis and progressively envelop it. By continued growth they may form layer upon layer of strengthening and thickening cortical tissue. Sometimes cells of this corticating layer may divide periclinally, as well, to build up a pseudoparenchymatous tissue (Figure 7-31,*F*). So complete is this compacting and fusion that in many species the initially filamentous construction, with its axial cell row, can be detected only in the very youngest apical regions. In others, the cell walls may be so soft that the individual filament branches can be separated and observed on a slide by pressing them out under the cover slip. Firm thalli can be treated with softening reagents and squashed to reveal their filamentous structure (see Chapter 18).

Polysiphonia is a type illustrative of a diverse array of red algae in which the derivatives from the apical cell cut off pericentral cells that surround the central axial filament cells. In *Polysiphonia*, these remain in tiers equal in length to the central axial cells to form what is called a polysiphonous structure.

As a member of the large family Rhodomelaceae, *Polysiphonia* illustrates the manner of origin of the pericentral cells which is precise in relation to the usual production of two kinds of laterals: ordinary branches, which in turn develop the polysiphonous structure, and uniseriate branches, called trichoblasts, which are often colorless and deciduous (Figure 7-29,*G*). The dome-shaped apical cell cuts off beneath itself a series of segments, some or all of which may produce a lateral. The initial of the lateral is cut off first from an upper side of a segment before longitudinal divisions begin in the formation of central and pericentral cells. The primary laterals are usually trichoblasts which usually arise in a right-hand spiral succession, often from each central axial segment. Next, the pericentral cells are formed successively, the first one being cut off beneath the initial of the lateral just formed at the top of the cell. Additional pericentrals (totaling from 4 to 20) are cut off alternately on either side of the first to close the ring. Like the parent axis, regular polysiphonous branches may arise either as a replacement of a trichoblast or from the basal cell of a trichoblast by its initiating a new apical cell (Figure 10-21).

In a number of other red algae, including fleshy types such as *Gracilaria* and *Gelidium,* the pericentral cells are cut off in a somewhat different manner (Figure 7-29,*D–E*) and become the apical cells of laterals which, by their repeated monopodial branching, build up the thick, primary thallus tissues.

Hypoglossum is one of the finest examples of apical cell development for student examination, for in this plant the complexities of the three-dimensional thallus are reduced by the organization of all the juxtaposed and fused thallus filaments in a single plane. Since the delicate blade is essentially monostromatic, it is possible to observe without any obstruction the sequence of development

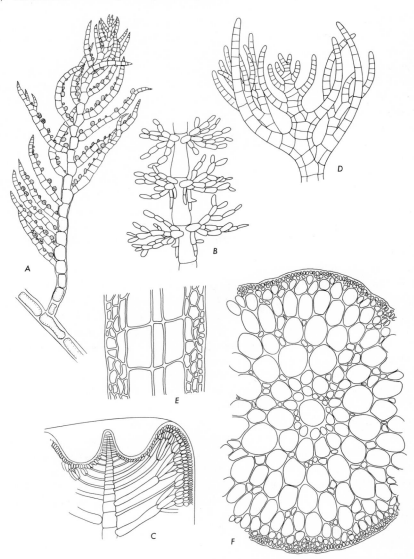

FIGURE 7–31. Representative examples of elaboration and compaction of tissues in algae of uniaxial construction: *A, Callithamnion,* showing simple uniaxial construction with all filaments free; *B, Sirodotia,* showing a uniseriate axis with whorled branches and downwardly developing corticating filaments; *C,* growing tip of *Chondria,* showing central axial filament and branches terminating in small cortical cells forming a complete covering, but with filamentous construction still evident (after Falkenberg); *D, Heterosiphonia,* showing development of a compact cortication by cell division near the sympodially branched apex (after Falkenberg); *E,* a fully corticated species of *Polysiphonia* in longitudinal section showing pseudoparenchymatous appearance of mature axis; *F,* transection of mature axis of *Chondria,* showing fully-developed pseudoparenchyma.

of almost every cell. The massive apical cell cuts off basally a lens-shaped segment, which by longitudinal divisions produces a central cell and four pericentral cells. (Of these, the two in the plane of a slide preparation are readily visible.) These two lateral pericentrals assume the function of lateral apical cells and proceed to cut off successive laterals of secondary, tertiary, and higher orders, each of which possesses a long, thin, apical cell whose tip reaches the thallus margin and shows by its position the order of derivation from the original pericentral cell (Figure 7-32,*A*). The clarity of the presentation is further enhanced by the absence of any intercalary divisions or secondary septation of the central axial cells, which merely continue to enlarge along with multiplication of the lateral filaments, and by the prominence of primary pit connections in the cell lineages.

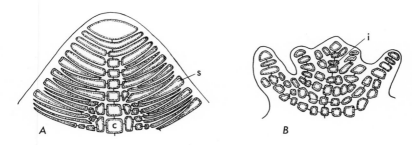

FIGURE 7-32. Apical cells in the Delesseriaceae. *A, Hypoglossum,* showing development of a central axial cell row (c) without intercalary divisions, and of secondary apical cells at the margins (s). *B, Phycodrys,* showing intercalary cell divisions developing in primary axial cell row (i) and throughout.

Some other members of the Delesseriaceae depart from the usual pattern of strictly apical growth in the red algae by exhibiting intercalary division in the primary cell rows from the apical cell. An example of this type of thallus expansion is provided by *Phycodrys* (Figure 7-32,*B*).

A further structural complexity in the uniaxial type results from the secondary development of rhizoidal filaments from young medullary and cortical cells. These descend by worming their ways between the cells of the inner parts of the thallus, thickening and strengthening the axis as they go. In soft thalli these filaments may actually pass through the gelatinous walls. Sometimes secondary filaments may become so numerous that they completely obscure a primary pseudoparenchymatous structure, although they may, instead, be limited to definite medullary or cortical areas of the thallus.

Gelidium serves as a good example of the latter type of dense thallus, in which the prominent apical cell develops filamentous derivatives that are completely consolidated into a pseudoparenchyma. At an early stage these in turn produce very slender, thick-walled rhizoidal filaments that become densely packed between the subcortical cells and greatly increase the tensile strength and elasticity of the thallus.

All of the foregoing have been examples of monopodial branching types. *Heterosiphonia* serves best as an illustration of the sympodial type, for several members of that genus are common, ecorticate forms in which the order of cellular development of the sympodium can readily be followed. Figure 7-31,*D* shows a sympodial organization in which the apical cell cuts off segments beneath it. The second or third of these segments produces the initial of a lateral. This initial assumes the function of the apical cell by deflecting to a side position the apical cell of the preceding generation immediately above it. Thus, the apical cell that had served the primary axis now provides increased length and branching of the pseudolateral, which remains uniseriate except near its base. The primary sympodial axis cells, on the other hand, undergo septation to form pericentral cells in much the same manner as in *Polysiphonia*.

Multiaxial Types

In these advanced types of thallus construction the growing apex consists of several closely juxtaposed filaments whose numerous branches make up a more or less compact cortex (Figure 7-28). In such red, brown, and green algae as *Nemalion (Dermonema), Myriogloia,* and *Codium,* respectively, the individual filaments and their branches are clearly evident and sufficiently free that one can readily recognize the multiaxial construction. On the other hand, firmer, more massive, and leafy thalli, as *Gigartina* and *Iridaea,* with entangled, filamentous medullary cells and dense, anticlinal cortical cell rows, give no superficial hint of their actual type of structure. This can be determined only by sectioning and laborious investigation. Such elaborate forms among red and brown algae often arise from a primary heterotrichous filament in which several or many threads of the erect system (rather than a single one) join in the development of the mature thallus.

The multiaxial structure of *Nemalion* is readily studied, for the thallus consists of a cylinder of ramified filaments in a mucilaginous intercellular matrix (Figure 7-33,*A*). A fragment on a slide can be squashed by gentle pressure of a cover slip, and the filaments can be sufficiently separated to permit individual examination. The apex of an axis shows a central core of longitudinal axial filaments, each terminating in an apical cell and each provided with much-branched lateral filaments of uniformly limited growth. These form a radiating envelope of pigmented assimilators around the colorless axial threads.

A series of gradual modifications toward compaction and solidification of the thallus of multiaxial forms may be traced from *Nemalion* through *Scinaia,* in which the matrix is firmly gelatinous and in which a differentiated cortex occurs; through calcareous *Jania* and *Corallina,* in which the filamentous structure of the stony thallus is readily observed after decalcification; to *Agardhiella,* in which the lateral filaments are firmly fused by their adjacent walls into a solid, pseudoparenchymatous tissue.

In *Agardhiella tenera* the apices exhibit a group of five to seven apical cells. The laterals that arise from these are compacted into the cortex, which shows large vacuolate inner cells and small external ones. The inner cells of the

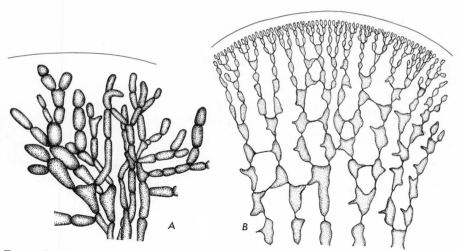

FIGURE 7–33. Apical growth of filaments in plants of multiaxial development: *A, Nemalion; B, Chondrus.*

laterals secondarily produce downwardly-growing rhizoidal cells that provide the characteristic filamentous core of the mature medulla in this plant.

Numerous other fleshy and foliose plants in the Cryptonemiales, Gigartinales, and Rhodymeniales show multiaxial construction of a solid tissue with greater or lesser evidence of the fundamentally filamentous character. In many of these the primary apical cells are numerous but are indistinguishable from the secondary apical cells of derivative laterals. At the terminus of an axis, in *Chondrus,* for example, the sequence of cell origins may be seen in the branched anticlinal filaments with their prominent primary pit connections. A short distance below, however, the cells of these filaments show rapid elongation and development of very thick gelatinous walls with prominent secondary pit connections that obscure the fundamental organization (Figure 7-33,*B*). Despite the lack of differentiation in the apex of such a coarse, multiaxial thallus, a precise and characteristic shape develops as a result of differential growth of the compacted, branching filaments.

Secondary Meristems

Secondary meristematic developments are present in great diversity among the benthic algae, and these provide most of the complexities of structure that so often make difficult the interpretation of algal anatomy. These meristems, both external and internal, may arise simply as a part of normal maturation of a thallus. Or they may form in response to injury or to modified local environment, as a mechanism for regeneration or vegetative proliferation. Regeneration from animal-grazed surfaces is common, as is proliferation after the sloughing away of larger, overshadowing plants.

Padina is an example of a change from a primary to a secondary meristem as the plant develops from its juvenile *(Vaughaniella)* stage with its single apical cell, to the adult, fan-shaped thallus. When this transition is to be made, the apical cell undergoes repeated longitudinal division in one plane to produce a broadening marginal row of initials, all of which develop dense protoplasmic contents and become meristematic.

The sympodial thalli of some *Rhodymenia* species show successive development of a new external, multiaxial meristem at the base of each mature blade as it initiates the next (Figure 7-34).

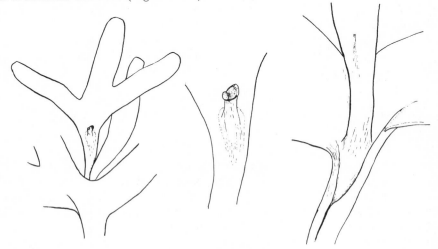

FIGURE 7–34. Secondary meristems in *Rhodymenia*. Sympodial development of a new blade from the base of a mature one is the result of a secondary, regenerative meristem.

Some of the various types of secondary tissue developments have already been mentioned, but they are so significant in an understanding of the structural characteristics of many plants that their importance cannot be over-emphasized to the beginning phycologist. Thus, one finds in almost all of the larger benthic algae as well as in many small ones, that some kind of cortical modification takes place a short distance below the tip by development of secondary corticating filaments. Similarly, the origin of downwardly-growing secondary medullary filaments that invade, fill, and expand the primary tissue may result in a completely different appearance of transections made at the apex and at a short distance below it.

The occurrence of the specially designated meristoderm in the stipes of Laminariales, and of the secondary development in some of these kelps of seasonal growth rings from cortical meristems, has been mentioned at the beginning of this chapter.

Regenerative meristems are common among the benthic algae and are especially conspicuous in foliose Rhodophyta, in which many species are capable of developing a new thallus from a small fragment of an old one.

Likewise, the animal grazing pressure is often so heavy that plants are found to be frequently and repeatedly regenerating new branches from old stubs. These proliferations from damaged tips and margins are often responsible for such bizarre, abnormal forms that the identity of a plant is recognized only with difficulty.

Some remarkable malformations have recently been reported by Japanese workers, evidently resulting from natural grafting of meristems. In two instances, thalli of two species of *Laminaria,* and, in one instance, the thalli of a species of *Alaria* and a species of *Laminaria,* have become coalesced in postgermling stages to produce a chimaera combining the vegetative characters of each component.

REPRODUCTIVE STRUCTURES

The slow development of cryptogamic botany in the eighteenth and early nineteenth centuries, compared with the burgeoning of seed-plant botany, was due in no small measure to neglect stemming from insurmountable difficulties of classification. These, in turn, were largely due to a lack of understanding of the morphological bases of reproduction. The neglect of marine algae was particularly widespread, for a great majority of these exhibited a confusing array of morphological variations and of reproductive bodies that defied interpretation. The confusion was compounded and understanding handicapped by a deep-seated belief in spontaneous generation and in the supposition that all organisms exhibiting movement should automatically be regarded as animals. Thus, the production of motile cells from an alga was widely held, until about a hundred years ago, as evidence of a plant changing into an animal. To these misconceptions, even in the face of obvious and unmistakable variability in nature, was added the stultifying concept of immutability of species. Against this background it is little wonder that there were few established facts concerning the reproduction of algae up to 1853.

The turning point came in that year, when Thuret, working with the eggs and sperms of *Fucus,* introduced a series of studies that soon established the occurrence of sexuality in a number of green, red, and brown algae. This led to an understanding of the long-observed process of conjugation in *Spirogyra,* and to an expanding explanation of the morphological inconsistencies in the benthic algae that had baffled marine botanists. Still it was left to Berthold in 1881 to observe nuclear fusion in a marine alga, and it was not until 1906 that Yamanouchi finally worked out the nuclear cycle of a red alga and correctly interpreted its life history.

We now recognize not only a large number of different kinds of reproductive bodies in the algae but a great diversity in the methods of reproduction that occur in the life histories. Some of the generalities under these subjects will be taken up here as a background for the more detailed examination of selected representative plants in later chapters.

Kinds of Reproductive Bodies

Sexual reproduction ordinarily results from the phenomenon of syngamy, or the sexual fusion of cells. It usually involves both plasmogamy (fusion of cytoplasm) and karyogamy (fusion of nuclei). These fusions, however, need not occur simultaneously, and in some red algae they are more or less separated in time. In some diatoms and euglenoids only karyogamy occurs, and it is called autogamy when two nuclei from the same parent cell fuse in the reproductive process. Syngamy, however, is prevalent in the algae and involves a fusion of gametes usually arising from separate sexual plants or, sometimes, from different fertile regions of the same plant.

The green algae serve as the best point of departure in considering sexual reproduction in the algae, for they include several independent evolutionary series, each of which show gametic union in their simplest primitive forms and a progression through several phases to the most advanced members of the group (see Chapter 11).

The several terms employed for the principal types of gametic fusion such as occur in these series have been mentioned above: isogamous, anisogamous, and oögamous. The latter two kinds of fusion, involving dissimilar gametes, are termed heterogamous. Except in red algae, where special terms are used, one may speak of the motile sexual bodies as zoögametes and of the nonmotile ones as oöspheres or eggs. Where fusion is accomplished within a common gelatinous envelope or through conjugation tubes, the nonmotile gametes are called aplanogametes.

A plant that produces gametes is called a gametophyte, and where there are separate male and female gametophyte plants the species is said to be dioecious. When separate male and female areas of the same plant discharge gametes, the species is monoecious.

The gametes are borne in gametangia, and in the great majority of algae these are unicellular structures. Apart from Charophytes, only in some of the Phaeophyta do multicellular gametangia occur, and in these a single gamete is usually produced in each cell (Figure 7-35). In a majority of the Chlorophyta the gametangia are not differentiated and are indistinguishable from vegetative cells until the zoögametes are released. Brown algal gametangia are usually more or less differentiated from vegetative cells and may be unilocular or plurilocular. Where distinctive spermatozoids (antherozoids) and eggs are produced, the respective gametangia are called antheridia and oögonia. In the red algae a special terminology is used, for the gametes are always nonmotile and are usually produced terminally on a filament. The male gamete (spermatium) is formed within the spermatangium and is liberated as a minute free cell. The female reproductive body is produced within the female sex organ, the carpogonium, and is never freed from the filament that bears it (the carpogonial branch).

In most instances the zygote resulting from syngamy does not reproduce the parent gametophyte plant, but instead develops directly or indirectly into a different kind of plant, the sporophyte, which produces some kind of meiospore.

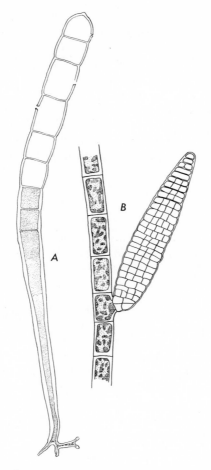

FIGURE 7–35. Two kinds of gametangia: *A,* a series of little-differentiated gametangia in *Chaetormorpha,* showing small apertures from which the zoospores have escaped; *B,* a well-differentiated, multicellular (plurilocular) gametangium as seen in *Ectocarpus.*

The meiospore, in turn, usually germinates to produce the gametophyte plant again and, thus, to complete what has been called an alternation of generations.

The meiospores produced by the sporophyte plants are of a number of kinds. In marine Chlorophyta they are almost always motile zoospores, usually with two or four anterior flagella. A number of these are produced in a sporangium (zoosporangium). Like the gametangia of green algae, the sporangia are often scarcely or not at all differentiated from vegetative cells until liberation occurs, nor are they superficially distinguishable from the gametangia except in cases of pigment differences. One usually must study the released swarmers to determine whether they are gametes or zoospores.

The brown algae also are mainly producers of zoospores from their sporophyte generation, either from unilocular or plurilocular zoosporangia. The principal exception is the order Dictyotales in which four or eight large, nonmotile aplanospores are produced. The unique and historically important situation in the fucalean brown algae will be discussed below in the consideration of life histories.

It is in the red algae that the characters of the spore (always nonmotile) find their greatest significance in taxonomy, for not only are a number of distinctive kinds produced, but these types are often representative of particular systematic groups and are extensively used in classification (Figure 7-36).

FIGURE 7-36. Kinds of sporangia in red algae, left to right: 2 forms of regularly divided zonate sporangia, an irregularly zonate sporangium, 2 cruciately divided forms, 2 tetrahedrally divided forms, an undivided monosporangium, a bisporangium, and a polysporangium.

In a large majority of the Rhodophyta the so-called "asexual" spores, from the meiosporophyte plants, arise by meiotic division of the contents of a one-celled sporangium and appear as a group of four tetraspores. The orientations of the walls resulting from the divisions within the sporangium are usually precise and may be: 1) transverse and parallel (zonate) to produce a row of four tetraspores; 2) at right angles to each other to produce a cruciate group; 3) tetrahedral to produce a tetrad of spores of similar shape. In a few forms the sporangium undergoes multiple divisions to produce polyspores, while in others two divisions of the tetrasporangium may be suppressed with a bispore result. A few species produce monospores (not necessarily on the sporophyte plant).

Fertile Structures

The manner in which the sporangia (or the sexual structures) are borne provides some of the most distinctive characteristics of the benthic algae. Although in many green algae sporangia and gametangia are undifferentiated cells, some forms, especially the higher siphonous types, have highly distinctive reproductive structures. The well-known "cap" of *Acetabularia* is a rotate group of gametangia. *Codium* bears male and female gametangia as lateral branchlets on the utricles. *Batophora* and *Dasycladus* have readily visible, deeply pigmented spherical gametangia among the lateral branchlets (Figure 7-37).

Zoosporangia in brown algae are often grouped in more or less extensive fertile areas called sori (Figure 7-38). The sorus may be borne on a special fertile blade called a sporophyll. In the Fucales the antheridia and oögonia are borne in cavities in the thallus called conceptacles. These are commonly aggregated in special fertile branches or branch-tips called receptacles (Figure 9-13, 9-14).

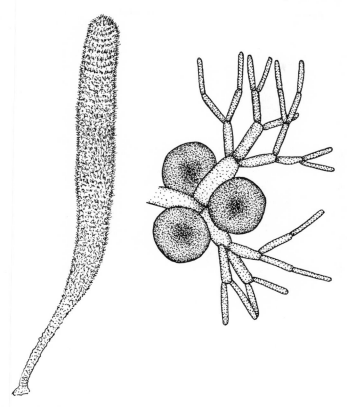

FIGURE 7-37. *Batophora oerstedi*, showing habit of a plant and the spherical gametangia among the verticillate branches.

In red algae the organization of the reproductive structures is particularly varied. The tetrasporangia and spermatangia may be borne superficially and scattered over the entire upper part of the thallus, or they may be grouped in various kinds of sori. Sometimes the sori are restricted to branch tips, to marginal or superficial leaflets, or to special branchlets (stichidia), or they may be in pits or hollows (conceptacles). In the coralline algae the conceptacles are especially definitive. Often the tetrasporangial sori have a distinctive structure (Figure 7-39). The sporangia may be borne among special anticlinal filaments (paraphyses) in a cushion-like sorus called a nemathecium. Sometimes they are geometrically oriented.

The prevalent macroscopic reproductive structure in the red algae is the cystocarp (Figure 7-40). Cystocarps are usually numerous on female gametophyte plants. On delicate plants they may be free. On larger thalli they may appear as small dark spots (1 to 2 millimeters in diameter) imbedded in the thallus, or as small domoid warts or papillae on the surface or margins of blades and branches. Embedded cystocarps consist usually only of a more or less spherical

FIGURE 7–38. Portions of fertile sporophylls of *Nereocystis,* showing sequence of development of zoosporangial sori which, when mature, fall out of the blade as a unit and drift to the bottom as discharge of zoospores ensues.

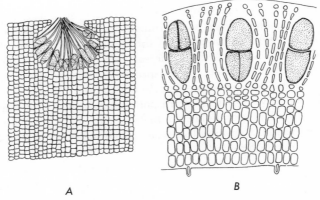

A   B

FIGURE 7–39. Specialized tetrasporangial sori: *A,* a conceptacle with sporangia and paraphyses as seen in vertical section in *Hildenbrandtia; B,* a nemathecium with sporangia and paraphyses as seen in a vertical section of *Peyssonelia.*

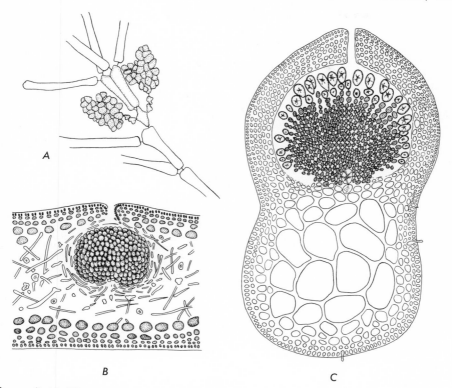

FIGURE 7–40. Three types of cystocarps: *A,* superficial, free carpospore masses of *Aglaothamnion; B,* an embedded cystocarp without definite envelope as seen in a transection of the blade of *Halymenia; C,* a domoid, emergent type as seen in *Gracilariopsis,* showing slight rostrate development around the ostiole, prominent, definitive pericarp, and carpospore chains from the gonimoblast within the cavity.

mass of deeply red-pigmented carpospores. External ones may have a pericarp surrounding the spore mass, and this may have one, two or several ostioles. The ostiole may be in a prolonged beak or rostrum, or may be encircled by coronate prongs.

The macroscopically visible cystocarp arises after fertilization from a minute and usually obscure carpogonial branch. This is the female reproductive apparatus proper, and usually consists of a filament of several cells. The terminal one is the carpogonium and bears a hair-like extension called the trichogyne (Figure 7-24,*F*). The trichogyne serves as the critical surface to which the spermatium adheres and through which the male nucleus enters to effect fusion directly or indirectly with the carpogonial nucleus. Sexual fusion initiates the development of a gonimoblast tissue that gives rise to the carpospores (as an embedded mass, or within a definitive pericarp that develops simultaneously) (Figure 7-40,*C*).

REFERENCES

Dawes, C. J., et al. 1960. Light and electron microscope study of cell walls of brown and red algae. *Science,* 132: 1163–1164.

Fritsch, F. E. 1935–1945. The structure and reproduction of the algae. Cambridge University Press. vol. 1 (1935), xvii + 791 pp.; vol. 2 (1945), xvi + 939 pp.

MacMillan, C. 1902. Observations on *Pterygophora. Minnesota Bot. Studies,* 2: 723–741.

Manton, I., and M. Parke. 1960. Further observations on small green flagellates. . . . *J. Marine Biol. Assoc. U.K.,* 39: 275–298.

Papenfuss, G. F. 1955. Classification of the algae. In: *A Century of Progress in the Natural Sciences, 1853–1953.* San Francisco: Calif. Acad. Sci., pp. 115–224.

Parker, B. C. 1963. Translocation in the giant kelp *Macrocystis. Science,* 140: 891–892.

Smith, G. M. (Ed.) 1951. *Manual of Phycology.* Waltham, Mass.: Chronica Botanica Co. 375 pp.

Thuret, G. 1854. Recherches sur la fécondation des Fucacées, suivies d'observations sur les anthéridies des algues. *Am. Sci. Nat. Bot.,* sér. 4(2): 197–214.

Tokida, J. et al. 1958. A chimera of *Alaria* and *Laminaria* found in nature. *Nature,* 181: 923–924.

Yamanouchi, S. 1906. The life history of *Polysiphonia violacea. Bot. Gaz.,* 42: 401–449.

8

Benthic Green Algae
(Chlorophyta)

Whereas the green algae are the dominantly conspicuous algae of terrestrial and fresh-water habitats, they are far less prevalent in the sea. Green algae are inconspicuous in the phytoplankton and rarely form dominant blooms. They reach their best quantitative development in quiet lagoon habitats of certain tropical, subtropical, and temperate areas.

A student of fresh-water green algae finds the marine forms mostly strange to him, for although several orders and families have both marine and fresh-water representatives, there are very few genera of fresh-water forms that have marine species *(Chlamydomonas, Cladophora)*. Some of the most important marine orders are without fresh-water examples (Siphonocladales, Siphonales, Dasycladales). These latter three orders are primarily of tropical marine occurrence, while three other orders with important marine representatives (Ulotrichales, Schizogoniales, and Cladophorales) are mainly of temperate distribution.

Marine benthic green algae, unlike fresh-water ones, are primarily macroscopic forms. A few minute species occur, but most are large enough to be recognized in the field as green algae simply by their color. A maximum size is reached in *Codium magnum* of Mexico, which sometimes attains a breadth of 25 centimeters and a length of 8 meters. An example of very heavy green-algal growth is seen in *Caulerpa sertularioides* which may occur, to the exclusion of most other vegetation, as a carpet at least 10 centimeters thick over many acres of shallow bay bottoms in the Gulf of California.

Marine green algae have well-defined, often thick and stratified cell walls consisting of an inner layer of cellulose or callose, and an outer pectic layer. This pectic layer is impregnated with calcium carbonate in all Dasycladales and in many of the Siphonales. Except for the chalkiness of calcareous forms, a majority of green algae are recognized by their grass-green color, for their pigment complex of chlorophyll *a*, chlorophyll *b*, xanthophylls, and carotenes is like that of flowering plants. The prevalent green pigments occur in well-defined chloroplasts. In many green algae these contain pyrenoids that are usually enveloped by plates of reserve starch.

Although most terrestrial green algae have uninucleate cells, a large majority of marine forms are multinucleate. Thus, the discrete cells of Cladophorales and Siphonocladales are multinucleate, as are the nonseptate filaments of Siphonales.

Reproductive life histories of many marine green algae are still not well known. Sexual reproduction has been established in all of the orders, but often on the basis of few representatives. An alternation of generations is known in several members of Ulotrichales, Cladophorales, and Siphonales. Where a sporophyte generation occurs it commonly produces zoospores in undifferentiated sporangia. Sexually reproducing plants may be dioecious or monoecious, and fertilization may be isogamous, anisogamous, or oögamous.

Examples of the various structural and reproductive types will be illustrated below by common and easily obtained representatives of the various families.

VOLVOCALES

Chlorangiaceae

The Volvocales is well known as a group consisting largely of planktonic fresh-water green algae in which the vegetative cells are flagellated and motile (*cf.* the classical colonial *Volvox*). A common marine form is *Platymonas,* which occurs in high, tidal spray pools fouled with sea-bird excrement. The small family Chlorangiaceae, however, includes several nonmotile forms. *Prasinocladus* is a common marine example, with species on both American coasts. It grows on rocks in high-level tide pools, and in its attached, vegetative state consists of a dendroid colony of unicellular bodies within terminal compartments in a branched or simple tubular stalk.

The life history of *Prasinocladus ascus,* worked out in culture by Proskauer (1950), demonstrates that this sessile form has been derived from a motile *Platymonas*-like type (Figure 8-1).

The mature plant consists of two or four oblong protoplasts lying in the upper end of the tubular stalk. These protoplasts are capable of producing flagella at any time. They may become motile in the tube and move up and down within its confines, or they may break through their chamber to escape

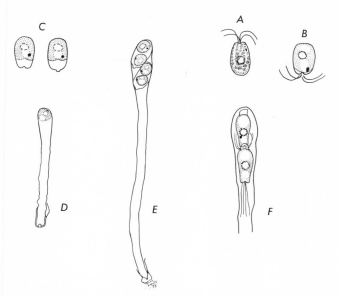

FIGURE 8–1. *Prasinocladus ascus: A,* a motile individual from a group of swarmers (resembling a vegetative plant of *Platymonas*); *B,* beginning of sedentary phase with throwing off of flagella; *C,* early developmental stages of sedentary phase; *D,* later stage in sedentary phase showing new, elongated inner wall after rupture of outer wall; *E,* mature plant with tubular stalk and division of protoplast into new vegetative individuals; *F,* vegetative individuals becoming motile, bearing flagella within the tube and capable of escape (after Proskauer).

as swarmers. The motile cells closely resemble vegetative *Platymonas* plants. They are about 22 μ long, have a definite wall, four flagella, an eyespot, and a chloroplast with an axial pyrenoid. After a period of motility, the sedentary phase is initiated by the settling of the swarmer by its anterior end, the throwing off of the flagella, and the secretion of a new wall inside the original one. The inner wall now elongates as the outer ruptures at its upper end, and a tube is formed beneath the protoplast which moves upward and proceeds to divide into two or more vegetative individuals. In *P. ascus* the tube may be unbranched and the compartment very long; in *P. marinus (P. lubricus),* short compartments and branched tubes occur.

ULOTRICHALES

This order contains marine, fresh-water, and aerial forms. The plants are filamentous or membranous and consist, typically, of uninucleate cells with a parietal chloroplast. There are four families with prominent marine representatives.

Ulotrichaceae

The family is well represented by the common and widespread genus *Ulothrix*. This plant consists of slender, unbranched filaments basally attached to rocks and woodwork on which it forms a silky green coating. The basal cell is somewhat modified to form a holdfast. The cylindrical filament is divided into numerous short, uninucleate cells, each with a single, parietal, band-shaped chloroplast (Figure 8-2).

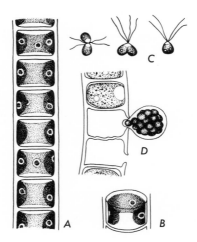

FIGURE 8-2. *Ulothrix* : *A–B*, vegetative filament and diagram of a cell showing brace-let-shaped parietal chloroplasts; *C*, free and copulating gametes; *D*, release of zoospores from fertile cells of filament.

Reproduction is by abundant swarmers which may arise from any cell but the basal one and are liberated through a lateral pore. These swarmers may be of three different kinds: quadriflagellate macrozoospores, biflagellate micro-zoospores, and biflagellate gametes. The macrozoospores are evidently the most frequently produced, and after a brief phase of movement they attach and develop directly into a new vegetative filament. Undischarged zoospores may be transformed into aplanospores. The gametes are isogamous, but arise from dioecious plants of plus and minus strains. The zygote is at first quadri-flagellate, but soon becomes a thick-walled resting zygospore, which remains inactive for 5 to 9 months. Meiosis occurs at the first division of the diploid zygote (zygospore), which releases quadriflagellate zoospores that grow into new filaments. The vegetative *Ulothrix* plant, thus, is haploid (Figure 8-2).

Several variations in marine *Ulothrix* life histories have recently been studied by Kornmann. Some species seem to reproduce exclusively by quadri-flagellate zoospores. One has been observed to produce biflagellate zoospores that develop into *Codiolum*-like unicells yielding quadriflagellate swarmers.

Chaetophoraceae

This family contains a number of genera and species of small, marine plants which characteristically grow on or in the tissues of seaweeds or in the shells and surface structures of animals. Many bore into calcareous materials. The plants are filamentous, and the filaments have either free or compacted branches.

Entocladia is a common, cosmopolitan genus that lives as an endophyte in the outer cell walls of various algae. The thallus forms a prostrate system of filaments radiating from a common center that, in some species, shows compaction of the filament cells into a pseudoparenchyma (Figure 8-3).

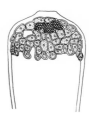

FIGURE 8–3. *Entocladia* in vertical section and in surface view as seen living in the end wall of a *Codium* utricle (after Setchell & Gardner).

Quadriflagellate zoospores are formed in groups of eight or more by cells near the center of the thallus. Sexual reproduction is by isogametes formed in the same manner.

Another widespread but commonly overlooked member of this group is *Phaeophila,* which commonly inhabits shells of living or dead marine annelids and mollusks on temperate and tropical shores.

Phaeophila engleri may be encountered in most North American salt marshes and quiet bays, growing on a variety of shells, including *Mya, Venus, Polynices, Anomia, Thais,* and *Spirorbis.* Other species have been detected in the calcareous stalks of *Acetabularia* and in the calcareous tissues of *Corallina* and *Lithothamnium.* The thallus is visible only after decalcification and consists of alternately branched, procumbent filaments extending in various directions. The cells are more or less cylindrical, but irregular in shape, 1 to 5 diameters long, and sometimes produce setae. They may have 1 to 5 nuclei (Figure 8-4).

Aplanospores may sometimes be seen, but reproduction is usually by zoospores produced in groups of 6 to 22 in irregularly shaped, usually intercalary sporangial cells. They are typically quadriflagellate, have a pyrenoid, an eyespot, and a pair of contractile vacuoles. Upon settling, the zoospore germinates by forming a tube from its anterior end. The tube effects entrance into the host shell and the cell contents follow its progression. Thus, the zoospore and the lower part of the tube become empty and are cut off by a septum. Sexual reproduction is unknown.

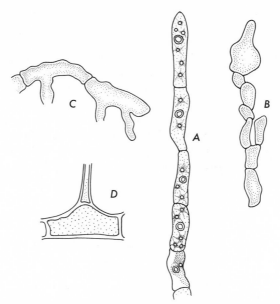

FIGURE 8–4. *Phaeophila engleri* as seen after decalcification of host shell: *A,* part of a filament showing multinucleate cells; *B,* a filament with developing sporangium; *C,* filament fragment with rhizoids; *D,* seta-bearing cell.

Monostromaceae

Monostroma, in the broad and traditional sense, is a widespread green alga of marine and brackish waters readily recognized by its membranous thallus consisting of a single layer of pseudoparenchymatous cells. The thallus begins as a small sac that ruptures to produce the expanding, unistratose membrane. In such quiet intertidal areas as occur in Puget Sound, the presence of these plants is particularly evident upon the inflow of a spring tide because of abundant release of swarmers that may turn the water soupy green.

Recent critical culture studies of various species of *Monostroma,* however, have revealed that this is by no means a genus of uniform characters, and that at least five different life histories may be recognized. Accordingly, those species that have been so studied are being separated by some workers into at least three genera within three different families in two orders, and *Monostroma* in the new sense becomes much restricted.

One of the common species under current study is *Monostroma grevillei,* in which a monophasic life history occurs. The macroscopic plants are haploid and dioecious, producing male and female biflagellate gametes that upon fusing produce a nonmotile zygote that remains dormant for several months. Germination is accompanied by meiotic division to produce usually 32 zoospores, half of which may develop into male plants and half into female. The germinating zoospore divides in such a way that the first eight cells enclose a central cavity. Further development produces the initial saccate thallus.

Such a life history as the above in *Monostroma (Ulvopsis) grevillei,* with its unicellular diploid phase alternating with a multicellular generation, is sharply distinct from that of the next family, Ulvaceae, whose members ordinarily exhibit an alternation of isomorphic sporophyte and gametophyte generations.

Ulvaceae

Members of the Ulvaceae, especially the genera *Ulva* and *Enteromorpha,* are the most conspicuous of the green algae in the oceans. They are usually bright green and often so large and abundant as to form a prominent component of most marine floras. They occur in all seas, and often are prevalent in brackish or polluted areas, or in salt marshes.

Enteromorpha is probably the most common of all benthic green algae, and occurs in a bewildering array of forms. The taxonomy has been complicated by attempts to describe species based upon vegetative characters, for these are now known to be extremely variable. Bliding (1963), the foremost worker with this difficult genus, has in recent years undertaken careful culture studies of numerous species and has worked out their life histories. He has demonstrated the inadequacies of species identifications of *Enteromorpha* based upon vegetative characters. The following are now accepted as important species characters: the presence or absence of a sexual generation, the size of gametes and zoospores, the number of pyrenoids per cell, and the size and arrangement of vegetative cells.

Enteromorpha plants may readily be recognized by their hollow, membranous construction. The tubular thalli are monostromatic (Figure 7-13,*E*), simple or branched, cylindrical or compressed. Sometimes the tubes are finely filamentous and only a few cells in diameter. The plants are attached by rhizoidal outgrowths at the base. The single chloroplast is commonly cup-shaped. The number of pyrenoids varies from 1 to as many as 10. There is usually an alternation of identical gametophyte and sporophyte generations, but several species are known to have lost their sexual generation and to reproduce only by zoospores.

The sporophyte plants may produce 4, 8, or 16 quadriflagellate zoospores (Figure 7-25,*A*) in any cell but the basalmost. They are liberated through a lateral pore. After swimming for a time, and after settling and losing their flagella, they divide transversely to initiate a uniseriate filament that develops a group of basal attachment cells and, by longitudinal division and expansion above, becomes hollow-tubular.

If a sexual generation occurs, zoogametes are formed and liberated much as are zoospores. Fertilization may be isogamous or anisogamous (Figure 7-24). Some species show parthenogenetic germination of gametes.

Recent evidence suggests that *Collinsiella,* a small warty green alga formerly ranked in the Chlorangiaceae, is a sexual phase of *Enteromorpha intestinalis,* probably representing a basal remnant of a previous season's tubular gametophyte thallus. An accessory method of repeated reproduction of the sporophyte generation by quadriflagellate mitospores (neutral spores) has also been demonstrated (Figure 8-5).

The typical life history of *Enteromorpha* (or *Ulva*) is one of the best illustrations of a regular alternation of isomorphic sporophyte and gametophyte generations, each with its distinctive motile reproductive cells (Figure 11-1).

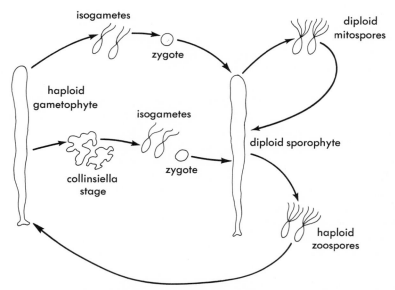

FIGURE 8–5. Life-history diagram of an *Enteromorpha* species showing usual alternation of isomorphic generations and two accessory methods of reproduction: by asexual diploid mitospores and by the "*Collinsiella* stage."

SCHIZOGONIALES

This is a small order, consisting mainly of marine forms of usually foliaceous habit and with uninucleate cells. It was formerly distinguished from superficially similar ulvoid algae mainly on the basis of chloroplast characters. The single chloroplast is stellate and located in the center of the cell. Recent investigations on the principal genus, *Prasiola*, have shown a highly distinctive kind of life history not otherwise known in the Chlorophyta (see Chapter 11).

Prasiolaceae

The genus *Prasiola* is represented by a number of species in north-temperate regions. The plants occur usually as dirty green patches at or above high-tide level, commonly in the spray zone and in areas fouled by bird excrement. They consist of small, thin, broadly ovate blades. In the Atlantic *P. stipitata*, which has been most closely investigated, the young vegetative thalli are diploid and have the potentiality to develop either into spore-forming or into gamete-forming plants (Figure 8-6). The formation of the two kinds of reproductive cells occurs in the distal region of the thallus, while the basal portion retains its vegetative character.

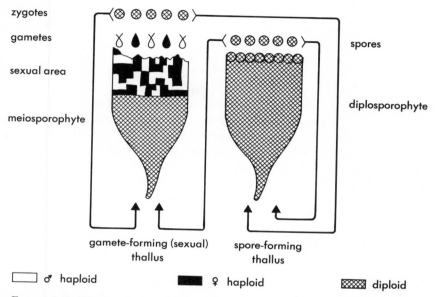

FIGURE 8-6. Diagram of the life history of *Prasiola stipitata* (after Friedmann).

A spore-forming thallus develops two to four layers in its apical part and produces a spherical, diploid aplanospore in each cell. These spores are thin-walled and germinate directly to produce new plants with the same reproductive capacities as the parent.

A gamete-forming thallus is composed of two parts. The lower part is diploid and remains like a spore-forming plant. It has been called the meio-sporophyte. The upper cells of the plant undergo meiosis and become haploid. These cells, called meiospores, develop further into a patchwork pattern of male and female tissue distinguished by the size of chromatophores in the cells. The haploid areas are arranged in pairs, and at maturity each cell produces a single gamete. Large numbers of gametes are discharged simultaneously during a dark period following illumination. The male gametes are anteriorly bi-flagellate; the female are nonmotile eggs. At fertilization, one of the male flagella is absorbed into the egg and the other remains functional in the swimming zygote. Later the zygote attaches to a solid surface, secretes a wall, and comes to resemble an aplanospore before germinating to produce a new diploid plant. The young thallus consists of an unbranched, uniseriate filament (the "hormidium" stage). The expanded, membranous thallus develops later through divisions in another plane.

CHLOROCOCCALES

A large number of diverse algal forms, mainly of fresh-water and terrestrial habitats, have been assigned to this order. The few marine species are mainly small, endophytic plants, and some formerly assigned here, such as *Codiolum,* have been shown to represent one of the alternate generations of other green algae.

Chlorococcaceae

Chlorochytrium is a unicellular endophyte in various red algae in temperate Pacific waters. *C. porphyrae* is sometimes so abundant in upper-level *Porphyra* plants as to color the host green in resemblance of *Ulva.* The solitary, ellipsoidal cells of *Chlorochytrium* do not divide vegetatively, but reproduction by quadri-flagellate zoospores is reported in some species. Sexual reproduction is by biflagellate isogametes. The zygote eventually invades the outer tissues or membrane of the host and develops into a vegetative cell (Figure 8-7).

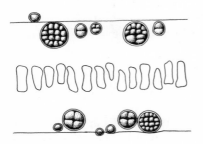

FIGURE 8-7. *Chlorochytrium porphyrae,* showing unicells within the membrane of a monostromatic *Porphyra* in various stages of development and division preparatory to gamete release (after Gardner).

CLADOPHORALES

Cladophoraceae

This family contains many fresh-water forms. Some of the large genera, such as *Cladophora,* have both fresh-water and marine representatives, but there are several strictly marine genera. The plants are composed of multinucleate cells arranged in uniseriate fashion in simple or branched filaments. The chloroplast is parietal and reticulate (Figure 7-22,*H*). The filaments are usually attached by rhizoids. Generic separations have traditionally been made on vegetative characters such as the presence or absence of branches, the kind of branches, and the form of the basal cell and its attachment rhizoids. Variations in these characters are such, however, that satisfactory separation of certain species in the closely related genera *Rhizoclonium, Chaetomorpha* (Figure 7-35,*A*), and *Cladophora* (Figure 3-3) have caused serious taxonomic difficulties.

Similarly, specific distinctions have been indefinite in such a genus as *Rhizoclonium* in which taxonomic characterizations have been virtually limited to cell size and shape. Accordingly, critical determinations often can be made only through culture practices involving observation of reproductive bodies.

Bliding (1957) has investigated two species of *Rhizoclonium* in culture. Similar studies of various species of *Chaetomorpha, Cladophora,* and other genera are needed.

In the cosmopolitan *Rhizoclonium riparium* the uniseriate filaments, about 21 μ in diameter, have cells 1.1 to 4.2 diameters long. They contain from 3 to 15 pyrenoids. The filaments are mostly unbranched, but have short rhizoidal branchlets here and there. Sporophytic filaments produce quadriflagellate zoospores from distinctly swollen cells (Figure 8-8). Most any vegetative cell may become fertile. The settled zoospore grows within 1 to 4 months into a sexual filament that is morphologically like the sporophyte. The sexual plants produce isogametes markedly smaller and more slender than the zoospores. The gametes are positively phototactic until copulation; then the zygotes instantly become negatively phototactic. The zygote germinates directly into a new filament.

FIGURE 8-8. Reproduction in *Rhizoclonium riparium: A,* a vegetative filament; *B,* rhizoidal branches of vegetative filaments; *C,* gametes; *D,* copulating pair of isogametes; *E,* germinating zoospore; *F,* young plant 16 days old from a zoospore; *G,* zoosporangia with some zoospores left (after Bliding).

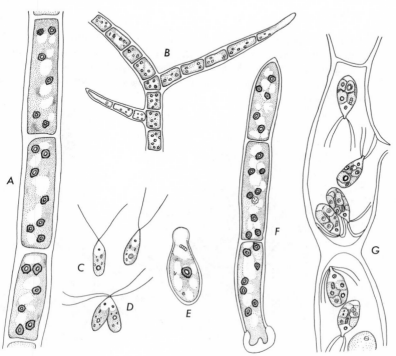

Spongomorpha

Spongomorpha is a common, *Cladophora*-like plant along the temperate and boreal American coasts. Recent investigations of *S. coalita* by Hollenberg (1958) and by Fan (1959) have revealed a life history showing alternation of *Spongomorpha* plants with the endophytic *Codiolum*, formerly treated as a member of the order Chlorococcales.

Codiolum petrocelidis is a common endophyte in *Petrocelis* in California. The plants consist of a globose, multinucleate cell embedded in the host and with a long, slender extension directed upward. The upward part is septate. Mature *Codiolum* cells produce in culture quadriflagellate zoospores that germinate to grow into a mass of radiating filaments. These develop into *Spongomorpha* plants with their regularly septate, branched filaments and characteristically hooked branchlets (Figure 8-9). These plants are sexual and dioecious and produce biflagellate gametes. After the pairing of the male and female gametes, which are of similar size, the zygote retains the resulting four flagella for a short time. Nuclear fusion may be delayed for about 20 hours after settling. After the zygote germinates on the surface of the host *Petrocelis*, it produces a penetrating projection. This becomes tubular and gives rise to a vesicular cell that enlarges deep within the host (Figure 8-9,*A*).

Demonstration of a heteromorphic alternation of generations in *Spongomorpha*, and similar evidence for a European *Urospora*, have pointed to the need for further extensive investigation of various kinds of *Codiolum* and of other small endophytic green algae.

Figure 8–9. The *Codiolum-Spongomorpha* alternation of generations: *A*, an isolated plant of *Codiolum petrocelidis* removed from its host (*Petrocelis*), showing numerous zoospores, each with an eyespot; *B*, a young *Spongomorpha* plant derived from the spores of *Codiolum*; *C*, typical hooked branchlet of *Spongomorpha* on a plant cultured from the spores of *Codiolum* (after Fan).

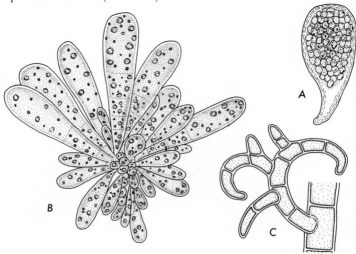

Anadyomenaceae

This is a small family of strictly marine, tropical algae formerly ranked in the Siphonocladales. The two principal genera, *Microdictyon* and *Anadyomene*, are delicate, reticulate, foliose plants in which the blade results from abundant branching of uniseriate filaments essentially in one plane. In *Microdictyon* the branches do not lie closely together as in *Anadyomene*, but form an open mesh (Figure 8-10).

Although the several genera of Anadyomenaceae show many morphological features suggesting close affinity with members of the Siphonocladales, they lack the special method of segregative cell division (see below) peculiar to that group. Furthermore, Iyengar and Ramanathan (1940, 1941) have established a life history for *Microdictyon* corresponding with that in the Cladophorales. Thus, morphologically indistinguishable vegetative plants were found to produce two kinds of swarmers. They established that diploid sporophyte plants form quadriflagellate, haploid zoospores after meiosis and that dioecious, haploid gametophyte plants produce biflagellate male and female isogametes. This alternation of generations, in which meiosis occurs at sporogenesis, sets this group off sharply from the other siphonous Chlorophyta, in which there is only one kind of vegetative plant (a diploid thallus) and in which meiosis occurs at gametogenesis.

FIGURE 8–10. *Microdictyon okamurai*, showing the network of uniseriate filaments making up the blade (reprinted from *Plants of Bikini* by W. R. Taylor, by permission of University of Michigan Press, copyright 1950).

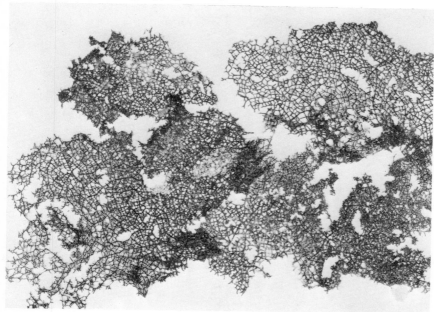

SIPHONOCLADALES

This order is wholly marine, and the plants consist of multinucleate segments, variously shaped, but definitely septate and basally attached by rhizoids. The chloroplasts are reticulate. Septation of the thallus occurs in a unique manner known as segregative division. The thallus begins to develop as a nonseptate, erect, tubular, primary vesicle. As expressed by Egerod (1952, p. 329), this primary "vesicle cleaves into several to many protoplasmic masses of varying size, each of which rounds up and secretes an enveloping membrane and then expands until it comes in contact with adjacent masses. The contiguous surfaces of the newly formed membrane cohere to one another and to the lateral walls of the parent cell, and in this way the vesicle is divided into numerous cells." This process is most clearly seen in *Siphonocladus* and in *Dictyosphaeria* (Figure 8-11). It is discussed in detail by Børgesen, who first observed it in 1905.

FIGURE 8–11. Segregative cell division as seen in *Dictyosphaeria* (A) and in *Siphonocladus* (B–E) (redrawn after Egerod).

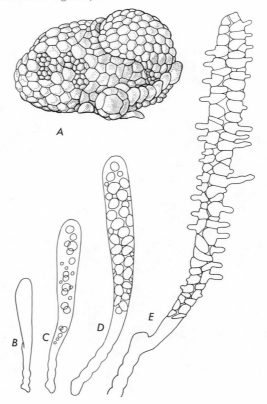

Valoniaceae

Valonia ventricosa is famous as the "largest single-celled alga" in that it seems to be a unicell that reaches the size of a hen's egg. It has been used in physiological experiments calling for large amounts of cell sap. Widely distributed in the tropics, it suggests to an underwater observer a glass flashbulb embedded in the benthic growth. It is not, however, a single cell, but a large, multinucleate vesicle the inner surface of which is beset with scattered, minute lenticular cells only about 250 μ across. The lower of these cells grows out into attachment rhizoids. Other species of *Valonia* consist of many subclavate vesicles (Figure 7-6,*D*), and the genus *Dictyosphaeria* forms a cushion of polygonal vesicles. The vesicles are 2 to 5 millimeters in diameter (Figure 7-3,*E*; 8-11). The usual absence of branching axes and the presence of the small lenticular cells formed along vesicle walls set the Valoniaceae apart from the next family. Only sexual reproduction is known. Biflagellate isogametes are liberated through several pores in the diploid vegetative thallus following gametogenesis, but fusion has not yet been observed.

Siphonocladaceae

This family consists of several predominantly tropical genera having a habit of loose clusters, tufts, or mats of freely branched axes. The largest genus is *Cladophoropsis,* some species of which extend into temperate regions. It has uniseriate, branched axes irregularly divided by transverse septa. Some species closely resemble *Cladophora,* but the lateral branches generally remain nonseptate at the base, or, if a wall is formed later, it is produced secondarily (Figure 8-12,*E*).

Boodleaceae

This small family contains two equally common pantropical genera, *Boodlea* and *Struvea.* In both of these the thallus is reticulate, composed of a branching network of uniseriate filaments. In *Struvea* the net is stipitate and forms a distinct blade (Figure 8-12,*C–D*), while in *Boodlea* an amorphous, spongiose mat is formed (Figure 8-12,*F*). The branches are cylindrical, and the net-like form results from anastomosis of the branches accomplished by means of special attachment organs, the tenacula, which consist of a much-reduced vegetative cell with a hapteroid attachment pad at its free end (Figure 8-12).

Little is known of reproduction or life histories in this family or in the Siphonocladaceae. Swarmers have been reported in most genera. In *Boodlea* they are liberated from a single pore, but it is assumed only on the evidence from *Valonia* that these may be gametes and that the vegetative plant is diploid. Much work remains to be done on these tropical siphonocladalean green algae by culture studies at marine stations in such areas as Hawaii, Florida, and the Bahamas.

FIGURE 8–12. *A, Bryopsis*, showing distichous pinnae of a vegetative branch. *B, Micro-dictyon*, showing enlargement of anastomosing segment and modification for attachment. *C–D, Struvea*, showing a young vegetative plant with reticulate blade (*C*) and detail of a tenaculum (*D*). *E, Cladophoropsis*, showing delayed septation of lateral branches. *F, Boodlea*, showing rhizoidal extensions of vegetative cells with terminal tenacula. *G*, A zoosporangium of *Derbesia*. *H–I, Halicystis* (after Hollenberg), showing mature sexual plant with forceful discharge of gametes from a pore in a fertile area (*H*); male and female gametes (*I*).

SIPHONALES

This order is now widely recognized as containing all the green algae in which the plant remains siphonous and essentially nonseptate throughout its vegetative phase. This order contains most of the green algae commonly recognized as coenocytes (Figure 7-16). Whereas the Siphonocladales contain single, reticulate plastids, the Siphonales possess numerous discoid or fusiform plastids and two distinctive xanthophyll pigments known as siphonein and siphonoxanthin. Within this large assemblage of plants Feldmann (1946) proposed a division into two groups based upon the occurrence in many of the tropical genera (such as *Caulerpa, Udotea, Halimeda, Penicillus,* and *Avrainvillea*) of a dual system of plastids: a photosynthetic plastid and an amylogenic plastid.

Development of the thallus in Siphonales, as in the Siphonocladales, begins with a primary vesicle, but the enlargement and ultimate ramification to produce thalli of diverse forms takes place mostly without septum formation.

Reproduction in the Siphonales, with the principal exception of the Derbesiaceae, is sexual, with biflagellate gametes produced, following meiosis, in the diploid multinucleate adult thallus.

Derbesiaceae

This small family has received a great share of attention in recent years because of the remarkable life history of the principal genus, *Derbesia. Derbesia* is a filamentous green alga frequently encountered along temperate and tropical coasts, consisting of a prostrate, interwoven basal portion supporting erect, subdichotomously branched filaments that are here and there provided with broad, plug-like septa. Globoid or ellipsoidal sporangia are produced as short, lateral branchlets cut off by a septum formed by annular ingrowth of the lateral wall (Figure 8-12). The zoospores are unusual in having a whorl of flagella at one pole. It has been established in recent years that the settled zoospore develops into an entirely different kind of plant (an unbranched vesicular thallus anchored by a perennial rhizoidal system) known for many years as the genus *Halicystis.*

Halicystis ovalis was exhaustively studied by Hollenberg (1935) who showed that the plants are dioecious and produce biflagellate anisogametes from certain reproductive areas in the undifferentiated vesicles (Figure 8-12). Kornmann (1938) and Feldmann (1950) have concluded that *Derbesia* plants are the sporophyte generation of gametophytic *Halicystis* plants, and this distinctive life history has suggested to some workers that a new order (Derbesiales) should be erected for the group. Much work, however, remains to be done. Few kinds of *Halicystis* are known, but many kinds of *Derbesia. Derbesia* often occurs where *Halicystis* has not been found. Nuclear phases of the life history remain to be worked out.

Caulerpaceae

This family contains a single, large, widely distributed genus, *Caulerpa,* generally characteristic of the tropics, but prominent in Australian temperate waters. *Caulerpa,* being aseptate, is remarkable in the size of the thallus and dimensions of its parts. Plants up to a meter long occur, with stem-like and bladelike parts several to many millimeters in diameter (Figure 7-17). There are no cross walls, and mechanical support is provided by an elaborate strutwork of internal trabeculae (Figure 7-16,*F*). Species have been distinguished mainly on remarkably diverse gross morphological characters, but these are so variable in some species complexes that quadrinomials have been used to designate the subspecific variants (Figure 8-13,*A*). Within the genus branch forms occur that may be described as plumose, pectinate, peltate, ovate, turbinate, spatulate,

FIGURE 8–13. *A, Caulerpa serrulata* var. *serrulata* f. *spiralis. B, Bryopsis,* showing stages in development of septation between gametangia and vegetative branches (after Oltmanns).

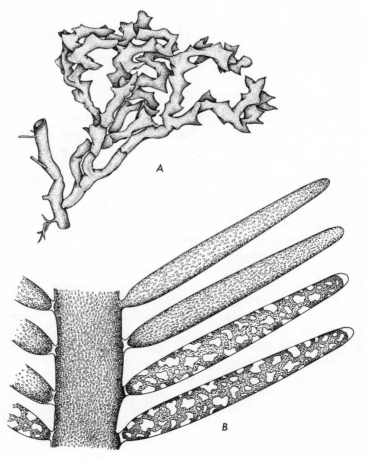

falcate, or obconical (Figure 7-16). The reproduction of only a few species of *Caulerpa* has been studied, but no alternation of generations has been recorded. In *C. prolifera* it has been shown that the vegetative thallus is diploid and that meiosis occurs at gametogenesis. Anisogametes are known in a few species, formed in unmodified areas of the vegetative thallus without separation by cross walls. They are liberated through superficial papillae.

Bryopsidaceae

This is another small family of only 2 genera, of which *Bryopsis* is widespread in most temperate and tropical regions. Unlike *Caulerpa, Bryopsis* has no internal network of trabeculae, and the filaments generally remain slender and less than a millimeter in diameter. *Bryopsis* usually has a distinct main axis with branchlets arranged radially, or pinnately in opposite or alternate fashion (Figure 7-16,*G*; 8-12,*A*). The mature lateral branchlets may become cut off from the axis by a transverse septum and function as gametangia (Figure 8-13,*B*). The mature thalli are reported to be diploid and dioecious, producing biflagellate anisogametes. As in most other Siphonales, zoospores are unknown.

Codiaceae

Of the 17 genera assigned to this family, 10 occur on the coasts of the United States, and these exhibit essentially the full range of morphological diversity found in the group (Figure 7-3,*A*; 8-14). The structure is filamentous throughout, but varies from the sparsely branched, loosely tufted thallus of *Chlorodesmis* to the quite dense and compact thalli of *Halimeda* and *Codium* (Figure 7-15). Some of the remarkable forms are indicated by the common names "Neptune's shaving brush" *(Penicillus)* (Figure 7-2,*C*) and "mermaid's fan" *(Udotea)* (Figure 8-16). The members of several genera characteristically deposit calcium carbonate around their filaments and are the largest and most conspicuous of calcareous green algae (Figure 12-4).

It is of extraordinary interest that despite their abundance and relatively large size, reproduction is practically unknown in all but two genera. Only in *Codium* is sexual reproduction known. Reproductive structures have been observed by a few workers in *Halimeda,* but their nature has not been determined. Sporangia-like structures have been reported in two other genera, but the information is fragmentary and unconfirmed. The lack of understanding of life histories in this family remains a major problem, for there is yet no clear indication of answers to the following questions: Does reproduction somehow occur in the unmodified filaments of the thallus? Have some members of the group lost sexuality? Do some reproduce only by vegetative fragmentation?

FIGURE 8–14. A typical association of Codiaceae such as may be seen along Florida and West-Indian shores. The dominant plant here is *Avrainvillea,* but small heads of *Penicillus* are also fixed in the muddy sand together with *Halimeda, Rhipocephalus, Udotea,* and various other Siphonales (reprinted from *Marine Algae of the Eastern Tropical and Subtropical Coasts of the Americas* by W. R. Taylor, by permission of University of Michigan Press, copyright 1960).

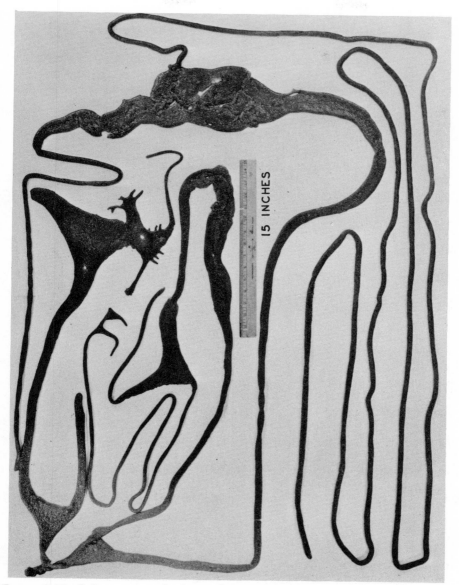

FIGURE 8–15. *Codium magnum,* the largest known siphonous, multinucleate alga, from Bahĭa de San Quintin, Baja California.

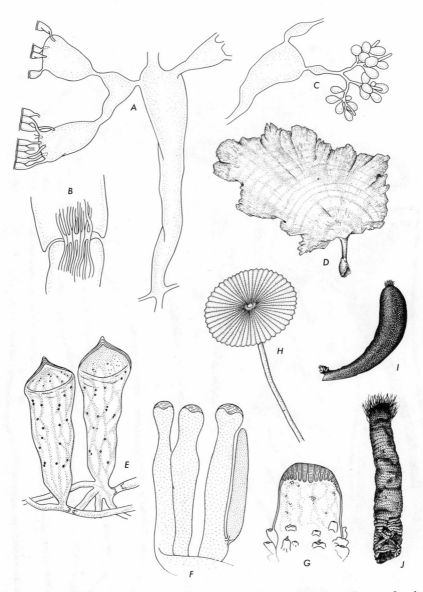

FIGURE 8–16. *A–C, Halimeda* structure (after Egerod): *A,* dissection of part of a decal-cified segment showing cortical utricles and inflated medullary filaments; *B,* diagram-matic representation of a flexible joint or node, showing anastomosis of medullary filaments; *C,* a group of reproductive structures. *D, Udotea palmetta,* one of the fan-shaped Codiaceae. *E–G, Codium* utricles, showing various modifications of the terminal wall (points, convex thickenings, trabeculate thickenings). Note the gametangium in (*F*) and the hair scars in (*G*). *H, Acetabularia crenulata,* showing adult sporangial disc. *I, Bornetella sphaerica. J, Neomeris annulata,* showing whorled organization.

Halimeda

These jointed, calcareous organisms were long considered to be animals, and later related to the coralline red algae. With the monograph of Barton (1901) the great morphological variation within species was recognized and an approach to classification was made on the basis of internal structure. This has been brought to considerable refinement in the recent treatise of Hillis (1959). The plants consist of conspicuous calcified segments separated by more or less flexible, little-calcified nodes (Figure 8-16,*B*). The longitudinally arranged filaments are provided in the segments with lateral branches that terminate in a distinctive surface layer of cortical utricles (Figure 8-16,*A*). These may cohere firmly even after decalcification.

Very infrequently, *Halimeda* plants bear clusters of bead-like reproductive structures on branched stalks arising from the surface of the segments (Figure 8-16,*C*). These are known to produce biflagellate swarmers, but whether they are gametes or zoospores is unknown.

Codium

This is a large genus of frequent occurrence throughout the warm-temperate and subtropical regions of the world, and occasionally in cold waters. Some species are narrow insular endemics; some extend into two hemispheres. Because of the somewhat amorphous character of a number of the species and the great variability of others, the taxonomy has been much confused and is only now being clarified by the critical studies of Silva (1960) and others.

Codium is composed of more or less compactly interwoven, multinucleate, scarcely septate filaments that form a spongy, macroscopic, green plant body. Most of the species are 6 to 20 centimeters tall or broad, but the gigantic *C. magnum* reaches 8 meters (Figure 8-15). The medullary filaments are colorless and interwoven, but these give rise to a palisade-like cortex of inflated, photosynthetic utricles (Figure 7-15) often of distinctive shape and sometimes with peculiar end-wall thickenings (Figure 8-16). The small discoid chloroplasts lack pyrenoids.

Most codiums are dioecious and the gametangia are borne laterally on the utricles, cut off by an annular ingrowth of the cell wall (Figure 8-16,*F*). Male and female zoogametes are of distinctive size and color, golden yellow and deep green, respectively. It has been shown that the gametophyte plants are diploid and that the reduction divisions occur at gametogenesis. The zygote evidently germinates immediately after rounding up and secreting a wall, although growth at first is very slow.

DASYCLADALES

Dasycladaceae

The modern-day Dasycladales embraces only about 10 genera in a single family, but it has an extraordinary fossil history of some 60 genera dating back to Ordovician times. Fossils of *Acetabularia* are known from the Cretaceous period. The living genera are all tropical and subtropical plants, with usually evident calcification. Seven of them occur along the warm Atlantic and Gulf coasts of America.

The members of this order are distinctive in a number of features that occur with such constancy in the various genera as to make the Dasycladales a remarkably homogeneous and clearly defined group: 1) The plants all have radial symmetry in which an erect main axis bears one to many whorls of lateral branches (Figure 7-37); 2) The vegetative thallus is uninucleate and a multinucleate condition develops prior to reproduction; 3) Gametes are formed in operculate cysts within specialized gametangia (Figure 7-37).

Reproduction within the group has become understood mainly through the long-term studies of Hämmerling, whose experimental cultures of *Acetabularia acetabulum* (*A. mediterranea*) have made it the best known of the siphonous green algae and one familiar to almost every student of general biology.

Acetabularia

The life history of *Acetabularia* provides a good generalization for the entire order. The zygote develops directly into a juvenile plant consisting of an irregularly shaped rhizoidal base and an undivided erect axis. This diploid thallus has a single large nucleus located in a lobe of the holdfast. Further development results in the formation of a whorl of sterile, deciduous, branched, hairlike appendages. As they are shed, these hairs leave an often distinctive pattern of persistent scars. The sterile thallus may die back to the perennial rhizoidal base and regenerate one or several times before producing a reproductive thallus. When the latter begins, the nucleus undergoes many mitotic divisions and the daughter nuclei move up into a whorl of developing gametangial rays (Figure 8-17). Uninucleate, operculate cysts (sometimes called aplanospores) are formed within each gametangium. These cysts, which may be strongly calcified, are liberated from the rays of the fertile disc and may pass several months before germinating. Meiotic divisions within each cyst result in haploid biflagellate isogametes, which are discharged through the operculum. The zygotes are quadriflagellate for a time before they settle.

Whereas *Acetabularia* consists at maturity of a naked stipe usually with a single gametangial disc at the apex, the axis of *Neomeris, Batophora,* and other genera of the group, is usually completely enclosed by whorls of lateral branches that may form a fairly solid cortication (Figure 8-16,*H–J*).

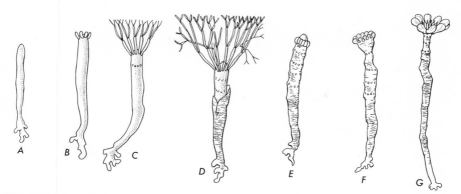

FIGURE 8–17. *Acetabularia* developmental series (after Egerod): *A–D,* initiation of whorls of vegetative branches on the axis, these soon being shed and leaving scars. The emergence of a new shoot is shown at (*D*). *E–G,* development of a reproductive disc at the apex of an older shoot, the gametangial rays composing the whorl elongating and bending outward.

MARINE CHAROPHYTES

This important and interesting group of fresh-water aquatics is of little significance in the marine habitat. About 13 percent of the known species of charophytes occur in brackish water, but they are not known from undiluted seawater. They occasionally inhabit coastal lagoons, ponds, and coves, and are recorded from inland salt lakes and springs. They are well represented in the Baltic Sea. Some species are common in salinities of 5 to 10 °/oo, and a few in salinities of 15 °/oo, but as far as known, at 20 °/oo growth stops and plants survive only for short periods.

Morphological and reproductive peculiarities of this group are described in standard textbooks of cryptogamic botany. The latest systematic review of the phylum is Wood and Imahori, 1964.

REFERENCES

Barton, Ethel S. 1901. The genus *Halimeda. Siboga Exped. Monogr. 60.* Leiden: Brill. 32 pp.
Bliding, C. 1957. Studies in *Rhizoclonium.* 1. Life history of two species. *Bot. Notiser,* 110: 271–275.
———— 1963. A critical survey of European taxa of Ulvales. *Opera Bot.,* 8(3):1–160.
Børgesen, F. 1905. Contributions à la connaissance du genre *Siphonocladus. Overs. K. Dansk. Vidensk. Selsk. Forhandl. 1905:* 259–291.
Egerod, Lois E. 1952. An analysis of the siphonous Chlorophycophyta. . . . *Univ. Calif. Publ. Bot.,* 25: 325–454.
Fan, K. C. 1959. Studies on the life histories of marine algae. 1. *Codiolum petrocelidis* and *Spongomorpha coalita. Bull. Torrey Bot. Club,* 86: 1–12.

Feldmann, J. 1946. Sur l'heteroplastie de certaines Siphonales et leur classification. *Compt. Rend. Acad. Sci.*, 222: 752–753.

——————— 1950. Sur l'existence d'une alternance de générations entre l'*Halicystis parvula* Schmitz et le *Derbesia tenuissima* (De Not.). *Compt. Rend. Acad. Sci.*, 230: 322–323.

Friedmann, I. 1959. Structure, life history and sex determination of *Prasiola stipitata* Suhr. *Ann. Bot.*, n.s., 6: 571–594.

——————— 1960. Gametes, fertilization and zygote development in *Prasiola stipitata* Suhr. *Nova Hedwigia*, 1: 333–362.

Hillis, Llewellya W. 1959. A revision of the genus *Halimeda*. . . . *Publ. Inst. Mar. Sci.*, Univ. Texas, 6: 321–399.

Hirose, H., and K. Yoshida. 1964. A review of the life history of the genus *Monostroma*. *Bull. Japanese Soc. Phycology*, 12: 19–31.

Hollenberg, G. J. 1935. A study of *Halicystis ovalis*. I. Morphology and reproduction. *Am. J. Bot.*, 22: 783–812.

——————— 1958. Observations concerning the life cycle of *Spongomorpha coalita*. . . . *Madroño*, 14: 249–251.

Iyengar, M.O.P., and K. R. Ramanathan. 1940. On the reproduction of *Anadyomene stellata*. . . . *J. Indian Bot. Soc.*, 19: 175–176.

——————— 1941. On the life history and cytology of *Microdictyon tenuis*. . . . *J. Indian Bot. Soc.*, 20: 157–159.

Kornmann, P. 1938. Zur Entwicklungsgeschichte von *Derbesia* und *Halicystis*. *Planta*, 28: 464–470.

——————— 1963. Die Ulotrichales, neu geordnet auf der Grundlage entwicklungsgeschichtlicher Befunde. *Phycologia*, 3: 60–68.

Proskauer, J. 1950. On *Prasinocladus*. *Am. J. Bot.*, 37: 59–66.

Scagel, R. 1960. Life history studies of the Pacific Coast marine alga, *Collinsiella tuberculata*. . . . *Can. J. Bot.*, 38: 969–983.

Silva, P. C. 1960. *Codium* (Chlorophyta) of the tropical western Atlantic. *Nova Hedwigia*, 1: 497–536.

Thivy, Francesca. 1943. New records of some marine Chaetophoraceae and Chaetosphaeridiaceae for North America. *Biol. Bull.*, 85: 244–264.

Van den Hoek, C. 1963. Revision of the European species of *Cladophora*. Leiden: Brill. viii + 248 pp.

Wood, R. D., and K. Imahori. 1964. A revision of the Characeae. Weinheim: J. Cramer. vol. 1, Monograph (by Wood), 960 pp.; vol. 2, Iconograph (by Wood and Imahori), 395 pls.

9

Benthic Brown Algae
(Phaeophyta)

CHARACTERISTICS

The Phaeophyta are the most strictly marine of all the seaweeds. The group includes only three genera of small fresh-water forms, and these have life histories similar to the marine ones. The abundance and large size of the brown algae on rocky shores of the north-temperate Atlantic has made them almost synonymous with "seaweed" in our European culture. Less numerous in species than Rhodophyta, they make up for this in bulk in nearly all temperate and high-latitude waters where they dominate the vegetation of coastal waters. Although characteristic of exposed shores, they occur in some areas as conspicuous salt-marsh plants, loose-lying and regenerating vegetatively. Brown algae are much smaller in size, in numbers, and in kinds in tropical areas than in high-latitude seas, but the genus *Sargassum* often retains a conspicuous prevalence, and the immense floating masses of this alga in the vast Sargasso Sea provide a classic example of an abundant, free-floating brown alga in the tropics.

All the brown algal families, excepting a few strictly austral ones, are represented in the northern hemisphere. The North-American flora includes examples of nearly all the important families. Twenty-one of these will be considered briefly in this account.

The marine brown algae are in large part macroscopic plants. There are no unicellular or colonial forms, nor any so simple of construction as an unbranched filament. The smallest forms of Ectocarpales consist of branched, uniseriate filaments endophytic in larger seaweeds, while the largest members of Laminariales or Fucales exhibit a size and an elaboration of form and structure exceeding that of any other algae.

The characteristic brownish color of Phaeophyta is due to the special accessory carotinoid pigment, fucoxanthin, which masks the other pigments, including chlorophyll *a* and *c*. The chromatophore may be solitary in a cell, but usually there are many small parietal chromatophores. Unlike large numbers of marine green algae, the Phaeophyta usually have cells with a single large nucleus. There is nothing comparable to the Siphonales among brown algae.

Various kinds of meristems occur. Most Dictyosiphonales show diffuse growth, while Sphacelariales, Dictyotales, and Fucales usually exhibit a distinct apical cell. Chordariales and Desmarestiales are classic examples of trichothallic growth, as are the Laminariales of intercalary meristems.

Except for the large order Fucales, the brown algae characteristically show an alternation of generations. The sporophyte generation is diploid, and meiosis occurs in unilocular sporangia to produce haploid zoospores (except in Dictyotales in which the haploid spores are not motile). Sexual plants arise from these spores. Sporophytic plants in some groups may also produce plurilocular sporangia, which release zooids without a preceding meiotic process. These diploid zoospores give rise to other diploid sporophyte plants.

The motile reproductive cells are distinctive. They are pyriform and are laterally biflagellate. The two flagella are unequal, the long one being anterior and the short one posterior, except in Fucales in which the reverse occurs.

The brown algae have been divided into three classes according to the type of life history. Further division of one of these into subclasses, and the arrangement of the orders, may best be understood from the key given below. This classification has received wide recognition and is used here for practical purposes although Papenfuss (1951) rejects the use of the classes and subclasses on phylogenetic grounds.

1. Plants with an alternation of generations 2

1. Plants without an alternation of generations. (Class Cyclosporeae)
Order: *Fucales*

2. With an alternation of macroscopic, usually isomorphic generations . . . . (Class Isogeneratae)
Orders: *Ectocarpales*
Sphacelariales
Cutleriales
Tilopteridales
Dictyotales

2. With an alternation of heteromorphic generations . . . .
. . . . (Class Heterogeneratae) . . 3

3. Thallus composed of filaments which adhere to one another to form a pseudoparenchymatous tissue. (Subclass Haplostichineae)

    Orders: *Chordariales*
              Sporochnales
              Desmarestiales

3. Thallus composed of cells dividing by intercalary longitudinal walls to form a true parenchymatous tissue . . . . . . (Subclass Polystichineae)

    Orders: *Dictyosiphonales*
              Laminariales

ECTOCARPALES

This order contains only two families of little-specialized brown algae. The Ectocarpaceae, exemplified by *Ectocarpus,* contains mostly small plants of free-filamentous construction. The Ralfsiaceae, exemplified by *Ralfsia,* is composed of definitive, crustose forms of pseudoparenchymatous structure made up of compacted filaments.

Ectocarpus

The thalli of *Ectocarpus* are composed of freely branched, uniseriate filaments differentiated into prostrate and erect systems (Figure 9-1). The prostrate parts are rhizoid-like and often penetrate the substrate. The variously branched, erect parts may remain uniseriate or in some species become partially corticated by descending rhizoidal filaments from some of the cells. Growth is diffuse or

FIGURE 9–1. *A, Ectocarpus breviarticulatus,* a species with entangled, felted, erect branchlets and extensive prostrate system, in habit view. *B,* Detail of a species of *Giffordia,* showing numerous discoid chromatophores, a unilocular sporangium, and a plurilocular sporangium.

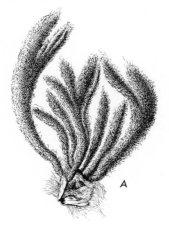
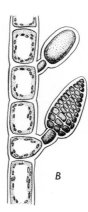

more or less clearly trichothallic with intercalary cell divisions confined to certain areas of the filaments.

This large genus has traditionally been divided into a group of species with band-shaped chromatophores (Figure 7-22,*C*) and a group with disc-shaped chromatophores. More recently, many workers have accepted generic segregation of *Giffordia* for species with numerous discoid chromatophores (Figure 7-22,*A*), and there are other generic segregates.

The classical *Ectocarpus siliculosus*, in which Berthold first observed fusion of gametes in 1881, has subsequently been studied intensively by numerous workers in many different areas. As a result, the life history of this alga has become well-known and confirmed.

The sporophyte plants are diploid and bear terminally on short branches either unilocular or plurilocular sporangia, or both (Figure 9-1,*B*). The plurilocular sporangia produce zooids by mitotic division, and these repeat the sporophyte generation. The unilocular sporangia, however, undergo meiosis, and the resulting haploid zoospores develop into sexual plants that are morphologically like the sporophyte plants.

The sexual plants are dioecious, although the plurilocular gametangial organs they bear are morphologically indistinguishable from each other and from the plurilocular organs of sporophyte plants (Figure 7-35,*B*). This circumstance makes it especially difficult to determine the sporophyte or gametophyte nature of plants that bear only plurilocular organs. The laterally biflagellate gametes look alike, but physiologically the male gametes have longer mobility, and fusion occurs after the female gamete has come to rest. The zygote develops directly into a new diploid sporophyte.

Ralfsia

The alternate sporophyte and gametophyte generations of *Ralfsia* are isomorphic plants of brown or blackish spreading crustose form, usually firmly adherent to rock surfaces at middle and upper intertidal levels along most temperate shores (Figure 7-2,*F*). Young plants may be more or less circular, but old ones become coalesced and overgrown to form extensive rock-covering patches. They may be attached to the substrate directly by the cell walls of the basal layer, or by short rhizoids. The basal layer of the thallus consists of branched, radiating, laterally coalesced filaments. Each cell of this nonphotosynthetic layer supports an erect or ascending assimilatory filament provided with chromatophores. The prostrate and erect filaments are all compacted into a firm tissue (Figure 9-2)

Fertile plants of *Ralfsia* are infrequently collected, for fruiting seems usually to occur in late autumn and winter. The sporophytes produce superficial sori resembling low, flat warts, in which the terminal cell of each erect, vegetative filament may produce an elongate, multicellular paraphysis and (or) a shorter, unilocular sporangium (Figure 9-2,*A,C*). After release of swarmers from the sporangia the fertile filaments are shed and the underlying parts continue to grow.

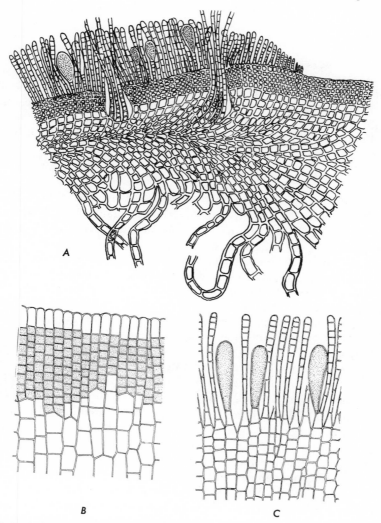

FIGURE 9-2. *A,* Portion of a plant of *Ralfsia expansa* as seen in vertical section, showing rhizoids, structure of compacted filaments, and unilocular sporangia among paraphyses (after Weber van Bosse). *B–C, Ralfsia pacifica*: *B,* upper portion of a fertile gametophyte showing uniseriate, plurilocular gametangia with terminal sterile cells; *C,* upper portion of a fertile sporophyte with unilocular sporangia (after Smith; reprinted by permission of Stanford University Press).

Gametophytes also produce their gametangia in superficial sori, but these are without paraphyses and consist of densely packed plurilocular organs interspersed with tufts of colorless, multicellular hairs. The gametangia, tipped with one or more sterile cells, arise distally on the assimilatory filaments and have their fertile cells in uniseriate, biseriate, or pluriseriate arrangement (Figure 9-2,*B*).

SPHACELARIALES

The members of this order are present in all seas, and a species of *Sphacelaria*, the largest genus, may be expected in almost any intertidal flora. They are usually short, densely branched, tufted plants up to a few centimeters in height. Among the Isogeneratae they are distinctive in that they possess well-marked apical growth from a large apical cell (Figure 7-29,*C*), parenchymatous structure, and usually radial organization.

Sphacelaria

The tufted, filamentous plants are attached by discoid holdfasts or by rhizoidal filaments. The erect axes are usually abundantly branched, sometimes in a regularly distichous manner. Each branch terminates in a conspicuous, cylindrical apical cell that undergoes a basal segmentation followed by longitudinal division of the segments to produce a polysiphonous structure (Figure 9-3,*A*). The maturing axis and branches, although undergoing septation into smaller and smaller cells, do not show any evident enlargement, so that filament diameters are essentially uniform from base to apex. Older axes, however, may in some species become corticated by downwardly growing rhizoidal filaments (Figure 9-3,*E*). Some plants may bear uniseriate hairs on the branches.

Many kinds of *Sphacelaria* show a peculiar type of vegetative multiplication that is widely used in classification. Small, specialized branchlets of distinctive form (propagula) are produced throughout vegetative parts of the plant, far more frequently than sporangia or gametangia (Figure 9-3,*B–D*). Each propagulum has an apical cell, and commonly two or three protuberances, rays, horns, or arms. Upon detachment and contact with a suitable substrate, any of these propagula can grow into a new plant. In many *Sphacelaria* species, only this vegetative method of reproduction is known.

Sporophyte plants are recognized by their sessile or pedicellate unilocular sporangia (Figure 9-3,*F*), which are borne singly here and there on the branches. It has been demonstrated that meiosis occurs in the unilocular sporangia and that haploid zooids so produced give rise to gametophyte plants. An accessory method of asexual reproduction may occur, in which zooids from plurilocular sporangia (presumable mitospores) germinate directly to repeat the sporophyte generation.

Gametophytes produce pedicellate plurilocular gametangia. These may be of different male and female kinds (Figure 9-3,*G–H*).

TILOPTERIDALES

This little-known order is represented in North America by only three rare species, each of a different genus (see Appendix B). They live mostly in deep

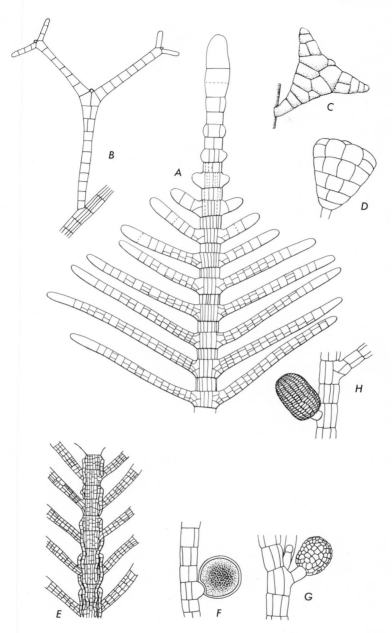

FIGURE 9–3. Growth and reproduction in *Sphacelaria*: *A,* apex of a growing axis show-ing prominent apical cell and successive divisions to form a polysiphonous axis; *B–D,* three forms of propagula; *E,* a corticated species showing downwardly growing rhizoidal corticating filaments; *F,* unilocular sporangium; *G,* a female plurilocular gametangium; *H,* a male plurilocular gametangium (mostly after Sauvageau).

water and seem to be sporadic and ephemeral. Many details in their life histories remain to be worked out.

The plants generally resemble *Ectocarpus* in filamentous habit, and show marked trichothallic growth. The lower parts may, however, become multiseriate somewhat as in *Sphacelaria*. The characteristic reproductive structures are globose or oblong monosporangia whose entire contents are liberated as a monospore. These are quadrinucleate, and some cytological investigations suggest that the four nuclei are the products of meiosis. The monospores, thus, may be considered a kind of primitive, undivided tetrad of spores. The sexual generation produces plurilocular gametangia, but fertilization and other details have not been described.

CUTLERIALES

This is another small order consisting of only three genera. The only species in the western hemisphere is *Cutleria hancockii*, which occurs commonly in the upper Gulf of California. The order is of unusual interest, however, in that both of the alternating generations are macroscopic but not always isomorphic. In this, it shows an advance toward strictly heteromorphic alternation of macroscopic and microscopic generations so prevalent among the more highly developed brown algae.

Cutleria

These plants are usually annuals of which the larger, rapidly growing, erect gametophyte may be found growing from among a cluster of prostrate, rhizoidally attached, more or less crustose sporophyte thalli (Figure 9-4). The latter were long thought to belong to a separate genus *(Aglaozonia)*. The gametophyte in *C. hancockii* is broadly fan-shaped with a fringe of fine assimilatory hairs along the leading margin by which the trichothallic mode of growth is achieved.

The life history has been worked out in the European species, *C. multifida*. The sexual plants are dioecious and the gametangia are of two kinds, produced laterally on hairs arising in superficial tufts. Both the male and female gametangia are multiseriate, but distinctly different in appearance. The motile gametes (Figure 7-24,*D*) are of markedly different size. Fertilization occurs after the larger female gametes have come to rest. The zygote germinates to develop into the diploid sporophyte *(Aglaozonia* stage.) Unfertilized female gametes may develop parthenogenetically into haploid, sterile *Aglaozonia* plants. The mature sporophyte produces unilocular sporangia in a dense, superficial sorus. The ripe sporangium, after meiosis, usually releases eight haploid swarmers through an apical pore.

Many variations of this life history in the Cutleriales present interesting problems for the student of comparative algal morphology and reproduction.

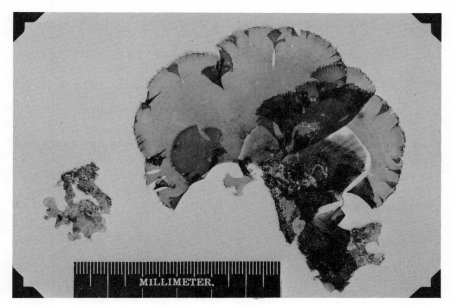

FIGURE 9–4. *Cutleria hancockii,* showing large, fringe-margined gametophyte (right) and prostrate sporophyte (*Aglaozonia* stage) at the left.

DICTYOTALES

Dictyotaceae

This distinctive order (which has a single family) is of widespread occurrence in tropical and subtropical regions. A number of species also occur in temperate waters, but among tropical brown algae *Dictyota* and *Padina* are next to *Sargassum* in abundance. The group shows an alternation of isomorphic generations, but differs from other Isogeneratae in some combination of the following characters: a prominent apical cell; a flat, membranous form; nonmotile meiospores; oogamous sexual reproduction.

Dictyota

The vegetative structure of this plant is distinctive in that the medulla consists of a single layer of large, quadrate, vacuolate cells (Figure 9-5,*C*) and the cortex of a single layer of smaller, pigmented cells. The closely related genus *Pachydictyon* in California differs in its thicker cortex at the blade margins.

The blades show dichotomous branching, and the division of the large apical cell to accomplish this provides a good demonstration of apical dichotomy (Figure 7-29,*A–B*). Attachment is commonly by a tangle of branched rhizoids which, in some plants of the order, become so abundant as to form a spongy basal cone. Tufts of colorless hairs are commonly scattered over both surfaces of the ligulate thallus.

Sporophyte plants in *Dictyota*, and characteristically for the order, bear peculiar unilocular sporangia that produce so-called tetraspores (Figure 7-25,*B*). These are of diverse arrangement in different genera and afford useful taxonomic application. In *Dictyota* they are spherical, superficial outgrowths, scattered in irregular patches and associated with tufts of sterile hairs. Meiosis occurs during the division of the nucleus of the developing sporangium, and cytoplasmic cleavage subsequently produces the four aplanospores (tetraspores). The spores are released by gelatinization of the sporangium apex and develop directly into new haploid gametophyte plants.

The gametophytes are usually of two sexes. (There are monoecious species.) The oogonial or antheridial sori are scattered over both surfaces of their respective thalli and may be recognized by color (Figure 9-5,*A–B*). The male sori show early disintegration of chromatophores in the cells destined to form the antheridia. The female sori remain dark brown. The oogonia each produce a single large, nonmotile egg. The plurilocular antheridia produce large numbers of uniflagellate antherozoids (Figure 9-5,*D*) which swarm around the egg when it is released into the water.

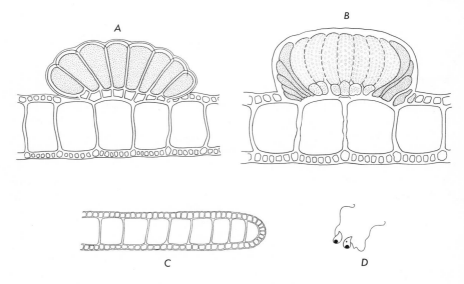

FIGURE 9–5. *Dictyota dichotoma*: *A,* vertical section of an oögonial sorus; *B,* vertical section of an antheridial sorus; *C,* transection of a sterile blade; *D,* spermatozoids.

The sexual reproduction of *Dictyota* shows, in different localities, varying kinds of rhythmic periodicity evidently related to tidal and light cycles.

CHORDARIALES

The four families of this order represented along American coasts are distinguished by trichothallic growth of the monoaxial or multiaxial sporophyte (Figure 7-28,*B*) and by isogamous gametic union (although gametes are still unknown for various genera and for most species.) The sporophyte plants range from minute, crustose epiphytes to erect, fleshy, or gelatinous plants up to 40 centimeters tall. The gametophytes (so far as limited knowledge goes) are microscopic, filamentous plants. They have been observed only by culturing zoospores.

Myrionemataceae

Myrionema

Myrionema is one of several genera of this family commonly occurring as epiphytes on stipes, blades, and pneumatocysts of Laminariales and on various other macroscopic algae. They give the impression, from their small size and simple structure, of being primitive forms, but there is some evidence that they are actually reduced forms, phylogenetically, of more complex types of the order. The sporophyte is a small, circular or irregular crustose thallus consisting of a monostromatic basal layer from each cell of which a short, erect filament arises. The erect filaments may be free or laterally adjoined, and among the short vegetative filaments are some basally meristematic, uniseriate hairs. Both unilocular and plurilocular sporangia may be produced in *Myrionema*, although the former are unknown in some species. *Myrionema* (Figure 9-6) is distinguished from the closely related *Compsonema* (Figure 9-9,*F*) by the uniseriate nature of the plurilocular sporangia.

FIGURE 9–6. *Myrionema primarium* as seen in vertical section, showing monostromatic basal layer, uniseriate hairs, a short vegetative filament, and several plurilocular sporangia.

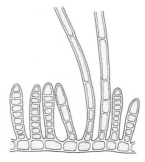

The plurilocular sporangia produce zoospores capable of repeating the sporophyte generation. The unilocular sporangia, however, are known in some species of *Myrionema* to produce haploid zoospores that develop into a loosely and irregularly branched filamentous gametophyte. In many species, on the other hand, the gametophyte plant is unknown. No gametangia have yet been reported for the family. Many of the plants assigned to the family Myrionemataceae, in fact, are so poorly known that they may ultimately prove to belong instead to some ectocarpalean group.

Elachisteaceae

Elachistea

These small, tufted or cushion-like plants are abundantly present in summer and autumn along the north-Atlantic coasts as epiphytes on *Fucus, Ascophyllum, Chondrus,* and various other coarse algae (Figure 9-7,*A*). The densely matted, colorless filaments of the basal portion often penetrate the host tissues. The basal stratum supports a tuft of long, free, uniseriate assimilatory filaments showing intercalary growth, and a crowded basal cluster of short paraphyses. Among these dense basal filaments the unilocular sporangia are borne. These appear in autumn, and in most species the zoospores germinate to produce a microscopic, branched, thread-like gametophyte that overwinters. In early

FIGURE 9-7. *A, Elachistea fucicola* growing as epiphytic tufts on *Fucus. B,* Portion of a fertile sporangial plant of *Chordaria flagelliformis* as seen in transection, showing unilocular sporangia at bases of cortical assimilatory filaments.

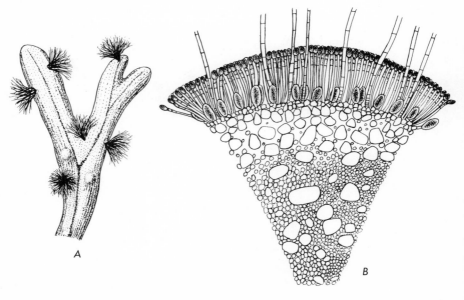

A

B

spring plurilocular gametangia develop and release isogametes. The zygote attaches to the host alga and develops into a new macroscopic *Elachistea* plant.

One of the commonest species, *E. fucicola,* has an atypical life history in which only unilocular sporangia are known (Figure 9-9,*I*), and the small, filamentous plant arising from germinating zoospores produces new sporophytes as lateral vegetative outgrowths. In this species there is evidently no haploid phase.

Chordariaceae

Chordaria

The members of this family are fairly large plants of gelatinous consistency and usually of branched filiform character. *Chordaria* is one of the commoner forms, especially along the northern Atlantic, and the large sporophyte may reach 7 decimeters in length. The slippery, cylindrical branched axes are up to 1.5 millimeters in diameter. They consist of a pseudoparenchymatous medulla of compacted, colorless longitudinal filaments bearing a dense cortex of short, radiating, assimilatory filaments. The cortical filaments are simple or branched and of clavate form. They are embedded in a thick jelly that provides the slimy texture. Growth is apical and trichothallic. Some members of the order are multiaxial, as *Myriogloia* (Figure 7-28,*B*) and *Chordaria.* There are also uniaxial types, as *Haplogloia* (Figure 9-8,*A*). Unilocular sporangia are produced among the bases of the cortical assimilatory filaments (Figure 9-7,*B*). These are pyriform structures up to 100 μ long. The zoospores of *C. flagelliformis* have been cultured to produce the microscopic gametophyte, but this has not been brought through to fertility, so plurilocular gametangia, gametes, and fertilization are unknown.

SPOROCHNALES

Sporochnaceae

The members of this small order (which has a single family) are mainly inhabitants of the Southern Hemisphere, but a few interesting species of very wide distribution, such as *Sporochnus peduncularis,* occur along the north Pacific and north Atlantic. They are almost exclusively deep-water plants (see Chapter 15) and may best be obtained by dredging on deep, sandy bottoms, although they occasionally appear in drift. Presumably, all show an alternation of macroscopic sporophyte and microscopic, filamentous gametophyte. The order is most distinctly characterized by the peculiar anatomy of the growing apices. The meristem at the branch tip is intercalary, consisting of a dome-shaped single layer of meristematic cells crowned by a tuft of simple hairs (Figure 9-8,*B*). The detailed ontogeny of this mode of growth has been worked out only in the European genus *Nereia.*

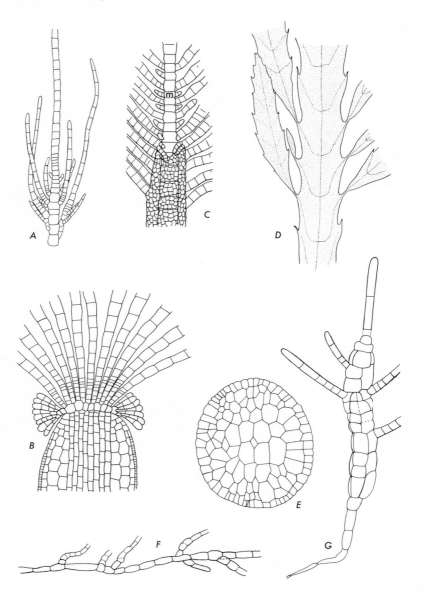

FIGURE 9–8. *A*, Apex of an axis of *Haplogloia andersonii*, showing trichothallic growth. *B*, Longisection of an apex of *Carpomitra* (Sporochnaceae), showing meristematic layer and origin of tuft of hairs. *C*, Apex of a growing axis of *Desmarestia aculeata* showing trichothallic meristematic area (m) in axial cell row, lateral hair branches, and development of cortical envelope. *D*, *Desmarestia munda*, showing midvein, opposite lateral veins, and pinnate branches. *E–G*, *Dictyosiphon foeniculaceus*: *E*, transection of a sporophyte thallus; *F*, portions of a gametophyte plant with gametangia; *G*, a young sporophyte arising from part of a plethysmothallus. (*B, E–G* after Sauvageau; *C* after Reinke)

DESMARESTIALES

The members of this order show a heteromorphic alternation of a large, erect, essentially pinnately branched sporophyte with a microscopic gametophyte. Growth is trichothallic and initiated by a single filament (Figure 9-8,*C*). Although the plants may be as large as many species of *Laminaria*, their structure is simple in comparison with the Laminariales. The sporophytes bear unilocular sporangia. The gametophyte plants, as in the Laminariales, are dioecious, and sexual reproduction is oögamous.

Desmarestiaceae

Desmarestia

Desmarestias are widely distributed in temperate waters and probably are best known because of their exceedingly acid character. They must always be kept separate from other algal collections to prevent damage from acid contact. Some of the species are finely divided, bushy plants, but several are large, ligulately branched forms of which some reach lengths of 4 meters or more with blades to 20 centimeters wide. Most species are readily recognized by their pinnate branches, usually with a distinct median vein (Figure 9-8,*D*). The apex bears a single uniseriate filament showing trichothallic growth (Figure 9-8,*C*), and, when growth is rapid, a fringe of deciduous hairs may be present along the margin of young blades.

Sporophyte plants bear unilocular sporangia which arise from superficial cells of mature blades and may be solitary or grouped in sori. Following meiosis, biflagellate zoospores are produced. These give rise to dioecious, microscopic, filamentous gametophytes (Figure 9-9,*G–H*). The smaller male plants develop terminal antheridial cells, each of which produces a single biflagellate antherozoid. The female gametophyte produces a terminal or intercalary oögonium from which an egg is extruded, but this remains attached to the apex of the oögonium where fertilization occurs and the young sporophyte begins development.

DICTYOSIPHONALES

This order has a large assemblage of brown algae in which the structure of the thallus is parenchyma-like throughout and in which both longitudinal and transverse divisions of intercalary cells occur. These are characters of the subclass Polystichineae used by various authors to include the orders Dictyosiphonales (sometimes treated as Punctariales) and the Laminariales.

Like the other orders of the class Heterogeneratae, a majority of the Dictyosiphonales show an alternation of a macroscopic sporophyte and a microscopic filamentous gametophyte (although there are several exceptions). They are, however, set off from the other orders by various characteristics: their solid, parenchymatous structure (Figure 9-8,E) easily sets them apart from the Chordariales; their lack of trichothallic growth, from the Desmarestiales; their diffuse or apical growth, usually without a restricted intercalary meristem, from the Laminariales.

The group is divided into seven families all of which are represented on North-American shores. The following families contain species of widespread and common occurrence that may conveniently be used for study.

Punctariaceae

Punctaria

The punctarias are annual plants in which the sporophyte consists of 1 or more erect blades from a discoid base. The blades are ligulate or broadly expanded from a short, slender stipe (Figure 9-9,C). They consist of three to seven layers of cubical cells (as seen in transection) with little difference in size between the interior and the superficial cells. The surface may be provided with tufts of hairs. Punctaria, and other members of the family, show an interestingly complex life history. In various species both unilocular and plurilocular zoosporangia are known to occur, either on the same or separate sporophyte plants and to function in different ways. The unilocular sporangia are formed by metamorphosis of superficial cells and are arranged in scattered sori immersed at the surface of the thallus. Meiosis occurs in these, and the haploid zoospores give rise to gametophyte plants which are of minute size and ectocarpoid form. These produce isogametes which fuse to initiate again the sporophyte generation. The sporophyte, however, also produces plurilocular sporangia (Figure 9-9,D-E), often grouped in minute sori and developing either concurrently with or before the unilocular sporangia. The zooids from these plurilocular organs serve as an accessory method of duplicating the sporophyte generation. The zoospores are diploid and grow into small filamentous plantlets known as plethysmothalli. These may form new sporophytes directly as lateral outgrowths, or they may produce plurilocular sporangia, the zoospores of which reproduce the sporophyte either directly upon germination, or sometimes through additional plethysmothallus stages.

Scytosiphonaceae

This family includes some of the commonest and most cosmopolitan of the brown algae. Both Scytosiphon (Figure 9-9,A-B) and Colpomenia (Figure 9-10) occur throughout much of the world, and Hydroclathrus and Rosenvingea are pantropical. These several genera are remarkable and distinct from other Dictyosiphonales in that the sporophyte produces only plurilocular sporangia. From this it has been presumed that the sexual generation has been lost. The

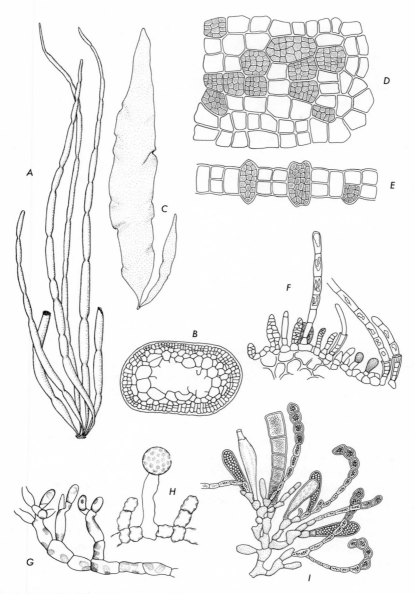

FIGURE 9–9. *A–B, Scytosiphon lomentaria*: *A*, habit; *B*, transection of a mid-portion (after Setchell & Gardner). *C–E, Punctaria* sp.: *C*, habit; *D*, plurilocular sporangia in surface view; *E*, in a transection of a blade (after Kylin). *F, Compsonema tenue* as seen in median optical view, showing unilocular and plurilocular sporangia (the latter pluriseriate) and vegetative hairs (after Setchell & Gardner). *G–H*, Gametophytes of *Desmarestia*: *G*, male; *H*, female with extruded egg ready for fertilization (after Schreiber). *I*, Portion of a fruiting part of *Elachistea fucicola*, showing unilocular sporangia, paraphyses, and the base of one assimilatory filament.

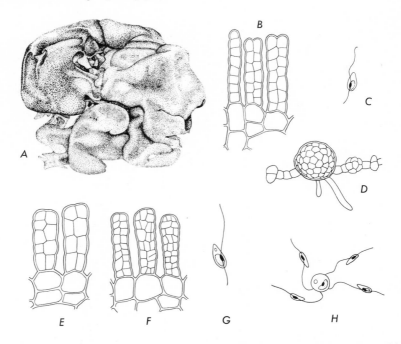

FIGURE 9–10. *Colpomenia sinuosa* life history (after Kunieda & Suto): *A*, habit; *B*, plurilocular sporangia; *C*, zoospore; *D*, young *Colpomenia* plants arising from a zoospore-derived protonema; *E*, plurilocular female gametangia; *F*, plurilocular male gametangia; *G*, female gamete; *H*, fertilization (4 male gametes and 1 female gamete).

life history of *Colpomenia*, however, as reported in Japan (Kunieda and Suto, 1938) suggests that the sexual generation may have been overlooked in some of these plants in which it may be morphologically like the sporophyte. The *Colpomenia* sporophyte's plurilocular sporangia were reported to produce zoospores that yielded dioecious gametophytes like the sporophyte parent. These produced two kinds of plurilocular gametangia yielding anisogametes that fused to reform the sporophyte (Figure 9-10). The cytology has not been worked out, and the anomaly of this life history calls for much further study of this group, particularly in view of the fact that unilocular sporangia (the seat of meiosis in brown algae) are unknown in members of this family.

Scytosiphon (Figure 9-9) is another of these common algae in which much clarifying work needs to be done. Conflicting reports on the activity of swarmers and their products makes it uncertain whether the *Scytosiphon* plant is sporophyte or gametophyte. The structure, however, makes it easily recognized, for it consists of an unbranched axis of tubular construction. The tube is made up of several layers of parenchymatous cells without intercellular spaces (Figure 9-9,*B*) grading outwardly to smaller size and more dense pigmentation. The tubes are often provided with constrictions and may be twisted into spirals.

Dictyosiphonaceae

The commonest and most representative member of this small family is *Dictyosiphon foeniculaceus,* inhabiting the northwest Atlantic from the subarctic to New Jersey and growing throughout the year on *Chordaria* or other algae in exposed places. The plants reach 10 decimeters in height and consist of a bushy cluster of abundantly branched filaments 1 millimeter or less in diameter. Young plants and young branches are clothed with delicate, deciduous hairs. The axis is typically solid and composed of a medulla of large, elongate cells and a thin cortex of small, densely pigmented cells (Figure 9-8,*E*). Older parts, however, may have a ruptured medulla which breaks down to produce a partially hollow axis. The large sporophyte plants produce unilocular sporangia in which meiosis precedes development of the zoospores. These germinate to form minute gametophyte thalli (Figure 9-8,*F*) which produce plurilocular gametangia. The gametes may germinate parthenogenetically to reproduce the haploid, ectocarpoid gametophyte plant, or they may fuse in pairs to produce a diploid zygote that develops into a minute, diploid, ectocarpoid plethysmo-thallus. This, in turn, produces plurilocular sporangia whose zoospores may reproduce the plethysmothallus; or the plethysmothallus may form lateral out-growths that develop into the diploid, macroscopic *Dictyosiphon* plant (Figure 9-8,*G*).

LAMINARIALES

This order contains the largest and most elaborately organized of all algae: the kelps. Many examples illustrating special features of these plants have already been mentioned in preceding chapters under such names as *Laminaria, Macrocystis, Nereocystis, Pelagophycus, Postelsia,* and *Eisenia.* The kelps are predominantly plants of cold water. They occur throughout the Pacific Coast from Alaska to Baja California and along the Atlantic as far south as New Jersey. High summer temperatures prevent their growth farther south, and none is to be found in the Gulf of Mexico or in the Caribbean area.

The order includes one small and three large families, each equally well represented on American coasts. The single genus *Chorda,* with its peculiar whip-like form (Figure 7-2) is treated as representing a separate family, Chordaceae. With this one exception, the kelps all show a large, coarse sporophyte genera-tion differentiated into holdfast, stipe, and one or more blades (Figure 7-6). Pneumatocysts occur in various members. Growth in length results from an intercalary meristem between stipe and blade which adds tissue to both. Secondary growth in diameter of the stipe occurs in some annual and in many perennial species (Figure 7-5). The plants have a highly developed internal structure, showing clear tissue differentiation. Whereas the sporophyte is the evident plant, the life history always is completed through an alternate, microscopic, filamentous gametophyte whose ecological requirements probably are more often the determining factors in the distribution of a given species.

The sporophytes of Laminariales produce superficial unilocular sporangia either on vegetative blades or on special sporophylls. These sporangia are sometimes (as in *Nereocystis*) in remarkably definitive sori. These mature in succession and fall out of the blade at maturity as an irregular plate, leaving a large hole that rapidly erodes (Figure 7-38). The sporangia are associated with unicellular paraphyses, both arising from the same basal cells (Figure 9-14,*D*). Meiosis occurs in the developing unilocular sporangia, which usually release 16 to 64 zoospores (32 in *Nereocystis*). The zoospores attach and form a wall after brief motility and germinate within a few hours to grow into haploid gametophytes. (Thirty-one chromosomes have been counted in *Nereocystis*). The gametophytes, which occur in a 1:1 ratio, are always dioecious, and this has now been determined in a large number of species in culture since the life history of Laminariales was first worked out by Sauvageau in 1915. The general appearance of the gametophytes is remarkably uniform throughout the order. All are small, filamentous thalli of relatively few cells in uniseriate arrangement. The male plants have smaller cells and are more abundantly branched than the female. Although these gametophytes have almost always been studied in culture, it is possible to observe them in nature. Neushul found at Friday Harbor, Washington, that gametophytes could be seen by examining the edges of the natural perforations in the blades of *Agarum* where they grow well in the freely passing water.

Sexual reproduction in Laminariales is oögamous. The oögonia are terminal or intercalary in position. Each forms a single egg which, though extruded, usually remains attached to the ruptured oögonium. The antheridia occur at the tips of branches or as outgrowths from intercalary cells of male gametophytes. Each releases a single biflagellate antherozoid, and the plant degenerates after the gametes are shed. The fertilized egg secretes a wall and soon undergoes division to begin the development of the sporophyte, but the female gametophyte persists during the early phases of this growth (Figure 7-26,*D*).

Laminariaceae

Nine genera of this family occur along temperate and boreal North America. All are characterized by an unbranched stipe terminating in a single blade. The genera are distinguished mainly on blade characters. Thus, *Laminaria* has a smooth or bullate, imperforate blade without ribs (Figure 7-1). *Phyllaria* is similar, but has tufts of hairs on the surface. *Costaria* has five percurrent ribs running through the blade. *Agarum* has a midrib, is perforated and expanded (Figure 7-1). *Thalassiophyllum* is perforated and has the fan-shaped blade spirally twisted and rolled up at the base like a scroll. In all genera the sporangial sori are produced on the vegetative blades and not on special sporophylls.

The genus *Laminaria* includes far more species than any of the other genera, some of which are monotypic. Twenty species of *Laminaria* occur on North American coasts. These range on the Pacific coast from the small, colonial *L. sinclairii* to the gigantic *L. farlowii,* which may reach 8 meters in length. Several species are distinguished by holdfast characters. *L. sinclairii* reproduces vegetatively by a prostrate, branched rhizome bearing many erect stipes and blades. Other species have a discoid or conical base rather than the more usual holdfast of branched haptera. The shape of the blade, the solid or hollow character of the stipe, and the presence or absence of mucilage ducts in the stipe provide other features for specific identification.

Lessoniaceae

This family, in North America, is exclusively of Pacific-Coast occurrence. It includes the largest of the algae and those that form the submarine kelp forests: *Macrocystis, Nereocystis, Pelagophycus* (Figure 7-6). These are plants with branched stipes in which a single blade terminates each branch of the stipe. It should be noted, however, that in such genera as *Nereocystis* and *Pelagophycus* the stipes are branched only at the apex above a large pneumatocyst.

In most of the genera the stipes are erect, prominent, and long, but *Dictyoneurum,* for example, has a flattened, prostrate stipe, and the plants are gregarious in groups of 25 to 100 individuals, forming dense, low clumps on intertidal rocks. The remarkable, hollow, resilient stipe of *Postelsia* has already been described and shown (Figure 7-4). The multiple, branched stipes of *Macrocystis,* capable of extensive regeneration, account for its development in submarine forest associations (see Chapter 15).

Perhaps the most readily available example of a massive member of the Lessoniaceae, and one well suited for class examination, is *Nereocystis,* which occurs in abundance from Alaska to San Luis Obispo, California, and may commonly be collected in shore drift. Although *Nereocystis* is an annual, it reaches a length of up to 40 meters. The plants have a rather small holdfast of densely compacted, branched haptera supporting a single stipe 1 to 2 centimeters in diameter for most of its unbranched length — which may be 36 meters! The upper 2 to 3 meters of the stipe gradually broaden and become hollow, forming a long pneumatocyst which is bulbous at the end and up to 14 centimeters in diameter. The top of the pneumatocyst bears four short extensions of the stipe which are 4 to 5 times dichotomous and support 32 to 64 blades (Figure 9-11). These are 3 or 4 meters long.

Nereocystis beds occur on rocky bottoms usually in 20 to 50 feet of water, and the inflated upper end of the stipe floats horizontally at the surface of the water with the blades hanging down vertically like curtains (Figure 7-18). In a quiet area, such as Puget Sound, the elongate stipes may allow the plants to stream out in one direction and then another with the movements of the tides.

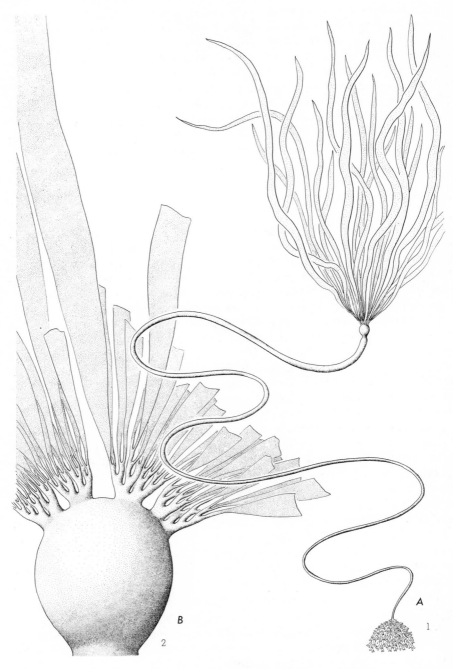

FIGURE 9–11. *Nereocystis leutkeana*: *A*, an entire plant; *B*, pneumatocyst and basal portion of blades (from Smith, reprinted by permission of Stanford University Press).

Alariaceae

Apart from the north circumpolar genus *Alaria*, these, also, are Pacific Coast plants in North America, and some of them range far south into Mexico *(Egregia, Eisenia)*. They are characterized by the presence of lateral, foliar outgrowths from the stipes (which may be branched or unbranched) or from the primary blade base, and by the restriction of sporangia to special sporophylls. The genera are distinguished on the basis of their stipe and blade characters. Almost all have blades restricted to groups at the upper end of the stipe. The sole exception is *Egregia*, in which lateral blades extend along either side of a flattened stipe for several meters, giving rise to the common name "feather boa" (Figure 9-12). *Eisenia* has the peculiar manner of development of the falsely branched stipe described above (Figure 7-7). *Pterygophora* has 1 terminal blade and laterals of approximately the same size and shape, while *Alaria* has a large terminal blade and a group of smaller lateral blades of different shape that function at maturity as sporophylls.

FIGURE 9–12. *Egregia laevigata*, the "feather-boa kelp."

Alaria is the most widespread and available representative of this group. Twelve species occur in New England and along the Pacific Coast. Some are large plants that reach lengths of more than 6 meters, but *Alaria nana* reaches only 70 centimeters. They are perennial algae with a single, rather short, unbranched stipe attached by a mass of spreading, branched haptera. The terminal blade is broadly expanded and undivided, sometimes 10 to 15 times as long as broad, and constitutes the bulk of the plant. It bears a conspicuous, flat, percurrent midrib. The unilocular sporangia are produced in a single large sorus occupying the greater part of each of the sporophylls.

FUCALES

This group is unique among the brown algae in lacking any reproduction by spores. There is a single diploid generation, and, consequently, no alternation of generations. Meiosis precedes gametogenesis as in animals. These peculiarities have led to the recognition of the Fucales as a single order of a separate class: Cyclosporeae.

Although *Fucus* is the prevalent and familiar example of this group in northern latitudes, the fucoids are a diversified assemblage found in nearly all seas. They are abundantly represented in tropical areas by many species of *Sargassum,* and are especially richly developed in austral regions where the largest fucoid, *Durvillea,* attains a size of 10 meters.

The fucoids show several unusual structural features. Growth of the branches is initiated in almost all cases by a single apical cell, usually sunken in an apical pit rather than prominent as in *Dictyota.* In most instances this is a three-sided cell (becomes four-sided in *Fucus*) that has remained functional since early germling stages (Figure 7-26). Divisions from the apical cell result in a parenchymatous structure, but the cortex may produce hyphae that invade the medullary area and complicate its anatomy.

Most of the North-American genera have a characteristic fucoid reproductive structure. The branches contain minute cavities (cryptostomata) in the outer cortex within which hairs are produced that commonly show as a microscopic tuft on the surface (Figure 9-13). When the plants become fertile, some or all of these cryptostomata located in terminal parts of branches become swollen and produce gametangia. The enlarged, fertile cryptostomata become the conceptacles. The swollen or otherwise modified branch ends bearing them are called receptacles (Figure 9-13). In some genera, such as *Fucus,* the receptacles are modified vegetative branches, while in the Sargassaceae, the receptacles are produced during a period of maturity when special fertile parts grow out of the vegetative plants.

Some genera of Fucales are dioecious and some are monoecious. Others have dioecious and monoecious species. In some monoecious species the sexual organs (oögonia and antheridia) are produced in the same conceptacle. The antheridia may be borne on the conceptacle wall or on branched paraphyses

FIGURE 9–13. A colony of *Fucus distichus* in Washington, showing both sterile vegetative blades and those with inflated receptacles. The immersed conceptacles show clearly as white specks where paraphyses protrude through the conceptacular pore.

in the cavity. The primary nucleus of the antheridium undergoes meiotic division and four mitotic divisions to produce 64 functional, biflagellate sperms. The sperms are extruded in a sac that gelatinizes in the exterior water and frees the zooids (Figure 7-24). These biflagellate zooids differ from those of other brown algae in that the longer of the laterally inserted flagella is posterior rather than anterior.

The oögonia are usually supported on a stalk cell developing from the wall of the conceptacle. The primary nucleus undergoes meiosis followed by 1 mitotic division of each of the 4 nuclei produced, so that 8 haploid egg nuclei are formed. Variation occurs, however, in the number of functional eggs produced in the various genera. Only in *Fucus,* among North American genera, is the full complement of eight eggs formed. In the other genera, some of the nuclei become nonfunctional and are extruded during the maturation of the oögonia. In *Ascophyllum* four eggs are produced. *Pelvetia* has two functional eggs, and the other genera have only one (Figure 9-14,*B,E–G*). The eight-egg condition is considered to be the primitive one.

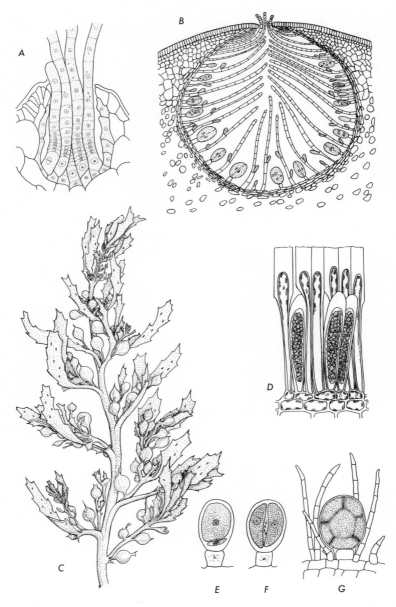

FIGURE 9–14. *A,* Vertical section of a young cryptostoma of *Sargassum filipendula,* showing hairs with basal meristem (after Simons). *B,* Diagrammatic representation of a monoecious conceptacle of *Pelvetia,* showing position of antheridia, oögonia, and paraphyses. *C,* Habit of upper part of a *Sargassum* plant, showing vesicles and "leaves" with cryptostomata. *D,* Vertical section of a sporangial sorus of *Laminaria,* showing unilocular sporangia and paraphyses. *E, Pelvetiopsis,* showing 1 egg in the oögonium; *F, Pelvetia,* showing 2 eggs in the oögonium; *Fucus,* showing 8 eggs in the oögonium.

Fucaceae

This family is characterized by a vegetative form in which the branching is dichotomous and in one plane. These are temperate and high-latitude plants. None occurs in the tropics. *Fucus* and *Ascophyllum* are common along the north Atlantic. *Fucus, Pelvetia, Pelvetiopsis,* and *Hesperophycus* all occur on the Pacific Coast where they are usually the most conspicuous intertidal plants at high levels (Figure 15-1). *Pelvetia* and *Hesperophycus* in southern California are particularly resistant to desiccation and may occur at virtually the highest levels occupied by seaweeds (Figure 9-15).

FIGURE 9–15. *Pelvetia fastigiata* on bare rocks at high intertidal levels in southern California.

Pelvetia is particularly favorable for study as an example of this family. The plants are firm, and young growing tips can easily be sectioned to reveal the pyramidal apical cell in the terminal pit. The development of the parenchymatous cortical tissue and the medulla of longitudinally "stretched" cells separated by gelatinous material, can also be observed. Occasionally the vertical division of the apical cell into two daughter cells may be encountered as a dichotomy of the frond is initiated.

Reproductive plants of *Pelvetia* may be found at any season. The terminal receptacles of mature plants will clearly show the immersed conceptacles by tufts of paraphyses projecting through the ostiole. The plants are monoecious, and both sexual organs are produced within the same conceptacle. The antheridia arise laterally from the bases of fertile paraphyses, and the oögonia are interspersed on single-celled stalks issuing from the wall of the conceptacle. The oögonial initial undergoes three nuclear divisions and produces an eight-nucleate protoplast. This cleaves into two eggs, each at first with four nuclei, but only one nucleus enlarges with each developing egg. The other three move to the dividing membrane, are extruded and cut off. Cleavage is sometimes irregular so that three to six eggs occasionally are formed.

In some instances sperm and eggs are forced out of the ostiole in a heavy mucilage as a plant shrinks under the effect of desiccation during tidal exposure. Upon reflooding by the tide, these are washed clear, and additional sperm and eggs are extruded from the conceptacles by the swelling of gelatinous material within. When released, the eggs are enclosed by a gelatinous gametangial wall (consisting of mesochite and endochite layers) and remain within this during the fertilization process. The sperm are released in a gelatinous envelope that soon dissolves and allows them to swim freely. They swarm in the vicinity of the pairs of enclosed eggs, penetrate the mesochite and fuse with the egg within. Both eggs are usually fertilized before the gelatinous gametangial wall finally disappears. The freed individual zygotes secrete a wall and germinate in a day or two. The germling of *Pelvetia* is much like that of *Fucus* (Figures 7-26; 7-30).

Sargassaceae and Cystoseiraceae

These plants are mainly tropical and subtropical in distribution, although a few are widespread in temperate regions. Unlike the Fucaceae, they are mostly of radial organization and the reproductive organs develop on special fertile branches at maturity. The upper branches commonly bear small, air-filled vesicles. These provide characters for ready recognition of several genera. *Sargassum* has solitary, individual, spherical vesicles, either smooth or with a mucro or crest (Figure 9-14,*C*). *Cystoseira* bears spherical vesicles in bead-like series. *Halidrys* has similar serial vesicles, but they are compressed and with foliar margins (Figure 9-16).

Sargassum is the most widespread genus and occurs in a bewildering number of species and subspecies that cannot readily be identified except on the basis of complete specimens including basal, vegetative, and adult fertile parts. Many of the existing type specimens of species in the literature are too fragmentary to be linked clearly with any natural species. Sargassums are among the most highly differentiated of the algae, for they approach the higher plants in the organization of the thallus into definitive parts (Figure 9-14,*C*). Thus, their basal attachment is well marked from the stem parts; the

FIGURE 9–16. *Halidrys dioica*: *A*, part of a mature plant showing woody holdfast, vegetative blades, and fertile part with compressed vesicle series; *B*, detail of a series of vesicles.

leaf-like photosynthetic blades have veins, specialized toothed or serrate margins and even a petiole-like base; the float vesicles and reproductive branches are further sharply differentiated. Many of the species are perennial and regenerate annually from the holdfast. A few species are capable of vegetative regeneration by fragmentation and can exist in the floating condition indefinitely. These have provided that great oceanic eddy, the Sargasso Sea, with its enormous mass of floating vegetation. These plants do not go through the normal sexual reproductive cycle, and it is not clear from which attached forms they may have originated, since many sargassums undergo some modification of their gross morphology after living in the floating state for some time.

REFERENCES

Gardner, N. L. 1910. Variations in nuclear extrusion among the Fucaceae. *Univ. Calif. Publ. Bot.,* 4: 121–137.

Kemp, L., and Kathleen Cole. 1961. Chromosomal alternation of generations in *Nereocystis leutkeana.* . . . *Can. J. Bot.,* 39: 1711–1724.

Kunieda, H., and S. Suto. 1938. The life history of *Colpomenia sinuosa* (Scytosiphonaceae) with special reference to conjugation of anisogametes. *Bot. Mag.* (Tokyo), 52: 539–546.

Kylin, H. 1947. Die Phaeophyceen der schwedischen Westküste. *Lunds Univ. Årssk.* N.F., Avd. 2, 43(4): 1–99.

Neushul, M. 1963. Studies on the giant kelp, *Macrocystis,* II. Reproduction. *Am. J. Bot.,* 50: 354–359.

Nizamuddin, M. 1962. Classification and distribution of the Fucales. *Botanica Marina,* 4: 191–203.

Papenfuss, G. F. 1935. Alternation of generations in *Ectocarpus siliculosus. Bot. Gaz.,* 96: 421–446.

——————————— 1947. Extension of the brown algal order Dictyosiphonales to include the Punctariales. *Bull. Torrey Bot. Club,* 74: 398–402.

——————————— 1951. Phaeophyta. In: G.M. Smith (Ed.) *Manual of Phycology.* Waltham, Mass.; Chronica Botanica Co. chap. 7, 375 pp.

Pease, V. A. 1920. Taxonomy and morphology of the ligulate species of the genus *Desmarestia. Publ. Puget Sound Biol. Sta.,* 2: 313–367.

Sauvageau, C. 1915. Sur la sexualité hétérogamique d'une Laminaire *(Saccorhiza bulbosa). Compt. Rend. Acad. Sci.,* 161: 796–799.

Setchell, W. A., and N. L. Gardner. 1925. The marine algae of the Pacific Coast of North America. III. Melanophyceae. *Univ. Calif. Publ. Bot.,* 8: 383–898.

Smith, G. M. 1944. Marine algae of the Monterey Peninsula, California. Stanford: Stanford University Press. 622 pp.

Yamanouchi, S. 1912. The life history of *Cutleria. Bot. Gaz.,* 54: 441–502.

10

Benthic Red Algae
(Rhodophyta)

A majority of the different kinds of seaweeds of the world are red algae. There are more of these (about 4000 species) than of all the several other major groups combined, and they occupy the entire range of habitats from highest intertidal levels to the lowermost limits of light. Less than 2 percent are fresh-water plants. They occur as minute filamentous epiphytes; as thin, epilithic films; and as large, fleshy, or membranous forms sometimes reaching a few meters in length. Most of them grow attached to rocks or other algae. Few are sand-dwelling forms like the calcareous greens, and there is no red alga capable of prolonged life in the floating state, as is *Sargassum.*

Although marine red algae occur in all latitudes, there is a marked shift in their proportional abundance as one goes from high to low latitudes. There are few species in north polar and subpolar regions where brown and green algae predominate, but in temperate and tropical regions they far out-number those groups. The average size of the plants also differs according to geographic regions. The larger species of fleshy red algae occur in cool-temperate areas, whereas in tropical seas, the Rhodophyta (except for massive calcareous forms) are mostly small, filamentous plants.

The relationship of the specialized accessory pigments of red algae to available light has been mentioned and will be elaborated in Chapter 13. In this regard, one finds that the great majority of deep-water algae are

Rhodophyta. Although some Chlorophyta and Phaeophyta occur in very deep and dimly lighted situations, the red algae hold the record for life at depths as great as 200 meters.

CHARACTERISTICS

The red algae may be distinguished from Phaeophyta and Chlorophyta by a number of characteristics, but color is not a uniformly reliable one. Although only infrequently will red and green algae be confused on account of color, there are kinds of *Grateloupia,* for example, that may be as green as *Ulva.* It is in the higher intertidal zone that the student most often mistakes Rhodophyta for Phaeophyta, for the pigments of some of the former may be so dense and the bright red phycoerythrin so masked by other pigments (see Table 3), that the characteristic red color is not recognizable. Well-shaded, or subtidal Rhodophyta, however, are almost invariably of pink or red color because of dominant phycoerythrin.

More definitive characteristics of the Rhodophyta are seen in their manner of sexual reproduction. Unlike the situation in brown and green algae, no flagellated reproductive bodies occur. The nonflagellated male gametes (spermatia) reach a fixed female reproductive cell (the carpogonium) by passive movement in the water medium (Figure 7-24,*F*). In a few red algae the zygote produces carpospores directly, but in a large majority of species there is a postfertilization stage (the carposporophyte) developed on the female gametophyte that gives rise indirectly to carpospores. A large majority of Rhodophyta show a triphasic alternation of this carposporophyte generation with sporophyte and gametophyte generations that are nearly isomorphic. Variations in this respect will be pointed out below.

With only two exceptions *(Porphyridium; Rhodosorus)* the marine Rhodophyta are all multicellular plants. The thallus is usually of fundamentally filamentous construction, although this may be obscured by dense compaction and modification of adult cells to form pseudoparenchymatous tissues. The cells are generally uninucleate, although many species have multinucleate cells. The nuclei are usually small and inconspicuous. In the Florideophycidae the occurrence of relatively large protoplasmic strands between adjoining cells (pit connections) is commonplace. Chromatophores, except for some of the more primitive forms, are usually discoid, without pyrenoids, and more than one to a cell. Carbohydrate reserves are usually in the form of floridean starch granules lying in the cytoplasm.

Although the general features of reproduction of the red algae are unique among plants (see Chapter 7), the very numerous variations in life histories among the large number of species, and the extreme obscurity of many of the critical details, have made the Rhodophyta a "difficult group" for phycologists.

The presently accepted classification of the red algae (mainly Florideophycidae) is the system first devised by Schmitz (1883) and refined through years of painstaking work by Kylin (1932) and others to a form finally adopted and presented by Kylin in his monograph of 1956. Modifications have been made in this system in recent years and continue to be made as life histories are worked out and new relationships of the reproductive phases are recognized. On the other hand, some authors (Dixon 1963) consider the system inadequate, unstable, and in need of complete revision.

The following is an outline of the distinctive characters of the marine orders as they are presently recognized by a majority of phycologists.

1. Cells usually without cytoplasmic connections; cell division intercalary; carpospores formed by direct division of the zygote . . . . **Bangiophycidae**
    2. Asexual reproduction only by monospores without cell division; sexual reproduction unknown . . . . .Goniotrichales
    2. Spore formation usually preceded by cell division; sexual reproduction present in most genera . . . . Bangiales
1. Cells with cytoplasmic connections; cell division rarely intercalary; carpospores produced in carposporangia borne on gonimoblast filaments . . . .
    Florideophycidae 3
    3. Life history usually without a free-living tetrasporophyte, or, if such present, then usually heteromorphic. . . . . Nemalionales
    3. Life history usually with a free-living tetrasporophyte; sexual and sporophytic generations isomorphic 4
4. Gonimoblasts growing directly from a carpogonium fusion cell . Gelidiales
4. Gonimoblasts growing mostly from an auxiliary cell. 5
    5. Auxiliary cell an intercalary vegetative cell . . . . Gigartinales
    5. Auxiliary cell not an intercalary vegetative cell 6
6. The auxiliary cell formed before fertilization 7
6. The auxiliary cell formed after fertilization and cut off directly from supporting cell of carpogonial filament. . . . . Ceramiales
    7. Auxiliary cell in a special filament and usually not borne on the supporting cell of the carpogonial filament . . . . Cryptonemiales
    7. Auxiliary cell the terminal cell of a usually two-celled filament borne on the supporting cell of the carpogonial filament. . . . . . . Rhodymeniales

It may be seen from the above that the characters by which most of the orders are distinguished are so difficult to observe and to interpret that it is commonly impossible to place a plant in its proper order by observation of the key characters of the order. Thus, to say that the order Gigartinales is distinguished by the auxiliary cell's being an intercalary vegetative cell of the female gametophyte, provides the student with only the most obscure clue to the recognition of the ordinal position of an unknown plant. Not only may the female gametophyte plant be rare or even unavailable, compared with sporophytic plants, but the usual absence of the precise stage of reproductive development at which an auxiliary cell may be found and recognized imposes an inordinate handicap against identification by this means. In fact, in a great majority of red algae, auxiliary cells have never been observed by anyone. Accordingly, the student of red algae must use numerous alternate clues in the vegetative, the sporophytic, and the sexual morphology of a plant to effect its identification. For the most part, only purely artificial keys based upon morphology and the more readily observed features of vegetative and repro-ductive anatomy are useful in this respect.

The brief survey of selected American genera within the various important families and orders of Rhodophyta is intended to point out some of the areas in which much work needs to be done toward the future development of an adequate treatment of the group.

SUBCLASS BANGIOPHYCIDEAE

This major subdivision of the red algae comprises a relatively small number of plants compared with the very large subclass Florideophycidae (Florideae). It is composed of relatively simple, primitive plants which, because of their pigments, have for nearly 100 years been regarded as related to the blue-green algae. A phylogenetic connection between red algae and Cyanophyta has been suggested through this line, although it is not considered a close one.

The Bangiophycideae contain many fresh-water as well as marine forms. They are mostly multicellular plants of filamentous or sheet construction and intercalary cell division. The cells are uninucleate and usually have a single stellate chromatophore (Figure 7-22,B). Reproductive structures are much less elaborate than in the Florideophycideae, although life histories may be fairly complex. Asexual spores may be produced by direct metamorphosis of a vege-tative cell (monosporangium) or by its division (Figure 7-36). Sexual repro-duction is poorly known for the group and has not been worked out thoroughly and convincingly for any species. No elaborate sexual apparatus, however, has been reported. The carpogonium (when recognized) is formed by direct metamorphosis of a vegetative cell, and the spermatia by division and sometimes redivision of vegetative cells. Carpospores develop directly by divi-sion of the zygote within its original cell.

It has generally been held that a fundamental difference between Bangiophycidae and Florideophycidae is the occurrence in the latter of pit connections between related cells and their absence in the former. Recently, however, pit connections have been reported in four genera of the group, but there have been no critical electron-microscope studies to determine whether there is any fine-structural resemblances between these pits and those of the Florideophycidae. There is evidence to suggest that several kinds of pit connec-tions occur in the Florideophycidae, and this provides a fertile field for electron-microscopic investigations.

GONIOTRICHALES

Goniotrichaceae

The genus *Goniotrichum* is a common, microscopic, epiphytic representative of this small order. It occurs on a wide variety of hosts and is almost cosmopolitan. It is readily recognized by its branched filaments of seriate cells with very thick, gelatinous walls (Figure 10-1). Only the simplest kind of asexual reproduction is known. The vegetative cells are directly transformed into monospores which are freed by dissolution or rupture of the adjoining gelatinous wall.

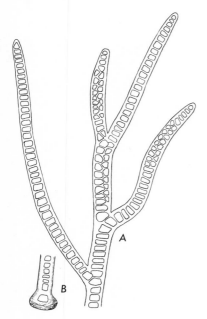

FIGURE 10–1. *Goniotrichum elegans,* showing the thick, gelatinous walls.

BANGIALES

Erythropeltidaceae

The remarkable plant *Smithora* is an obligate epiphyte on *Phyllospadix* and *Zostera* along the Pacific Coast, and consists of several small blades issuing from a perennial cushion-shaped base (Figure 10-2). It was long considered to be a diminutive species of *Porphyra* until Hollenberg (1958) elucidated its morphology and reproduction and placed it in this small family of plants characterized by having erect parts arising from basal cushions or discs, and

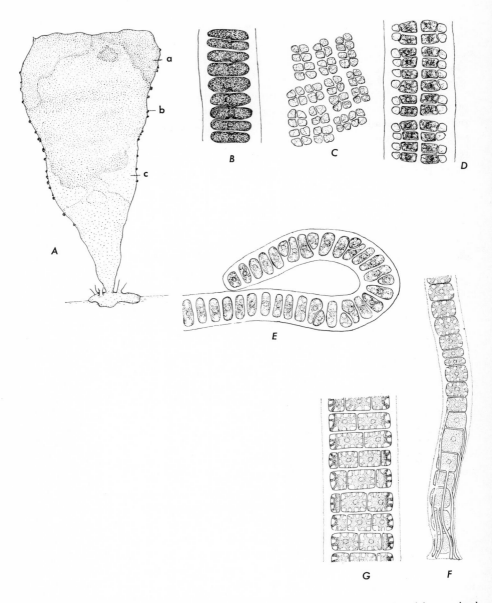

FIGURE 10–2. *A–E, Smithora naiadum*: *A*, habit sketch showing a blade with terminal deciduous sori, numerous marginal sori, and spermatangial sori; *B*, section through a mature terminal, deciduous sorus; *C*, surface view of a portion of a spermatangial sorus; *D*, section through one of the small marginal sori showing formation of "neutral spores." *F–G, Bangia fuscopurpurea*: *F*, basal part of a plant showing rhizoids; *G*, mid-part showing stellate chromatophores and gelatinous walls. (*A–E*, after Hollenberg; *F–G*, after Smith, reprinted by permission of Stanford University Press).

lacking rhizoidal processes from the lower cells of the blades. The blades of *Smithora* produce both sexual and asexual reproductive bodies, but the asexual ones are by far the more abundant. Most common are the terminal "deciduous sori" which are shed as units and in which the cells become gelatinous and cause the shed thallus fragment to stick to various objects. The relationship of these to the development of the epiphytic thallus on marine phanerogams has not been determined, although they seem to constitute some special vegetative type of reproduction. Another kind of asexual reproduction is observed in which small marginal sori release what appear to be neutral spores.

What has been considered to be sexual reproduction may less frequently be observed on the same plants. Carposporangial areas, consisting of spore groups in packets of 8, occur near the tips of blades. In addition, Spermatangial areas (Figure 10-2, *C–D*) occur in median parts of the blades and show spermatia cut off singly from pigmented cells. Repeated efforts to detect anything resembling a carpogonium with a trichogyne or with attached spermatia have been unsuccessful, and, as in the Bangiophycidae generally, convincing evidence of the actual occurrence of fertilization has never been obtained.

Bangiaceae

Two representatives of this family, *Bangia* and *Porphyra*, are widely distributed on American coasts. In recent years, both have been the subjects of intense study because of the discovery of the remarkable heteromorphic alternation of generations in which the shell-inhabiting *Conchocelis* phase is considered the sporophyte (see Chapter 11). *Bangia* is a small, slender, unbranched plant of cylindrical to ribbon-shaped form usually found at high intertidal levels during the summer and autumn (Figure 10-2,*F–G*).

Porphyra

The purple lavers, of which various species are extensively cultivated in Japan for food (nori; see Chapter 17), are usually membranous plants of medium size consisting of a single layer of cells or of two layers. The blades arise from a disc-shaped holdfast composed of rhizoids and develop by diffuse growth throughout most of the blade. The cells, depending upon the species, contain one or two stellate chromatophores. The species may be monoecious, dioecious, or sometimes both. In monoecious species, such as the common *P. perforata* of the Pacific Coast, the spermatangia and carpospores occur in irregular patches along the margins and are easily recognized by their contrasting colors. Generally, the male areas are pale yellowish and the spermatangia, according to the species, are borne in packets of 16, 32, 64, or 128 and arranged by a specific cell-division formula. The carpospores at maturity, forming reddish patches, are similarly arranged in packets of 4, 8, 16, 32, or 64. The carpogonium, from which upon fertilization these packets of carpospores presumably arise, bears a very short trichogyne, and some authors have thought they observed adherent spermatia. Fertilization has not, however, been demonstrated convincingly. The carpospores, unlike those of most other Rhodophyta, may be haploid, for in some species meiosis is reported to occur during the series of divisions to form the packet. Other authors, however, report the absence of such meiosis in other species. The carpospores usually germinate to produce a prostrate, creeping filament which, under natural conditions, usually penetrates a piece of dead mollusk shell within a few days. This develops into a pinkish growth that has been known for decades as *Conchocelis rosea*. In most of the species of *Porphyra* investigated, the *Conchocelis* phase produces conchospores that germinate to form new *Porphyra* plants. Miura, however, has recently described a species of *Porphyra* whose *Conchocelis* stage produces the leafy blades directly from bud-like swellings of the *Conchocelis* filament.

A majority of *Porphyra* species also seem to have an asexual method of reproduction of the leafy thallus by neutral spores (Figure 11-11). Similarly, the *Conchocelis* phase in some species may repeat itself.

SUBCLASS FLORIDEOPHYCIDAE (PREVIOUSLY KNOWN AS FLORIDEAE)

Despite great variation in size, habit, texture, and aspect in this highly diversified subclass of algae, there are several fundamental similarities in anatomy and reproduction that unite the assemblage. In all cases (except subfamily Nitophylloideae) the thallus consists of branched filaments. These may be either free or compacted by close mutual application. Growth of these filaments is almost exclusively by division of apical cells at the tips of branches. Every derivative of one of these apical cells is connected to it by a strand of cytoplasm (the pit connection). These strands provide a means of tracing the sequence of divisions in the development of the young thallus.

Except for certain genera of the Nemalionales, most Florideophycidae show an alternation of gametophytic and sporophytic generations. In most cases these generations are isomorphic and the sexual generation consists of separate male and female plants. The male plant produces its usually colorless, minute, nonmotile spermatia both on young and older parts of the plant in a variety of ways that provide useful toxonomic characters (Figures 10-3; 10-15; 10-20; 10-23). The female plant bears the female sex organ, the carpogonium, on a special carpogonial filament, usually produced in the very youngest apical parts of the plant. Usually, carpogonial filaments are of three or four cells and lack chromatophores. Their denser protoplasts often distinguish them from vegetative cells, especially when stained. The carpogonium, itself, is often relatively conspicuous because of the long trichogyne. When a spermatium reaches the trichogyne, the walls at the point of contact break down and the spermatial nucleus enters the trichogyne to move down to fuse with the carpogonial nucleus in the lower part of the cell. In some genera of Nemalionales meiosis of the zygote nucleus is said to occur, but in most other Florideophycidae meiosis occurs in the tetrasporophyte generation.

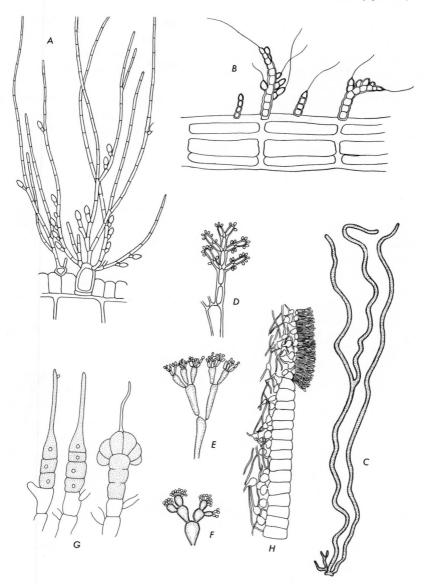

FIGURE 10–3. *A, Acrochaetium sinicola,* epiphytic on *Dictyota,* showing specialized basal cell and monosporangia. *B, Kylinia arcuata* (Acrochaetiaceae) epiphytic on *Polysiphonia. C, Nemalion elminthoides,* habit. *D,* Spermatangial branch of *Nemalion. E–F,* Spermatangial branches of species of *Liagora. G,* Postfertilization stages of *Nemalion:* at fertilization; at formation of first transverse wall in carpogonium; at early gonimoblast development from upper cell with breakdown of other transverse cell walls to form a fusion cell. *H,* Part of a longitudinal section of a male plant of *Scinaia* (Chaetangiaceae) showing compact cortical layer, filamentous medulla, and part of a dense spermatangial sorus.

The immediate postfertilization occurrences in the Florideophycidae are of utmost importance according to the presently accepted system of classification. They result in the development of gonimoblast filaments that ultimately produce carpospores. This occurs in a variety of ways. The gonimoblast filaments may grow directly from the carpogonium or its fusion cell, without movement of the zygote nucleus. In most instances, however, the zygote nucleus or one of its descendants moves directly or indirectly into another cell, the auxiliary cell, from which the gonimoblast filaments are initiated. Sometimes the auxiliary cell is at a considerable distance from the carpogonium and must be reached by a tubular outgrowth called a connecting filament, or oöblast. In other instances the gonimoblast filaments arise from a fusion cell arising from the breakdown of cell walls of a number of cells in the vicinity of the carpogonium and a nearby auxiliary cell to form a multinucleate mass.

The development of the diploid gonimoblast is usually accompanied by the development of haploid tissue of the female gametophyte to form some kind of enclosing envelope or enclosure around the maturing carpospores, called a pericarp. The pericarp, with its enclosed mass of gonimoblast filaments and sporangia, constitutes the traditional fruiting body, or cystocarp, of the Florideophycidae. We now recognize that this consists of tissues of two separate generations of the plant, the diploid carposporophyte, enclosed by haploid tissue of the female gametophyte. The term cystocarp is also applied to embedded "fruits" that do not have pericarps.

The carpospores are usually diploid and, upon germination, produce a diploid sporophyte plant similar to the gametophyte. The free-living sporophyte plant is usually a tetrasporophyte, for in a great majority of species the sporophyte produces sporangia containing four spores (Figure 11-6). Meiosis occurs in the division of the tetrasporangia. The haploid tetraspores germinate to produce gametophytes. In experiments with some species it has been shown that two of the spores from each sporangium are capable of developing into male plants and two into female plants.

NEMALIONALES

This order contains a curious assemblage of diverse plants that have generally been considered primitive among the floridean red algae. Structurally, they range from minute, uniseriate epiphytes *(Acrochaetium)* to complex, multiaxial, corticated, and calcified forms *(Galaxaura)*. Traditionally, the group is thought of as lacking a free-living sporophyte phase in the life history, but there are well-known exceptions such as *Galaxaura* and *Actinotrichia*. Recent studies have revealed the occurrence in several genera of a sporophyte generation that had previously been known as a member of some other family of red algae and have indicated further complications in life histories. Current culture studies on various members of the order are providing some of the most exciting discoveries of relationships among marine plants.

Monospores are a widespread method of asexual reproduction in this order. They are thought to repeat the phase of the plant that produces them.

Acrochaetiaceae

This family contains a large number of minute epiphytic and endophytic plants of uniaxial, branched-filament construction (Figure 10-3,*A–B*). The largest genus is *Acrochaetium* with about 150 species. A large majority of these are known to reproduce only by monospores formed in terminal or lateral sporangia on the erect filaments (Figure 10-3,*A*). A small number of species produce bispores or tetraspores, and fewer still are known to exhibit sexual reproduction (Abbott, 1962).

In the past, these plants were generally treated as species of *Chantransia,* and many fresh-water species were recognized. It has been shown, however, that these fresh-water chantransias are almost without exception phases in the life history of the well-known fresh-water genera, *Batrachospermum* and *Lemanea.* Current studies of marine *Acrochaetium* and *Rhodochorton* species are revealing similarly remarkable relationships. Thus, in the laboratory of von Stosch of Marburg, culture of carpospores of a species of *Liagora* (Helminthocladiaceae) has yielded tetrasporic plants of *Acrochaetium,* and the *Acrochaetium* spores have produced *Liagora* plants. Clearly, there are many opportunities for discoveries through culture work in the Acrochaetiaceae that may help to solve problems of life histories in the Nemalionales.

Helminthocladiaceae

Nemalion

This plant is a widely distributed member of the order, and a classical one for presentation of the supposedly primitive features of carposporophyte development in the order. The plants are multiaxial (Figure 7-33,*A*) and composed of irregularly branched, interwoven filaments in which the cortical parts are little differentiated from the medullary parts (Figure 7-28,*C*). Both male and female organs occur on the same plant, but the spermatangia are usually produced before the carpogonia appear (protandry), and the plants, thus, seem to be dioecious, though they are really monoecious. The spermatangia occur on modified tips of the assimilatory filaments (Figure 10-3,*D–F*). The carpogonial filaments, which may be observed by squashing a bit of the terminal portion of an axis, consist usually of three to four cells, the terminal one of which is the carpogonium with its projecting trichogyne (Figure 7-24,*F*). Fertilization is accomplished by movement of the spermatangial nucleus down the trichogyne to union with the female nucleus at the carpogonial base. The zygote nucleus divides into two, a transverse wall is formed in the carpogonial cell between these, and the gonimoblast develops from the upper of the two cells (Figure 10-3,*G*). An enclosing envelope is not formed around the developing gonimoblast which matures as a subspherical mass of carpospores appearing as dark specks in the gelatinous thallus. For many years the carpospores have been thought to reproduce the sexual parent plant without the occurrence of an alternate phase. Germination, reportedly, has been accomplished by the protrusion of a germ tube and the migration of most of the spore contents into the tube which becomes cut off by a wall to form the initial apical cell (Figure 7-26). Magne (1961), however, has observed carpospores of *Nemalion elminthoides* that give rise to small plants thought to be diploid tetrasporophytes. Evidently, there is still much to be learned about *Nemalion*.

Chaetangiaceae

The plants of this family are all of moderate size and bushy habit, multiaxial in structure, and with a continuous surface layer of specialized, compacted cells (Figure 10-3,*H*). The cystocarps are immersed and the gonimoblast enveloped by a pericarp of slender, crowded filaments that form a sac-like conceptacle with a superficial discharge pore. Both calcified and uncalcified genera are placed in the family.

Galaxaura

Galaxaura is a tropical genus of wide distribution and of unusual interest because of the strong dimorphism exhibited by the alternating generations. The plants are branched, calcified forms (Figure 10-4) with highly differentiated thalli, as compared with *Nemalion*. The cells of the cortex are particularly distinctive and provide characters for specific identification (Figure 10-6,*A*). The curious feature long recognized in the genus is that since the plants of the alternate generations differ so much in general morphology and in cortex structure, each of them has been named as a separate species. Largely through the work of Svedelius, we now know that these are alternate diploid and haploid phases of natural species. The plants are so dimorphic, however, that the matching pairs cannot in most cases be recognized easily (see Chapter 11), and culture techniques for carrying these plants through a life cycle have not yet been perfected.

Bonnemaisoniaceae

Much attention has been focused recently on the life histories of several members of this family because of discoveries of heteromorphic generations. J. and G. Feldmann, working with gametophyte *Asparagopsis* in 1942, and Harder and Koch, working with gametophyte *Bonnemaisonia* in 1949, found that *Falkenbergia* and *Trailliella*, previously classed in the Ceramiales, are sporophyte generations of these plants (see Chapter 11). Chihara has now cultured various

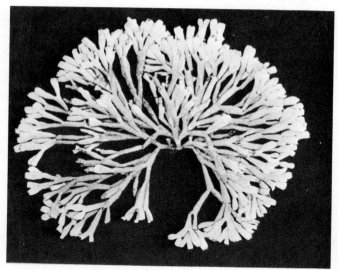

FIGURE 10–4. *Galaxaura fastigiata,* one of the more heavily calcified sexual "species" of the genus.

members of this family in Japan, and his work, together with that of several other investigators, has established that there are at least 3 types of life history represented in the family. Chihara calls these: (1) the *Asparagopsis* type, in which a macroscopic gametophyte generation *(Bonnemaisonia, Asparagopsis)* alternates with a microscopic, filamentous sporophyte generation *(Trailliella, Falkenbergia);* (2) the *Nemalion* type, in which the carpospores of the macroscopic gametophyte generation germinate to reproduce the parent *(Ptilonia, Delisea);* (3) the *Polysiphonia* type, in which there is an isomorphic alternation of macroscopic gametophyte and tetrasporophyte (an Australian species of *Delisea).*

Bonnemaisonia hamifera

The *Bonnemaisonia* stage is an annual plant reaching several centimeters in height and consisting of cylindrical axes with slender, opposite, distichous branches here and there replaced by an enlarged, hook-like branch (Figure 10-5,*L*). Growth of *Bonnemaisonia* plants is from an apical cell. The plants are dioecious, and mature cystocarps quickly shed their carpospores in early summer. The carpospores are discharged through an ostiole in the pericarp, and soon fasten to the substrate to germinate in the manner of *Fucus* (Figure 7-26), producing a primary rhizoid and an erect shoot. Within 10 days the developing, uniseriate vegetative filament produces at the distal end of each cell the alternate vesicles characteristic of *Trailliella* (Figure 10-5).

Trailliella plants, as they occur in nature, are tetrasporic. The sporangia are produced singly and irregularly in the uniseriate filament and are dis-

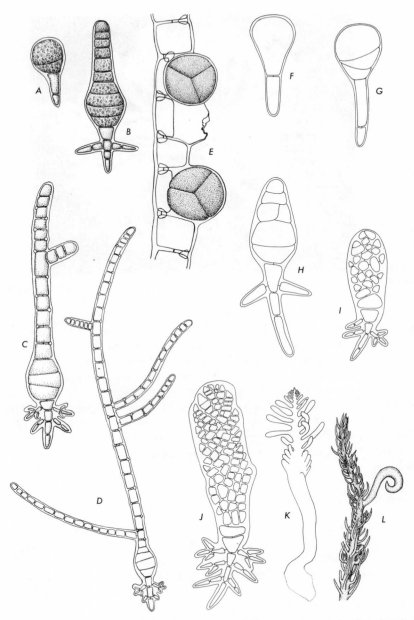

FIGURE 10–5. *Bonnemaisonia hamifera* life history: *A–B*, early stages in germination of carpospores; *C–D*, germlings (6-day and 30-day old) showing development of *Trailliella* structure; *E*, tetrasporangia in a filament of the *Trailliella* stage; *F–K*, early stages in germination of tetraspores of *Trailliella* stage and development into juvenile *Bonnemaisonia* plants; *L*, part of a mature *Bonnemaisonia* plant with characteristic hooked branchlet (*A–K* after Chihara).

charged through a split in the wall (Figure 10-5,*E*). The tetraspores germinate to produce a primary rhizoid and an erect shoot that soon develops an apical cell and proceeds to form the distichously branched thallus of *Bonnemaisonia* (Figure 10-5,*F–K*).

Magne (1960) has reported in one species of *Bonnemaisonia* a delay in meiosis to tetraspore development, indicating a triphasic alternation similar to that of most red algae, except for the extreme dimorphism of sporophyte and gametophyte generations.

GELIDIALES

This small order contains only a few genera in two families, but some of the species are common and very widely distributed. Some are of considerable economic importance (Chapter 17). The Gelidiales show an alternation of isomorphic generations, although there is often a great disparity in the proportion of sporophyte and gametophyte plants. The sexual plants are dioecious and distinguishable only when fertile. Most members of the order are plants of moderate size, of firm, cartilaginous consistency, of uniaxial construction, and of monopodial branching. The carpogonial filaments are single-celled and deeply embedded in the cortex of very young thallus parts. The gonimoblast develops directly from a multinucleate fusion cell formed from the carpogonium alone or as a result of the fusion of the carpogonium and certain neighboring cells.

Gelidium

This is the prevalent genus of the order, and the variable species range from the minute, cosmopolitan *Gelidium pusillum* (less than 1 centimeter tall) to the Pacific agar weed, *G. cartilagineum* var. *robustum,* attaining a meter in stature. The plants are perennial and cartilaginous, compressed to cylindrical and usually abundantly branched. The apical cell (Figure 7-29,*D*) provides a good clue for recognition together with the occurrence of rhizoidal filaments, which are slender, thick-walled, wire-like cells produced mainly between the subcortical and outer medullary cells of mature plants (Figure 10-6,*E*). These arise as outgrowths from internal cells of very young thallus parts and grow downward between these internal cells as they expand and mature.

Male plants, which are not easily recognized, bear elliptical spermatangial nemathecia on the flattened faces of branches.

Female plants bear their carpogonial filaments in the ultimate branchlets just back of the growing point. These filaments are one-celled, elongate structures consisting of a carpogonium tapered to a trichogyne with an inflated, protruding end. Simultaneously with the development of the carpogonial cells, chains of small nutritive (nurse) cells grow out from the basal cells of the vegetative filaments arising from the central axis (Figure 10-6,*B*). Following fertilization,

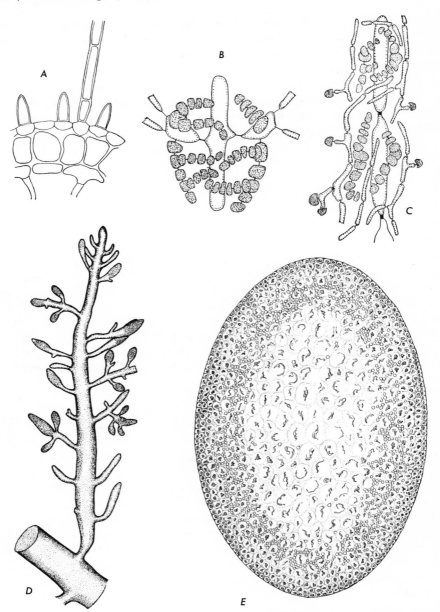

FIGURE 10-6. A, Part of a transection of a gametophytic *Galaxaura* plant, showing cortical cells, an extended assimilatory filament, and specialized spinulose cells. B–C, *Gelidium cartilagineum,* showing development of nutritive cells (B) and postfertilization extension of gonimoblast filaments among these (C) with initiation of carposporangia (after Kylin). D, Tetrasporangial branch of *Gelidium purpurascens. E,* Typical transectional appearance of mature *Gelidium* showing abundant rhizoidal filaments packed in among the subcortical cells, and very few in the medulla (after Loomis).

the carpogonium and the supporting cell coalesce and an irregular fusion cell is formed. From this the gonimoblast grows out as a branched, multicellular structure and extends longitudinally along the axial filament among the nutritive cells (Figure 10-6,*C*). The gonimoblast filaments from several different carpogonia become intertwined and form an aggregation of carposporophytes within a single pericarp. In *Gelidium*, the cystocarp develops an ostiole on either side of the bearing branch. In the closely related *Pterocladia*, there is only one ostiole.

Tetrasporangial plants are vegetatively indistinguishable from sexual plants. The tetrasporangia are borne in sori in the somewhat swollen ends of fertile branchlets (Figure 10-6,*D*). The reduction divisions are presumed to occur at division of the young tetrasporangium, as in most other Florideophycidae.

CRYPTONEMIALES

This is a large order of almost 100 genera, and of species showing greater diversity of form, structure, and substance than any other group. Gelatinous, fleshy, cartilaginous, and calcareous types occur in remarkable array. All of these have in common the fact that the auxiliary cell is formed before fertilization and is borne on a special filament of the gametophyte. The auxiliary cell filament usually resembles the carpogonial filament in its dense cytoplasm and may be distinguished before fertilization. It may be borne far removed from the carpogonial filament, or both may arise from a common cell.

There are 12 families in the order as recognized by Kylin (1956), and 6 of these are well represented by common species on the American coasts.

Dumontiaceae

Dumontia

Dumontia contorta (D. incrassata) is a frequent inhabitant of tide pools and the immediate sublittoral along the New England coast. The plants occur in somewhat gregarious tufts and reach 2 to 6 decimeters in length. The irregular branches are 2 to 5 millimeters in diameter and partially hollow, often compressed or irregularly inflated and twisted (Figure 10-7,*A*), tending to decay at the ends of older parts.

Growth is from an apical cell that gives rise to an axial filament bearing radiating branched filaments whose closely appressed outer cells form the cortex (Figure 7-19,*C*). The cross section of a mature plant shows a pseudo-parenchymatous cortex and a single axial strand surrounded by rhizoids, the axis becoming centrally hollow with age. The tetrasporangia are immersed in the cortex (Figure 10-7,*E*). The carpogonial branches, arising from the inner cortical filaments (Figure 10-7,*B*), are distinctive in consisting of five cells in a hook-like row. The auxiliary-cell filaments are similar, but of four cells (Figure 10-7,*C*). The carpogonium, upon fertilization, usually fuses with the third cell

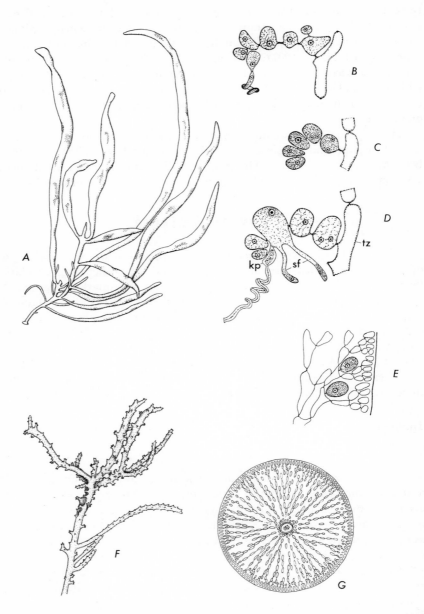

FIGURE 10-7. *A–E, Dumontia contorta*: *A*, habit of a plant showing irregularly inflated upper branches; *B*, a 5-celled carpogonial branch on its supporting cell; *C*, a similar 4-celled auxiliary-cell branch; *D*, postfertilization stage showing fusion of carpogonium with third cell of the carpogonial branch and development of oöblast filaments; *E*, young, undivided sporangial initials in the cortex. *F–G, Endocladia muricata*: *F*, habit of part of a plant; *G*, transection showing prominent axial filament. (*B–E* after Kylin)

of the carpogonial branch, and this sends out two or three oöblast filaments (Figure 10-7,*D*), each of which may contact an auxiliary cell in its special filament somewhere in the vicinity and carry a diploid nucleus to it. The gonimoblast then develops from the auxiliary cell and forms a carpospore mass in the cortex without any pericarp investment.

Endocladiaceae

Endocladia

Endocladia muricata, which is a common high-level intertidal plant of the Pacific Coast (Figure 13-4), provides an interesting series of contrasts with *Dumontia.* It is a small, bushy plant with cylindrical branches covered with minute spines (Figure 10-7,*F*). Its apical cell gives rise to a very prominent axial filament from which the medullary and cortical filaments radiate (Figure 10-7,*G*).

The irregularly cruciate tetrasporangia are borne among long, unbranched paraphyses in nemathecia on the surface of young branches.

The carpogonial filament (which has only two cells) and the auxiliary-cell filament arise from a common cell (the supporting cell) in the medullary tissue of the thallus and constitute a procarp (Figure 10-15,*D*). (The term "procarp" is applied in those cases in which a carpogonium is closely associated with an auxiliary cell or an auxiliary mother cell to form a well-defined, unified organ.) The gonimoblast develops inwardly from the auxiliary cell, and its growth and enlargement is accompanied by the development of an urn-shaped pericarp enclosing the carpospore mass.

Squamariaceae

Whereas the preceding two families consist of plants of clearly filamentous construction and erect habit, the Squamariaceae are prostrate, crustose forms of pseudoparenchymatous structure. Some are calcareous. The most widespread members are species of *Peyssonelia.* These are usually plants of circular outline firmly fastened to a rock or shell substrate by ventral rhizoids. The crust usually shows a monostromatic basal cell layer called the hypothallium from which short, laterally compacted vertical or ascending rows of cells arise (Figure 7-14,*C*).

Reproduction is usually by tetrasporangia. These are borne in nemathecia on the surface of the crust as slightly elevated, pale, warty areas. The elongate, cruciately divided tetrasporangia stand among slender paraphyses of gelatinous consistency (Figure 7-39).

Sexual reproduction is rarely encountered. The carpogonial and auxiliary-cell filaments, usually four-celled, are borne separately on the basal cell of a paraphysis in a nemathecium. A cystocarp consists of only a small cluster of carpospores in the nemathecium.

Corallinaceae

This is the largest family of the order and is made up of a great diversity of forms almost all of which are heavily calcified. There are two subfamilies, the Melobesioideae, comprising the crustose and nodular corallines, and the Corallinoideae, comprising the articulated, or jointed corallines. Plants of both groups are widespread and occur in all seas (see Chapter 12).

Apart from the heavy calcification, the Corallinaceae differ from other Cryptonemiales in the occurrence of the reproductive organs in conceptacles opening to the exterior by one or more pores. In some genera the tetrasporic conceptacles differ markedly from sexual conceptacles in having numerous small pores in the roof rather than a single pore (Figure 10-8,*A–B*). The sexual plants are dioecious, and there are usually marked differences between male and female conceptacles. Both male and female organs are borne in nemathecia

FIGURE 10-8. *A,* Part of a tetrasporangial plant of *Melobesia* in vertical section, showing tetrasporangia in conceptacular cavities and multiple pores in the roof. *B,* A prominent tetrasporic conceptacle of *Heteroderma* in vertical section, showing single pore (ostiole) in roof. *C,* A deeply immersed cystocarpic conceptacle of *Lithophyllum,* showing cellular structure of thallus, ostiole, degenerating procarps, and large fusion cell with marginal gonimoblast development of carposporangia. *D,* Part of a fertile plant of *Bossiella,* showing sagittate intergenicula, short, flexible genicula, and superficial conceptacles. (*C* after Suneson)

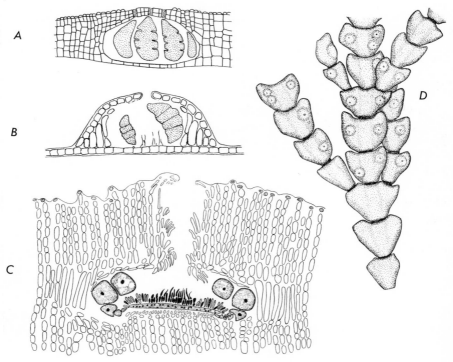

which develop on the floor of the conceptacle. Spermatangia are cut off abundantly from short filaments on the floor and may fill the cavity of the conceptacle. Female reproductive organs are specialized but unelaborated. The procarps are markedly simplified. A two-celled carpogonial filament arises from a basal cell that functions as the auxiliary cell. The long trichogynes from the many carpogonia project through the conceptacular ostiole. After fertilization, a short oöblast from the carpogonium joins the auxiliary cell at the base. Then all of the auxiliary cells of the conceptacle fuse to form a large fusion cell, or placental cell, from the margins of which issue the gonimoblast filaments that cut off the carposporangia (Figure 10-8,*C*).

Tetrasporangia are easily recognized by the zonate arrangement of the tetraspores.

MELOBESIOIDEAE

Three important genera may be mentioned briefly as representatives of this group.

Lithophyllum is a large genus of crustose and nodular forms that may be recognized by the structure of the thallus. It consists of numerous layers of cells in which the cells are all similar in form and without marked distinction of size (Figures 10-8,*C*; 10-9,*A–B*). The conceptacles may be embedded or superficial and domoid, but both sexual and sporangial conceptacles have a single circular ostiole (Figure 10-8,*C*).

Porolithon, the major constituent of many algal reefs (Figure 12-2), resembles some forms of *Lithophyllum* in its massive crustose structure, but is readily distinguished when decalcified and sectioned by its rows of heterocysts scattered through the vegetative tissues (Figure 10-10).

Melobesia is one of several genera of minute flake-like epiphytes on marine phanerogams and fleshy algae (Figure 10-9,*F–G*). The crusts are only 1 cell thick at the margins and composed of laterally adjoined radiating filaments. This is one of the genera (*Lithothamnium* is the common more massive one, Figure 10-9,*C–E*) in which the tetrasporangial conceptacles provide a means of recognition by their multiple pores. The tetrasporangia are separated in youthful stages by vertical rows of sterile cells that degenerate as the conceptacle ripens. The conceptacular roof then develops a small pore external to each sporangium, but until the spores are discharged this is closed by what appears to be a gelatinous plug (Figure 10-8,*A*).

CORALLINOIDEAE

The articulated corallines are among the most attractive red algae of the shore, and in many Pacific-Coast areas species of *Corallina* and *Bossiella* may form dominant intertidal associations (Figure 10-8,*D*). These calcareous plants with noncalcified articulations are related to the crustose members of the family through such intermediates as the genus *Yamadaea* that bears erect parts with

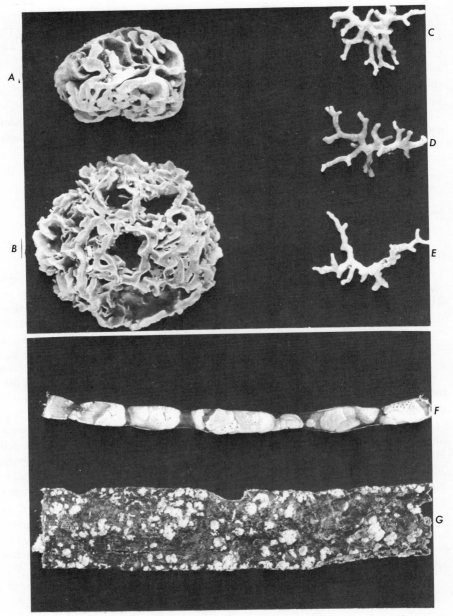

FIGURE 10–9. *A–B,* Two forms of *Lithophyllum veleroae.* *C–E,* Forms of the deep-water nullipore, *Lithothamnium australe.* *F–G,* Forms of *Melobesia mediocris* growing on leaves of *Phyllospadix* and of *Zostera.*

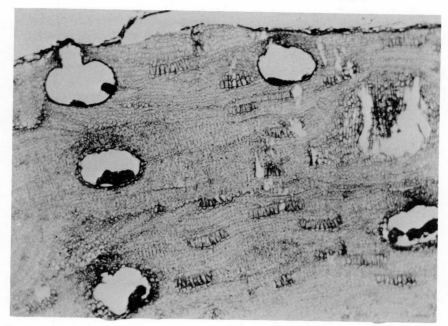

FIGURE 10-10. Vertical section through a thallus of *Porolithon* showing embedded, empty conceptacles and rows of heterocysts (reprinted from *Plants of Bikini* by W. R. Taylor, by permission of University of Michigan Press, copyright 1950).

only 1 or 2 segments from a spreading crust (Figure 10-11). The widespread genus *Corallina* also shows the indefinite expansion of a crustose base, but the erect parts are elaborated into abundantly branched, bushy fronds. The flexibility of the erect parts is achieved by the noncalcified genicula that consist of slender, thick-walled cells usually arranged in dense, parallel fashion. The calcified intergenicula have their medullary cells arranged in tiers of varying pattern in the different genera and species.

Cryptonemiaceae

Grateloupia

This is a genus of lubricous plants in which the medullary cells are somewhat stellate in form, with long, filamentous processes. The cortex arises from these as compact rows of short, branched, small-celled, anticlinal filaments forming a smooth thallus surface. Growth is by a group of apical initials.

The two-celled carpogonial filaments are borne in special bushy clusters in the outer medulla. The auxiliary-cell filaments are separate and scattered, like the carpogonial filaments, through the very young apical parts of a fertile

FIGURE 10-11. A crust of *Yamadaea americana* overgrowing a rock and worm tubes, and showing 2 fertile articulated erect branches.

thallus. They are also bushy and of many cells, but with a single cell at the base of the cluster enlarging and functioning as the auxiliary cell.

The fertilized carpogonium sends out several oöblast filaments each of which may grow out to connect and fuse with an auxiliary cell. The auxiliary cell is then stimulated to put out branched gonimoblasts. These grow toward the thallus surface while overlying cortical tissue becomes modified to provide an ostiole for the deeply embedded cystocarp that does not possess a pericarp, proper, and resembles that of *Halymenia* shown in Figure 7-40,*B*.

Tetrasporangia, which are cruciately divided, occur throughout most of a mature sporophytic plant and are scattered through the cortex just below the thallus surface.

Kallymeniaceae

Callophyllis

The structure and reproduction of the Kallymeniaceae, a highly specialized family of membranous, foliose red algae, has recently been elucidated by Norris (1957). *Callophyllis* is one of the larger genera of the group and is represented on the Pacific Coast by a number of species, several of which are commonly encountered in drift from the sublittoral. The blades are narrowly or broadly flabellate, dichotomous, or palmate, and without ribs or veins. The structure is multiaxial. The most distinctive character of the mature blades is the pseudoparenchymatous structure in which the medulla is composed of large, thin-walled cells intermingled with small cells. The latter arise as elongate cells and filaments from the inner cortical cells and invade the medulla as it matures (Figure 10-12,*A*). The cortex shows progressively smaller cells to the thallus surface.

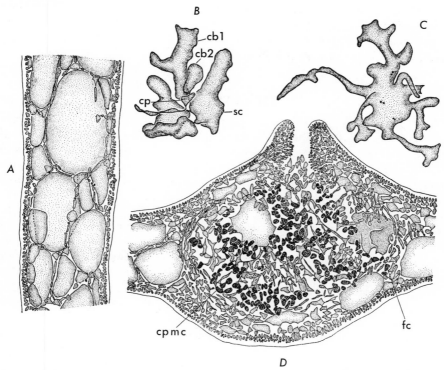

FIGURE 10–12. *Callophyllis heanophylla*: *A,* longisection of a blade showing large medullary cells and smaller invading filament cells; *B,* a mature procarp (c: carpogonium; cb1, cb2: first and second cells of carpogonial branch; sc: supporting cell); *C,* fusion cell; *D,* vertical section through a young cystocarp, showing fusion cell (fc) and carposporangium mother cells (cpmc).

The female reproductive apparatus and the postfertilization stages of development of the cystocarp are complex and difficult to interpret. A squash technique is best used to observe the structures that cannot be dissected out nor understood through observation of sections. The procarp consists of one or more 3-celled carpogonial branches arising from a large, much-lobed supporting cell. The first cell of the carpogonial branch is also much lobed as are several side-branch cells (Figure 10-12,*B*). The supporting cell functions as the auxiliary cell. After fertilization, a connection is established between the carpogonium and this auxiliary cell, and the diploid nucleus migrates into it. A large, irregular fusion cell, involving the supporting cell (auxiliary cell) and numerous cells in its vicinity (Figure 10-12,*C*), is then formed. At the tips of some of the fusion cell's arms gonimoblast filaments develop and extend through the surrounding vegetative tissue. The developing cystocarp bulges on one or both sides of the thallus and acquires one to three ostioles that may be more or less rostrate (Figure 10-12,*D*).

Male plants have superficial spermatangial sori, but these rarely have been observed in *Callophyllis*. Tetrasporic plants are the most commonly encountered. The cruciately divided tetrasporangia, produced by the cells of the inner cortex, are usually scattered over the blades.

GIGARTINALES

This large order includes almost as diversified an assemblage of algae as the Cryptonemiales, but, with few exceptions, the members are fleshy and noncalcareous forms. The plants are of monoaxial or multiaxial construction and of cylindrical to foliaceous form. Only a few are prostrate or crustose, and none is filamentous or microscopic.

According to Kylin's system, the order is technically distinguished by the auxiliary cell being an intercalary vegetative cell and not a cell borne in a special filament. It should be pointed out, however, that in some Gigartinales the supporting cell may function as an auxiliary cell and that this presents a seeming contradiction. A parallel situation obtains in the Cryptonemiales and makes these ordinal distinctions extremely obscure except to the experienced specialist. One should realize, furthermore, that in only a relatively few plants, either of Cryptonemiales or of Gigartinales, have the details of the sexual reproductive process been worked out. Genera continue to be moved from one order to the other as new facts become established. There are instances, too, in which the details of postfertilization development of the carposporophyte are so difficult to unravel and to interpret that different viewers may see different things from the same microscopic preparation. Such problems have led Dixon (1963) to point out in a recent review that "The apparent stability [of the present system of classification] is largely an illusion, and of the orders of the Florideophycidae, only one, the Ceramiales, is at all well founded." Clearly, a great deal more work is needed on details of reproductive, and more especially on vegetative developmental morphology, before a new revisionary approach can be made to general red-algal classification. Although most of the families can be defined with fair clarity, their ordinal arrangement at present is quite uncertain.

Cruoriaceae

This is a good example of the statements above, for until recently this small family of crustose red algae has been treated by various workers as belonging in the Cryptonemiales near the Corallinaceae. In habit it resembles the Squamariaceae to some extent, but structurally it is easily recognized by the fact that the erect filaments arising from the hypothallium are not firmly adjoined but have gelatinous walls that allow them to separate from one another very easily.

The sexual reproduction was worked out by Kylin in one species of *Cruoria*. In that plant he found that the carpogonial branches, which are two to three-celled, are branches of erect, vegetative, assimilatory filaments; that after fertilization a connecting filament develops from the carpogonium and fuses directly with an unspecialized cell of another vegetative filament; and that the gonimoblast develops from the connecting filament. Such details have not been verified in other plants assigned to the group.

The most common genus, *Petrocelis*, is now well-known as the host in the recently studied *Codiolum* problem (see Chapter 8). The plants are usually tetrasporic and show cruciately divided tetrasporangia developed from inter-calary cells of the perithallial filaments and in certain species lying in a zone well below the surface (Figure 10-13).

FIGURE 10–13. Vertical section of part of a fertile crust of *Petrocelis ascendens*, showing intercalary tetrasporangia.

Solieriaceae

Agardhiella

The several genera of this small family may be recognized rather easily by the occurrence of zonately divided tetrasporangia combined with multiaxial thallus development. *Agardhiella* (Figure 10-14, *C*) is the most common and most widespread member on American shores. Although superficially similar in habit to certain other genera of red algae, such as *Gracilariopsis*, it is quickly distinguished by its structure. The axes are cylindrical and show a transectional structure largely of pseudoparenchymatous cells grading to smaller and smaller size toward the surface. The center of the medulla, however, consists of a core of parallel, longitudinal filaments. The cystocarps are deeply embedded and form on the surface localized swellings that show an ostiole. The carposporangial mass is surrounded by a thick, felted layer of nutritive cells penetrated by haustorial filaments of the developing gonimoblast. Spermatangia are borne in superficial sori of varying size on separate male plants.

Hypneaceae

Hypnea

This small family is represented in the northern hemisphere only by the genus *Hypnea* and its minute parasite, *Hypneocolax*. Species of *Hypnea*, however, are among the more common fleshy algae of almost all warm seas, and the widespread *H. musciformis*, with its distinctive hooked branchlets, occurs as far north as Massachusetts.

The plants are bushy, tufted, or clustered forms with cylindrical branches provided with many short, spine-like lateral branchlets (Figure 10-14, *B*). Growth is from an apical cell, and the single axial filament is usually clearly evident at maturity, centered in a pseudoparenchymatous tissue of large, medullary cells and small cortical cells (Figure 10-14, *A*).

The tetrasporangia are zonate and produced in swollen sori on the short, lateral branchlets.

The female reproductive apparatus consists of procarps produced just back of the apex. The carpogonial branch is 3-celled, and the supporting cell also bears the auxiliary cell (Figure 10-15, *B*). After fertilization, the carpogonium fuses with the auxiliary cell (Figure 10-15, *C*) and the gonimoblast develops within a rapidly expanding pericarp. The maturing, hemispherical cystocarp shows a central mass of developing spores whose nourishment is facilitated by nutritive filaments from the pericarp. In some species an ostiole is formed, and in some not.

Plocamiaceae

Plocamium

This is another small family, and one consisting of a single free-living genus and its minute parasite, *Plocamiocolax*. There are about 50 species of *Plocamium*, mostly in the southern hemisphere. *P. coccineum* is a common European one which also occurs abundantly along Pacific America as a robust form. It is one

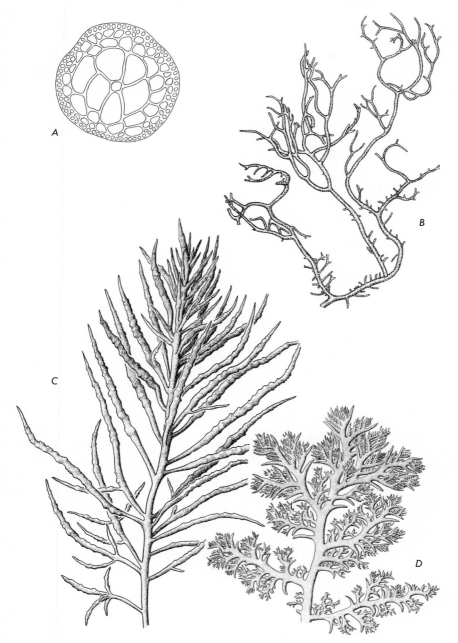

FIGURE 10–14. *A–B, Hypnea cervicornis*: *A*, transection; *B*, habit. *C*, Part of a cystocarpic plant of *Agardhiella tenera*. *D*, Upper part of *Plocamium coccineum* var. *pacificum*, showing sympodial branching. (*C–D* after Smith, reprinted by permission of Stanford Unversity Press)

of the more brilliantly colored and attractively branched representatives of the red algae.

The plant is uniaxial and is one of the best examples of sympodial, distichous, pectinate branching (Figure 10-14,D).

The tetrasporangia are zonately divided and are confined to stichidium-like, fertile ultimate branchlets that are somewhat swollen. The spermatangia are also limited to the ultimate branchlets that they cover as a superficial sorus.

Procarps are formed in the tips of young branchlets. They consist of a three-celled carpogonial filament whose supporting cell functions as the auxiliary cell. Like some hypneas, the cystocarp develops a hemispherical pericarp without an ostiole, but the gonimoblast stands free within the cavity on a pedicel originating from the auxiliary-cell fusion cell and without nutritive filaments to the pericarp.

Gracilariaceae

Gracilaria

This family includes several genera that have small numbers of species, and a large one, Gracilaria, with about 100 species widely distributed throughout temperate and tropical waters of the world. The plants are all fleshy types tending to be flattened to foliose and of pseudoparenchymatous sturcture without filamentous cells in the mature vegetative thallus.

The tetrasporangia are cruciately divided and occur continuously, or in irregular sori, in the outer cortical tissue of mature plants (Figure 10-15,F).

Spermatangial sori are of particular interest, although male plants are infrequent, for they afford diagnostic characters for many of the species. In some they occur entirely superficially over broad areas of the thallus, in others as sori of irregular shape and sunken as shallow channels or pits in the cortex. In several species the spermatangial sori consist of deeply sunken cavities or pockets in which the spermatia originate from fertile cells that line the walls (Figure 10-15,G).

The simple, two-celled carpogonial filaments are exceedingly inconspicuous and must be sought with great diligence. After fertilization, the carpogonium fuses with a large number of neighboring cells to form a massive fusion cell. This serves as a basal structure from which the upward growth of the gonimoblast filaments produces a hemispherical carposporophyte within a prominently developed pericarp with a central, terminal ostiole. The development of the chains of carpospores in Gracilaria is aided by nutritive filaments that grow out from the gonimoblast to connect with the cells of the pericarp (Figure 10-15,E). In the closely related genus Gracilariopsis, such nutritive filaments are not present, and the basal cells of the gonimoblast are more compact, less vacuolate and serve for transport of nourishment from the broad cystocarp base (Figure 7-40,C).

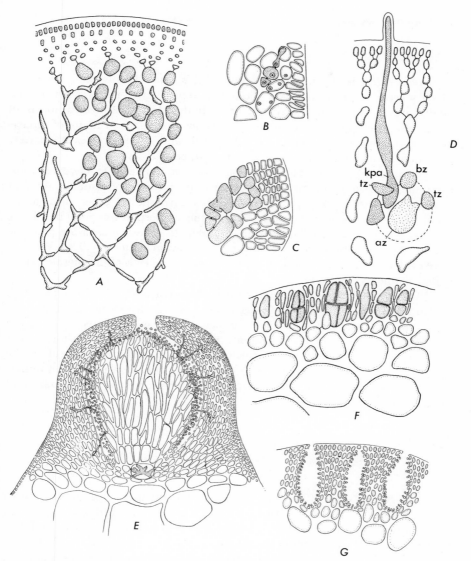

FIGURE 10–15. *A*, Part of a transection of a tetrasporic plant of *Gigartina leptorhynchos*, showing structure of cortex and medulla and origins of chains of tetrasporangia (undivided) from outer medullary filaments. *B–C, Hypnea musciformis: B*, procarp; *C*, early postfertilization fusion of carpogonium and auxiliary cell. *D, Endocladia muricata*: a procarp ready for fertilization (kpa: carpogonium; tz: supporting cell; bz: basal cell of fertile branch; az: auxiliary cell). *E*, Mature cystocarp in *Gracilaria*, showing subparenchymatous gonimoblast, basal fusion cell, nutritive filaments to the pericarp, and release of carposporangia. *F*, Tetrasporic sorus in *Gracilaria* as seen in vertical section. *G*, Vertical section of a male sorus in *Gracilaria coronopifolia*, showing deep, conceptacular spermatangial cavities. (*A–D* after Kylin)

Phyllophoraceae

Gymnogongrus

Gymnogongrus is the principal genus of this small family of 5 genera in which several atypical and even anomalous reproductive features occur. The plants are mostly erect, cartilaginous, cylindrical to compressed forms of repeatedly dichotomous branching. They show a compact structure of moderately large, somewhat angular medullary cells and a thick cortex of sparsely branched, compacted anticlinal rows of small cells.

Tetrasporophytes are known in some species, but seem to have been lost from the life history of others. Several species have carpogonial thalli that produce ordinary cystocarps bearing normal carpospores; other carpogonial thalli bear tetrasporic nemathecia where the carpospores should be. These peculiar wart-like structures were long thought to represent separate parasitic genera that were known as *Colacolepis* or *Actinococcus* (Figure 10-19,*A*). We now have evidence that these develop from the supporting cells of degenerate carpogonial filaments.

Male plants have seldom been clearly or convincingly described, although in two species of Pacific Coast *Gymnogongrus,* normal, superficial spermatangial sori occur as a colorless layer on the upper parts of male plants.

The relationship of the tetrasporic nemathecia to the life history is not clear, for details of fertilization, nuclear behavior, and development of the cystocarp are largely unknown. Such deficiencies provide a number of opportunities for the study in this family of peculiar reproductive adaptations and modifications.

Gigartinaceae

Gigartina

The genus *Gigartina* includes among its 90-odd species the most massive of the fleshy red algae, some of which reach a meter in breadth and more than twice that length. Many of the species are perennial from a discoid holdfast that produces new blades after the seasonal breakoff or decay of the old blades.

Growth is multiaxial (Figure 7-33,*B*) and the structure of the thallus is filamentous. The medulla shows a loose, interlacing of filaments in a clear, gelatinous matrix. The cortex is of branched, anticlinal rows of pigmented cells of decreasing size to the surface (Figure 10-15,*A*).

Gigartina is usually recognized by the short, papillate, superficial outgrowths that cover the surface of the thallus. The tetrasporic sori are usually borne on or around the base of these (Figure 10-16), and the procarps are essentially confined to them. The procarps are borne on the inner cells of cortical filaments and consist of a supporting cell bearing a 3-celled carpogonial branch and a branched, sterile filament. The supporting cell serves as the auxiliary cell and

Figure 10–16. *Gigartina armata* var. *echinata,* showing a tetrasporangial plant (left) with sporangial sori occupying the papilla, and a carpogonial plant (right) with maturing pedicellate cystocarps.

receives the diploid zygote nucleus through a short connection formed by the carpogonium. The gonimoblast develops inwardly and causes the swelling of the superficial papilla so that the mature cystocarp often appears as a pedicellate sphere (Figure 10-16).

Just as in a majority of red algae, tetrasporic plants of many species of *Gigartina* are found in far greater numbers than are sexual ones. In one census of a Mexican *Gigartina* colony the writer found tetrasporic plants to be about 100 times as frequent as cystocarpic ones.

RHODYMENIALES

The structure and reproduction of a number of representatives of this group have been described recently by Sparling (1957, p. 319) who has summarized the distinctive features of the order as follows.

The members of the Rhodymeniales are "characterized by multiaxial growth, by a three or four-celled carpogonial branch, by the presence of a procarp with one or occasionally two auxiliary cells that are not part of the vegetative system, and by having the auxiliary-cell branch (that is produced by the supporting cell and is usually composed of two cells) initiated before fertilization. The mature tetrasporangia are either cruciately or tetrahedrally divided. The life cycle is almost always diplobiontic."

This is a small order of Florideophycidae and presently includes only two families that, however, have representatives throughout the world. These two families seem to differ consistently in only one vegetative character.

Champiaceae: Most of the thallus, or at least the reproductive part hollow and with longitudinal filaments bordering the cavity; tetrasporangia generally tetrahedrally divided, but some genera with polysporangia.

Rhodymeniaceae: Thallus solid or hollow (Figure 7-2,*D–E*; 7-27), but if hollow, longitudinal filaments lacking; tetrasporangia generally cruciately divided.

Rhodymeniaceae

Rhodymenia

This is a genus containing perhaps 50 species of foliose plants usually with dichotomously or palmately branched blades (Figure 7-34). The structure of mature blades is entirely pseudoparenchymatous (Figure 7-19,*B*). The medulla is of large, thin-walled, vacuolate cells and the cortex of smaller, more densely protoplasmic, pigmented cells. The tetrasporangia occur variously in sori or dispersed over the blades. They are embedded in the cortex, which may be unmodified, or distinctly nemathecially modified by their presence. In *R. palmata*, the commonest of our North American species, only tetrasporic and male plants are known, and the carposporic phase has evidently been lost. The life history of that plant remains to be worked out.

Spermatangia, where known, occur in small superficial sori, usually near the apices of the lobes of the blades.

The procarps consist of a supporting cell bearing a three-or-four-celled carpogonial branch and a two-celled auxiliary-cell filament. The gonimoblast develops outwardly and concurrently with the formation of a domed pericarp. The mature cystocarp is projecting, hemispherical, and ostiolate (Figure 10-17,*A*).

FIGURE 10–17. *A,* Mature cystocarp of *Rhodymenia,* showing prominent, ostiolate pericarp and pedicellate gonimoblast. *B,* Small part of a cystocarpic plant of *Lomentaria.* *C,* Part of a sporophytic plant of *Lomentaria,* showing cortical cavities bearing the tetrasporangia.

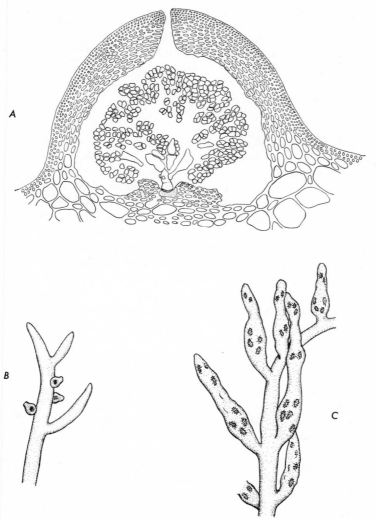

Champiaceae

Lomentaria

Two genera may be mentioned as examples for study of this small family: *Lomentaria* and *Gastroclonium*. The lomentarias are usually delicate, branched, tubular plants in which the hollow parts are closed at the points of branching. The tetrasporangia (or polysporangia) are borne in groups beneath the surface of the cortical layer, which is often inwardly sunken to form a depression or pit-like cavity (Figure 10-17,*C*). The cystocarp develops much as in the Rhodymeniaceae and matures as a projecting, spherical, ostiolate body almost equal in diameter to the bearing branch (Figure 10-17,*B*).

Gastroclonium is a coarser plant that occurs commonly in California. It consists of solid, cylindrical, branched axes bearing short, constricted, and septate hollow branchlets. The tetrasporophytes bear tetrahedrally divided sporangia embedded just beneath the thallus surface, but polysporangia with 15 to 20 spores are produced at times.

CERAMIALES

This is by far the largest order of the red algae and contains over 250 genera. It is also the best circumscribed of the orders, and has been divided into only four well-defined families. A vast majority of the members are relatively delicate, filamentous or membranous forms. Few are species of coarse texture or large size. The life histories are typically triphasic, with isomorphic sporophyte and gametophyte generations. The order shows marked uniformity in the structure and development of the reproductive organs. The procarp is peculiar in that the auxiliary cell, borne directly on the supporting cell of the four-celled carpogonial filament, is formed after fertilization. The gonimoblast is consistently of compact form. On the other hand, a wide variation occurs in the vegetative organization of the thallus, and distinctions and relationships throughout the order are based largely upon the morphology of the vegetative system.

Ceramiaceae

This large family is composed mainly of very delicate plants mostly of cylindrical construction. They may be uniseriate, uncorticated filaments (Figures 7-11; 7-13; 7-31; 7-29,*F*), or they may be partially or wholly corticated, but the corticating cells are never as long as the cells they enclose (not polysiphonous). The cystocarps are distinctive in lacking a fully enclosing pericarp, although there may be an involucre of short branchlets around the gonimoblast. In many forms the gonimoblast is naked (Figure 7-40,*A*). Sporophytes usually bear tetrasporangia, although several genera produce polysporangia (Figure 7-25,*E*).

Antithamnion

The genus *Antithamnion* is representative of a group of genera of uniseriate plants in which there is no cortication of the axis. In this instance the axis is provided with branches in opposite pairs or in verticils of three or four, these branches usually being equal in length and producing a symmetrical form. In many species hyaline gland cells occur in distinctive positions.

The gametophytes are dioecious. Male plants bear clusters of spermatangia on the adaxial side of the branches. Female plants show the simplest organization in this order. They bear their 4-celled carpogonial filaments on the lowermost cell of lateral branches and with the trichogyne directed apically. The supporting cell cuts off an auxiliary cell which, after receiving the diploid nucleus, develops into a fully exposed gonimoblast without an involucre.

Sporophyte plants are most commonly found. They produce their sessile or pedicellate, cruciately divided tetrasporangia on the adaxial side of the branchlets (Figure 7-25,*D*).

Ceramium

This is a large genus that is prevailingly of epiphytes on larger algae in warm waters or calm situations. It is a ready representative of those Ceramiaceae with corticated axes. The central axial filament is characteristically large-celled compared with the small corticating cells that may form bands at the junctures of the axial cells (the nodes) (Figure 10-18), or that may cover the axis more or less completely by upward and downward growth. The branching is commonly dichotomous and the apices often forcipate or even circinate. Sexual plants are infrequently seen, and diagnostic characters are found mainly in the tetrasporic plants in which the tetrahedrally dividing sporangia may be borne in a variety of ways: solitary at the nodes; whorled and naked; involucrate by upward growth of a whorl of cortical cells; or embedded in a complete cortex (Figure 10-18,*B–D*).

Delesseriaceae

This family of about 70 genera is one of the most attractive of all the algae. The plants are mostly delicate, membranous forms of brilliant reddish color and of marvelously clear anatomical structure. Many are unistratose forms in which, as in *Hypoglossum* (Figure 7-32,*A*) the sequence of development of the thallus can be traced back through many generations of cells. In others, the pattern of midribs and veins suggests that of the leaves of flowering plants (Figure 7-19,*D*).

The great number of generic distinctions that have been pointed out reflect the diversity of structure and the clarity with which diagnostic characters can be recognized in this assemblage. The systematics and taxonomy of the group were elaborately revised by Kylin in 1924. More recently the morphology of a number of representatives of the family has been worked out by Wagner (1954).

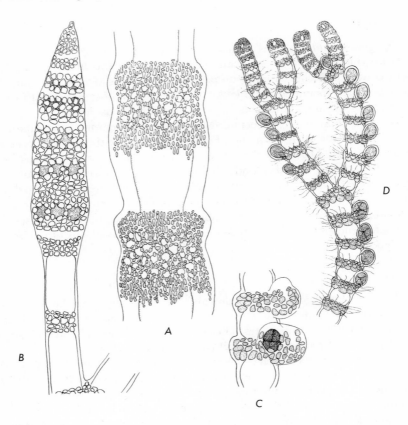

FIGURE 10–18. Structure and reproduction of *Ceramium*. *A,* 2 nodes of a partially corticated species, showing large axial cells and small cortical cells, the outer ones with a tendency to basipetal growth over the internodes; *B,* embedded tetrasporangia in a terminal fertile branch; *C,* a tetrasporangium partially enveloped by an involucre of cortical cells; *D,* habit of a typically dichotomous species, with forcipate apices and solitary, naked tetrasporangia at the nodes.

The family is divided into two subfamilies and several generic groups primarily according to the following characters:

1) whether the procarps are scattered over the fertile blades (Nitophylloideae) or confined to the midrib region (Delesserioideae).
2) whether the blades develop by means of a single transversely dividing apical cell, or from numerous marginal initials.
3) whether or not intercalary cell divisions occur back of the apical cells (Figure 7-32,*B*).

DELESSERIOIDEAE (DELESSERIEAE)

Membranoptera

Several species of these delicate, pink membranopteras occur on the Atlantic and Pacific coasts, either on rocks or on coarse algae. The blades are
monostromatic except at the percurrent midrib, and some species have delicate
lateral veins. Growth of each blade segment is by an apical cell. As in
Hypoglossum (whose growth has been described in Chapter 7, Figure 7-32,*A*)
there are no intercalary divisions in the axial cell row, but unlike that genus,
not all of the apical cells of the cell rows of the third order reach the thallus
margin. Plants are dioecious. Spermatangia are borne variously in sori at the
blade tips, on either side of the midrib, or on small proliferations. The procarps
are borne along the midrib, each arising from an axial cell. The supporting cell
is always a pericentral cell cut off from an axial cell. It bears the four-celled
carpogonial filament and also cuts off two sterile cells, one of which develops
into a two- or three-celled sterile filament. The auxiliary cell is cut off from
the supporting cell after fertilization. The gonimoblast filaments develop toward
the thallus surface, and the mature cystocarp takes on a domoid form with an
ostiolate pericarp.

Tetrasporangia are tetrahedrally divided and borne in sori variously
situated like the spermatangial ones.

Species distinctions are usually made on vegetative characters such as venation (if any), shape, and serration of the blade margins (Figure 10-19,*B*).

NITOPHYLLOIDEAE (NITOPHYLLEAE)

Polyneura

This is one of the more common Delesseriaceae found on the Pacific
Coast and one of the most attractive by its rosy color and interesting pattern
of anastomosing veins. It is also a large plant that may reach 30 centimeters.
The erect blades are stipitate, broadly cuneate, and more or less deeply incised
and lacerate (Figure 10-19,*C*). Younger parts are monostromatic, but older
parts become more than one cell thick. Growth is marginal by a meristem of
numerous cells.

Tetrasporangia are borne in small sori scattered over both surfaces of the
blades, several in each of the small areas between the veins. Spermatangial sori
are similarly situated. Procarps develop throughout the blade. The supporting
cell bears a pair of 4-celled carpogonial branches and also a single group of
sterile cells. The mature cystocarps are prominent, hemispherical structures
with ostiolate pericarp.

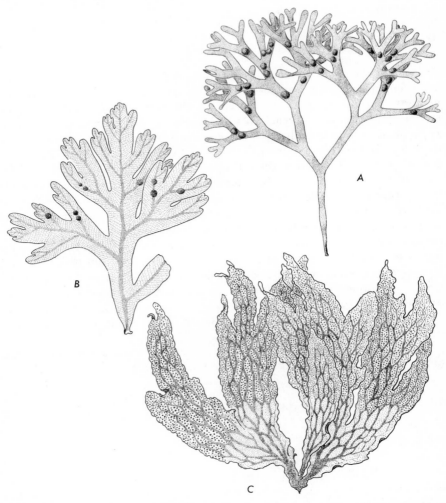

FIGURE 10–19. *A,* Habit of *Gymnogongrus platyphyllus,* showing large sporangial nemathecia. *B, Membranoptera multiramosa,* showing midrib, parallel lateral veins and cystocarps on the midrib. *C,* A mature plant of *Polyneura latissima,* showing anastomosing veins and scattered tetrasporangial sori (after Smith, reprinted by permission Stanford University Press).

Dasyaceae

Dasya

The structure of *Dasya* is a relatively complex one among Ceramiales, and care must be exercised in the preparation of material for examination in order to reveal the distinctive features. The plants consist of slender, cylindrical,

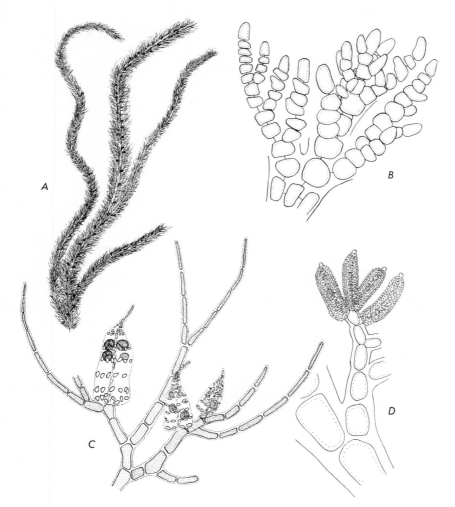

FIGURE 10–20. Structure and reproduction of *Dasya*: *A*, habit of *D. pedicellata*, show-ing abundant pseudolaterals and position of cystocarps; *B*, apex of a branch to show spiral sympodial branch origins; *C*, tetrasporangial stichidia; *D*, spermatangial branchlets in *D. sinicola*.

solid axes clothed with abundant fine hairs which tend to obscure the apical development. Growth is sympodial. Thus, a persistent apical cell does not occur, but successive segments produce laterally a new growing point that dis-places the preceding apex as in *Heterosiphonia* (Figure 7-31,*D*). The latter con-tinues development to produce one of the lateral tufts of colored monosiphonous filaments (the pseudolaterals) which, by their abundance, usually conceal the young apical structure (Figure 10-20,*A–B*). An axial cell row is formed around which 5 pericentral cells are developed very early behind the growing point.

These produce downwardly growing rhizoidal filaments that soon envelop the axis with a more or less heavy cortication. Tetrasporangia occur in distinctive stichidia (Figure 10-20,C). Spermatangia occur as subcylindrical, sheathing clusters around mid-parts of the lateral filaments (Figure 10-20,D). Procarps appear near the base of the lateral tufts of filaments. The 4-celled carpogonial branch and a group of sterile cells arise from a fertile pericentral cell. Cystocarps develop with an ovate, short-stalked pericarp provided with a large, apical pore.

Rhodomelaceae

This family includes a great diversity of vegetative types, but a remarkably well-defined and uniform reproductive development. It is generally accorded a status of advanced evolution and placed last among the Ceramiales and all the red algae in current classification. At the same time, with more than 100 genera, it is the largest of all the families. Most of its members are delicate plants of cylindrical construction, but there are prostrate, dorsiventral forms and erect, flat forms. Relatively few are coarse plants of fleshy or cartilaginous consistency. Growth is characteristically by means of a persistent apical cell (Figure 7-29,G) that produces an axial cell row. Branched or unbranched uniseriate hairs (trichoblasts) are usually produced in spiral succession at the apex. These may be persistent or deciduous, pigmented or nonpigmented.

FIGURE 10–21. Transverse sections (A–F) through first 6 segments of *Polysiphonia*, showing sequence of formation of pericentral cells (p1, p2, p3, p4) and trichoblasts (i–vii) (after Rosenberg).

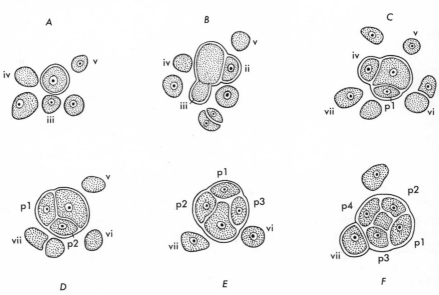

The most striking character of the Rhodomelaceae is the polysiphonous structure whereby axial cells cut off by longitudinal walls a series of pericentral cells according to a regular sequence (Figure 10-21). The first develops directly under an initial that in some genera forms the trichoblast for the segment. Subsequent pericentral cells are cut off to the right and to the left of this one. Further cortication may occur as the result of division of the pericentral cells or by the development of appressed rhizoidal downgrowths from the pericentral cells and cortical cells.

Tetrasporangia develop internally from segments of the pericentral cells.

Spermatangia occur in tufts, clusters, or cones arising from special fertile trichoblasts around the apices.

Procarps also arise immediately behind the apex from trichoblast segments. The carpogonial branch is usually four-celled and its supporting cell also bears several sterile cells. The position of the carpogonial branch in relation to the sterile cells in the fertile segment is remarkably precise. The auxiliary cell is cut off from the supporting cell after fertilization. Fusion of the carpogonium with the auxiliary cell is followed by the formation of a fusion cell. This first involves fusion of the auxiliary cell and the supporting cell as the gonimoblast filaments begin to develop. Later the fusion cell enlarges as other cells are incorporated. The developing group of gonimoblast filaments becomes enclosed by an ostiolate pericarp.

Polysiphonia

The cosmopolitan genus *Polysiphonia* has long been a classic representative of the red algae, and it is one of the few genera in which the nuclear aspects of the entire life history have been well established. It is also the most readily available material to illustrate the polysiphonous structure of Rhodomelaceae (Figure 7-13,*D*; 7-31,*E*). The manner of origin of the trichoblasts and pericentral cells has been described in Chapter 7. Most species are not corticated, and the most commonly encountered ones are those with four pericentral cells. In these one will usually note the development of the colorless trichoblasts in a regular spiral sequence with 90° divergence at each segment (never more than one per segment). The trichoblast is usually early deciduous and leaves its small basal cell (scar cell) prominently connected with the central axial cell row. This usually reveals the spiral sequence through mature parts of the plant (Figure 7-29,*G*). Some species, however, have few scar cells, or these may be irregularly arranged. The indeterminate branches often show a relationship to the scar cells, because they replace trichoblasts, or because they arise either axillary to them (Figure 10-22) or from the scar cells.

The young procarp arises on young trichoblasts very near the apex, one to each trichoblast. It is always formed on the second segment from the base of the trichoblast, which becomes polysiphonous by the cutting off of pericentral cells. One of these, the last to be cut off, is the fertile pericentral cell that

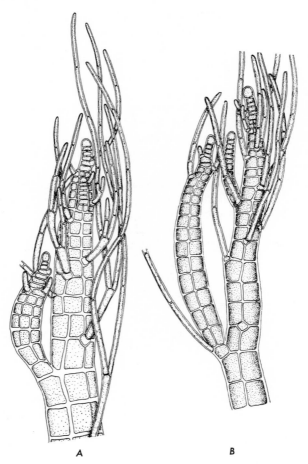

A   B

FIGURE 10–22. Structure of *Polysiphonia*: *A, P. mollis,* showing 4 pericentral cells, trichoblasts, regular scar cells at 1/4 divergence, and a branch replacing a trichoblast or a scar cell; *B, P. flaccidissima,* showing similar structure, but with branches in the axils of trichoblasts (after Hollenberg).

gives rise to the procarp. This one divides unequally to form a larger carpogonial branch initial and a smaller supporting cell. The carpogonial branch initial then forms a row of four cells (rarely three), of which the top one is the carpogonium. Meanwhile the supporting cell cuts off a basal sterile cell and, toward the side, two lateral sterile cells.

After fertilization, the carpogonium enlarges and the trichogyne is cut off by a wall. The fusion nucleus begins to undergo division and at the same time the sterile cells multiply, the basal cell into two and the lateral two into four. The supporting cell also enlarges and cuts off an auxiliary cell directly below the carpogonium. After formation of the auxiliary cell, a small connecting cell is, in some species, cut off from the base of the carpogonium. This cell fuses with the auxiliary cell and establishes a communication with the carpogonium. At this stage the fusion nucleus enters into anaphase and one of the daughter groups of chromosomes is thought to enter the auxiliary cell, while the other remains inside the carpogonium and degenerates. The carpogonium then is cut off by a wall and degenerates along with the other cells of the carpogonial branch. By this time, the protoplasmic connections between the supporting cell, the auxiliary cell, and the sterile cells enlarge as open communications. The fusion nucleus in the auxiliary cell divides and the auxiliary cell cuts off a gonimoblast mother cell toward its outer side. This, in turn, cuts off a number of gonimoblast cells, each of which gives rise terminally to a carpo-sporangium and then divides laterally to form more gonimoblast cells. Mean-while, the supporting cell, the auxiliary cell, the central cell, and the sterile cells fuse to form a large, irregular, multinucleate fusion cell. The cystocarp is at this stage mature and has formed its ostiolate pericarp.

Chondria

The genus *Chondria,* and the equally common *Laurencia,* provide examples of fleshy Rhodomelaceae with extensive cortical development. The apical cell, that in *Chondria* may be either in an apical pit or emergent (Figure 7-31, *C;* 7-3,*D*), cuts off successive cells of an axial cell row. These, in turn, cut off trichoblast initials and five pericentral cells (Figure 10-23,*A*). The pericentral cells divide to build up the cortical tissue and lose their identity as the ma-turing thallus becomes pseudoparenchymatous (Figure 7-31,*F*). The trichoblasts are deciduous early and leave a scar cell that remains capable of giving rise to a lateral branch.

Procarps are found arising from fertile trichoblasts immediately behind the apical cell. Growth of the cystocarp may be so rapid that within a fraction of a millimeter of the apex a fairly prominent hemispherical protuberance is visible.

Male reproductive structures in *Chondria* are unusual in having the form of a pedicellate fan (Figure 10-23,*B–C*). They originate from trichoblasts that produce both spermatangial branches and sterile branches.

Tetrasporangia are initiated very near the fertile apex by the cutting off from a pericentral cell of a sporangial initial and two or more cover cells (Figure 10-23,*F–G*). These undergo very rapid enlargement, and the tetra-sporangium matures and is discharged within a few millimeters of the apex.

REFERENCES

Abbott, Isabella A. 1962. Some *Liagora*-inhabiting species of *Acrochaetium. Occ. Papers B. P. Bishop Mus.,* 23: 77–120.
Balakrishnan, M.S. 1961. Studies on Indian Cryptonemiales, I. *Grateloupia. J. Madras Univ.,* 31: 11–35.

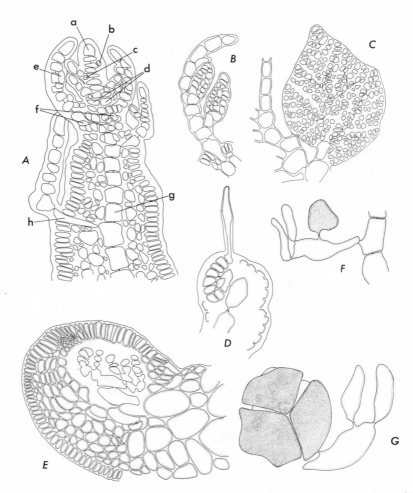

FIGURE 10–23. Structure and reproduction of *Chondria nidifica*: *A,* apex of a primary axis, the lower part shown in median longitudinal view (a: apical cell; b: first trichoblast initial; c: first pericentral cell; d: two of the developing ring of five pericentral cells; e: trichoblast branch; f: cortical cells developing from pericentral cells; g: axial cell row; h: basal cell of trichoblast which becomes the scar cell; i: outer palisade cortex). *B–C,* development of fan-shaped spermatangial sori on trichoblasts; *D,* median optical view of a young cystocarp ready for fertilization, showing 4-celled carpogonial branch; *E,* cystocarp in early postfertilization stage; *F–G,* tetrasporangium development from a fertile pericentral cell bearing 2 cover cells.

Chihara, M. 1961–1962. Life cycles of the Bonnemaisoniaceous algae of Japan, I–II. *Sci. Reports Tokyo Kyoiku Daigaku*, Sec. B, 10(153): 121–154; 11(161): 127–153.

Dawson, E. Y. 1961. Marine red algae of Pacific Mexico, pt. 4. Gigartinales. *Pacific Naturalist*, 2: 191–344.

Dixon, P. 1963a. The Rhodophyta: some aspects of their biology. *Oceanogr. Marine Biol. Ann. Rev.*, 1: 177–196.

————— 1963b. The taxonomic implications of the "pit-connexions" reported in the Bangiophycidae. *Taxon*, 12: 108–110.

Fan, K.C. 1961. Morphological studies of the Gelidiales. *Univ. Calif. Publ. Bot.*, 32: 315–368.

Hollenberg, G. J. 1959. *Smithora*, an interesting new algal genus in the Erythropeltidaceae. *Pacific Naturalist*, 1(8): 1–12.

Hommersand, M. H. 1963. The morphology and classification of some Ceramiaceae and Rhodomelaceae. *Univ. Calif. Publ. Bot.*, 36: 165–366.

Iyengar, M.O.P. and M.S. Balakrishnan. 1950. Morphology and cytology of *Polysiphonia platycarpa* Børg. *Proc. Indian Acad. Sci.*, 31: 135–161.

Kurogi, M. 1961. Species of cultivated porphyras and their life histories. *Bull. Tohoku Reg. Fish. Res. Lab.*, (18): 1–115.

Kylin, H. 1924. Studien über die Delesseriaceen. Lunds Univ. Årsskr., N.F., Avd. 2, 20(6): 1–111.

————— 1928. Entwicklungsgeschichtliche Florideenstudien. Lunds Univ. Årsskr., N.F., 24(4): 1–127.

————— 1932. Die Florideenordnung Gigartinales. Lunds Univ. Årsskr., N.F., Avd. 2, 28(8): 1–88.

————— 1956. Die Gattungen der Rhodophyceen. Lund: Gleerup. xv + 673 pp.

Magne, M. F. 1960. Sur le lieu de la meiose chez le *Bonnemaisonia asparagoides*. . . . . *Compt. Rend. Acad. Sci.*, 250: 2742–2744.

————— 1961. Sur le cycle cytologique du *Nemalion helminthoides*. *Compt. Rend. Acad. Sci.*, 252: 157–159.

Miura, A. 1961. A new species of *Porphyra* and its *Conchocelis* phase in nature. *J. Tokyo Univ. of Fisheries*, 47: 305–311.

Norris, R. E. 1957. Morphological studies on the Kallymeniaceae. *Univ. Calif. Publ. Bot.*, 28: 251–333.

Scagel, R. F. 1953. A morphological study of some dorsiventral Rhodomelaceae. *Univ. Calif. Publ. Bot.*, 27: 1–108.

Schmitz, C. J. F. 1883. Untersuchungen über die Befruchtung der Florideen. Berlin: Sitzungsber. K. Preuss. Akad. Wiss. (1): 215–258.

Sparling, Shirley R. 1957. The structure and reproduction of some members of the Rhodymeniaceae. *Univ. Calif. Publ. Bot.*, 29: 319–396.

Svedelius, N. 1953. Critical studies of some species of *Galaxaura* from Hawaii. *Nova Acta Reg. Soc. Sci. Upsaliensis*, iv, 15(9): 1–92.

Wagner, Florence S. 1954. Contributions to the morphology of the Delesseriaceae. *Univ. Calif. Publ. Bot.*, 27: 279–346.

11

Seaweed Life Histories

It should be emphasized at the outset that our concepts of life histories in the seaweeds are based upon factual evidences provided by many different investigators, using different techniques and suffering different handicaps. Much of the evidence is imperfect, and very often sweeping generalizations have been made with regard to large taxonomic groups on the basis of incomplete knowledge of the life history of a single species. On the other hand, it is now becoming evident that even races of the same species may show differences in life history. Accordingly, one should look upon the present status of seaweed life histories as open to frequent and extensive change. Indeed, significant discoveries may be made through the critical study of almost any species.

The term "life history" has been defined by Drew (1955, p. 349) as "the recurring sequence of somatic and nuclear phases characteristic of the species under consideration." Thus, a life history must be considered in terms of both morphology and cytology. One observes in nature or in culture that the thalli that succeed each other in reproduction are often morphologically similar (isomorphic), but that this is not always true. Many other plants produce distinctive resting stages or small phases of very different morphology from the preceding plant (heteromorphic), and these different phases may each bear distinctive types of sexual or asexual reproductive bodies. For these reasons it is evident that an alternation of generations may not readily be recognized in the gross morphology of a plant, either because of too much similarity or too much difference. The male, female and sporophytic plants of *Gelidium* species, for example, look so much alike that one does not recognize from casual observation more than one kind of plant. On the other hand, the microscopic gametophyte plants of the Laminariales give no clue in themselves of relationship with their massive alternate sporophytes. One must undertake careful culture experiments with these to demonstrate the origin of one phase from another, and make cytological examination of the nuclear phases in order to interpret the meaning of the sequence.

It became evident a number of decades ago that two cytological events, karyogamy (nuclear fusion) and meiosis (reduction division) are obligately involved in sexual life histories. The corresponding nuclear states are known as the haploid (following reduction division) and the diploid (following fusion). On the basis of these nuclear phases, Svedelius introduced in 1931 the modern study of algal life histories by distinguishing three types, the names for which are still widely used:

1) haplonts: types in which the zygote is the only diploid cell
2) diplonts: types in which the gametes are the only haploid cells
3) diplohaplonts: types that show an alternation of a diploid and a haploid vegetative phase.

It was soon realized that this simple classification would not accommodate all the kinds of life histories. Much modification and extension of Svedelius' scheme have occurred, and continue as new discoveries are made. Nevertheless, it provides us with a means of beginning a consideration of diverse life histories.

EXAMPLES

We can observe in the green algae organisms with the simplest possible life cycle. Thus, in *Chlamydomonas*, a vegetative cell produces motile daughter cells that may function as gametes to produce a zygote. This divides meiotically to produce zoospores that function directly as vegetative plants. In this instance the life history consists of an alternation of a one-celled haploid phase that produces gametes, and a one-celled diploid phase that produces zoospores. From this simplicity one can recognize among green algae a progressive complexity in the development of multicellular conditions either in the haploid or diploid phase, or in both. In most of the fresh-water green algae the vegetative multiplication of cells occurs in the haploid stage. Meiosis occurs in the germinating zygote, and these algae, thus, are haplonts.

A considerable number of marine forms, of which *Ulva* is representative, are diplohaplonts. In these, vegetative division occurs upon germination of the zygote, but reduction division is delayed until the formation of zoospores. These zoospores in turn initiate another phase of vegetative cell division essentially like the former, but it results in the production of gametes. *Ulva*, thus, exhibits the alternation of a macroscopic diploid generation with a macroscopic haploid generation, and, since these are essentially identical in appearance, they constitute an isomorphic alternation (Figure 11-1).

Another evolutionary line has given rise to diplonts, of which *Codium* is a good example. Here, despite the fact that cell division does not include cross-

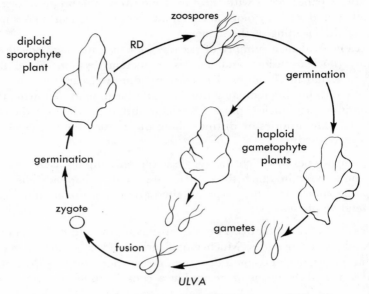

FIGURE 11–1. Diagrammatic life history of *Ulva*.

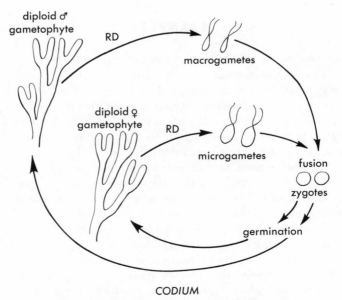

FIGURE 11–2. Diagrammatic life history of *Codium*.

wall formation, the diploid nucleus resulting from syngamy undergoes repeated mitotic division as the multinucleate thallus develops. The macroscopic *Codium* plant is diploid, and the reduction division is delayed until gamete formation (Figure 11-2).

The fact that either gametes or zoospores may be produced by the diploid or the haploid generation makes it clear that the sexual or asexual nature of a thallus is not necessarily tied to its nuclear phase. Thus, in the algae, a gametophyte, though usually haploid, may be diploid; and a sporophyte, though usually diploid, may be haploid. This is in contrast to the pattern of life cycles in the bryophytes and pteridophytes, in which there is usually an obligatory alternation of a haploid gametophyte and a diploid sporophyte.

In the Phaeophyta three types of life histories are readily recognized, two diplohaplontic and one diplontic.

Ectocarpus is generally used to illustrate the alternation of similar gametophyte and sporophyte generations (isomorphic diplohaplontic), although members of the genus often show accessory reproductive phases in addition to the basic alternation (Figure 11-3).

Laminaria is exemplary of the heteromorphic diplohaplont type that is widespread among brown algae. The conspicuous *Laminaria* plant in nature is the sporophyte generation. The gametophytes are so small that they are rarely seen except in culture dishes. The fusion of gametes is oögamous, and reduction division is delayed through the diploid sporophyte generation to zoospore formation (Figure 11-4).

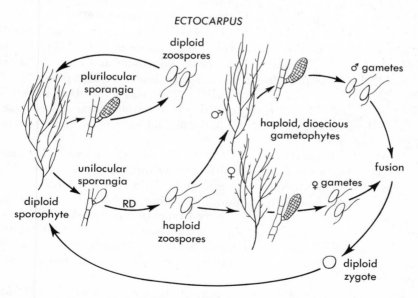

FIGURE 11-3. Diagrammatic life history of *Ectocarpus*.

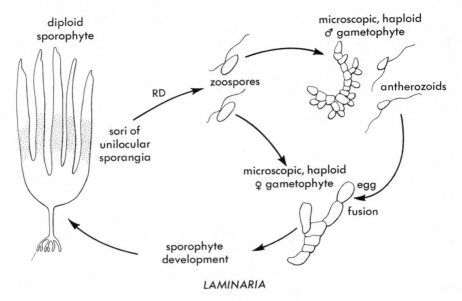

LAMINARIA

FIGURE 11-4. Diagrammatic life history of *Laminaria*.

The diplont among Phaeophyta is exceptional, and is confined to the order Fucales. Nevertheless, it has been the object of some of the most significant investigations of marine algal life histories. It was Thuret's classical work on *Fucus* and his observations of fertilization of eggs by spermatozoids that provided in 1853 a major breakthrough in our knowledge of algal life histories. As an unusual type of fertilization in the marine algae, the oögamous condition in *Fucus* remained a point of confusion for many years, until diploidy was established in 1897 and until meiosis in the oögonium and antheridium was confirmed in 1909 to provide the first example among benthic plants of a life history analogous to that of animals. In 1925 it was shown that *Codium* is a diploid alga, and it is now recognized that in the siphonalean green algae as well as in the Fucales and the diatoms, the diploid soma is the gamete-producing generation as in animals.

Among the Rhodophyta, particularly the overwhelmingly large group, Florideophycidae, we encounter a distinctively different kind of life history from any of the Chlorophyta or Phaeophyta. For a new generation, namely, the carposporophyte, which is unique in being dependent on the female gametophyte, is introduced. Two common types of alternation of generations occur, involving this carposporophyte, a diphasic type, and a triphasic type.

Nemalion multifidum is one of the best known of the diphasic types and consists of the alternation of a haploid gametophyte plant and a haploid carposporophyte borne upon it.

The triphasic type of life history is much more widespread in the Florideophycidae and constitutes the most commonly observed life-cycle phenomenon

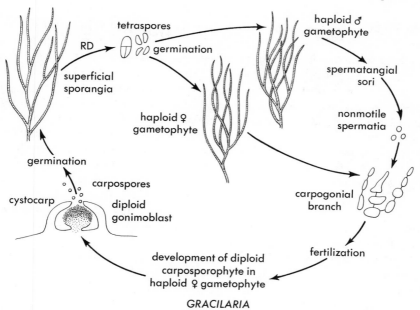

GRACILARIA

FIGURE 11–5. Diagrammatic life history of *Gracilaria*.

of the red algae. *Gracilaria* serves as an example of this type (Figure 11-5). It shows an alternation of isomorphic, haploid gametophytes with a diploid carposporophyte and a diploid tetrasporophyte. The plant is a diplohaplont according to Svedelius' old scheme, but the life history clearly is of an entirely different kind than in diplohaplontic *Laminaria*. *Polysiphonia* (see Chapter 10) is another well-known example of this triphasic type.

A large number of variations and anomalies in life histories have come to light in recent years, so many in fact that one wonders if "exceptional cases" may not soon outnumber the "typical" ones. These have called for a marked expansion in the classification of algal life histories, and the elaboration of terminology used to describe them. The new data have not yet provided any solid evolutionary picture based upon adaptationally significant structures. They are, however, bringing about significant taxonomic changes, for many plants long treated as independent species are now being recognized as but stages in the life histories of dimorphic or trimorphic natural species. Several of the more recent discoveries along this line may be reiterated, but it should be borne in mind that in most cases the evidences are incomplete, and seldom has indisputable cytological confirmation been provided.

Perhaps the most widely publicized case among the green algae is the *Halicystis-Derbesia* life history (see Chapter 8). Five species of the vesicular *Halicystis* are described from various parts of the world, as are 22 species of filamentous *Derbesia*. *Halicystis* species are seldom encountered and have been considered to have restricted ranges, whereas *Derbesia* species appear frequently in collections. In 1938 Kornmann cultured the common *Derbesia marina* and first found that its zoospores grow into aseptate filaments that eventually produce characteristic vesicles of *Halicystis*. Subsequent culture of zygotes from *Halicystis* showed a development into *Derbesia* thalli that, after two months, produced typical sporangia and zoospores. Although the nuclear situation has not been determined, certain morphological observations suggest that meiosis precedes gametogenesis and that the life history consists of the alternation of a vesicular, unicellular, multinucleate, diploid gametophyte with a tubular, unicellular, multinucleate diploid sporophyte. This would be termed a dimorphic diplont. On the other hand, should meiosis be proved to occur preceding the formation of asexual spores, it would be a dimorphic diplohaplont. A further unsolved complication is provided by some evidence that zoospores liberated from a *Derbesia* plant may in some instances repeat the *Derbesia* phase, and that for some of the many species of *Derbesia* there may be no gametophytic, *Halicystis* phase. All of the species of *Halicystis* and *Derbesia*, thus, remain pregnant subjects for cultural and cytological study.

Another study of an apparently dimorphic diplohaplontic life history is that of the *Spongomorpha-Codiolum* alternation described in Chapter 8. The discovery that *Spongomorpha* gametes fuse to give rise to *Codiolum* plants, and that *Spongomorpha* plants arise from zoospores of *Codiolum*, raises even more questions than the *Halicystis-Derbesia* story. *Spongomorpha* (and the possibly identical genus *Acrosiphonia*) number more than 20 species, whereas only three or four kinds of *Codiolum* have been described. Some of the *Spongomorpha* species are scarcely distinguishable from species of the large genus *Cladophora*. Furthermore, it has been suggested that a European species of *Codiolum* is the sporophyte generation of another filamentous green alga, *Urospora*, though experiments in California with *Urospora* do not confirm that finding. Other studies of *Urospora* are in progress, but results have not been published as of this writing.

Taxonomically, the nomenclature of these algae with pleomorphic life histories has presented some interesting problems in the application of the principal of priority. In the *Spongomorpha-Codiolum* combination, priority does not violate usage, for *Spongomorpha* was described in 1843 and *Codiolum* in 1855. There are other instances, however, in which it is necessary to employ the name of the smaller, lesser-known phase of the life history to designate a complete natural species, in order to abide by the international rules of priority in nomenclature.

Important aspects of life histories in some algae have been overlooked for a long time despite extensive taxonomic and ecological study. The membranous green alga, *Prasiola* (see Chapter 8) is a remarkable example. Although there were 5 monographs on the genus between 1848 and 1936, and numerous papers on its anatomy, development, cytology, and floristics, so significant and even conspicuous a structure as the gamete-forming thallus was unobserved until some 30 years ago. Even then its existence was not believed by many prominent phycologists until it was elucidated beyond doubt in 1955. Friedmann has provided the best-documented account of this interesting genus, as represented by *Prasiola stipitata*, the life history of which is of a type previously unrecorded in the algae (Figure 8-6). It uniquely exhibits two of the cytological phases as a single morphological and physiological unit.

Among Rhodophyta, the studies of "exceptional" life histories have centered around certain members of the order Nemalionales, in which some divergences from the characteristic diphasic, haplontic life cycle have been known for some time. The first significant cytological evidence, showing that species of *Galaxaura* are diplohaplonts, was provided by Svedelius in 1942. In *Galaxaura* (see Chapter 10), it had long been recognized that some of the "species" are always tetrasporic and some are always sexual. Svedelius showed that these *Galaxaura* "species" are paired alternates in a diplohaplontic life history. The sporophyte and gametophyte generations, thus, proved to be heteromorphic (different in appearance) but not very markedly so. There is still, however, limited information as to which "species" constitute natural pairs.

Concurrently with the work of Svedelius in Sweden, the Feldmanns of Paris studied two other Nemalionalean genera, *Bonnemaisonia* and *Asparagopsis,* in which only carposporic plants were known. They germinated the carpospores and found that they grew into different kinds of plants that corresponded with members of the known genera *Hymenoclonium* and *Falkenbergia,* respectively. These latter genera, however, had previously been recognized in a different order! Subsequent work by Harder and Kock showed a similar relationship between carpospores of *Bonnemaisonia hamifera* and the small, filamentous plants previously known as *Trailliella intricata.* Japanese workers have established that these are gametophyte and sporophyte generations, respectively, of the same species. Magne has very recently shown that reduction division occurs at sporogenesis in the *Bonnemaisonia* life history. Thus, we have a triphasic, diplohaplont life history in which the sporophyte and gametophyte are extremely heteromorphic. This condition, and that of the less markedly heteromorphic *Galaxaura,* have led some authors recently to recognize a new order, Bonnemaisoniales, to contain these plants. Hardly had this been done, however, when Magne in 1961 discovered that carpospores of *Nemalion elminthoides* do not divide meiotically to grow directly into a new gametophyte plant, but give rise to small plantlets that are presumed to be tetrasporophytes. This calls for critical further investigation and review of the *Nemalion multifidum* life history that has been considered established as a type since 1919. Further, Chihara has pointed out (1962) that several different kinds of life cycles occur in the bonnemaisoniaceous assemblage. These emphasize that in the floridean red algae the relationship between kind of life history and classification is neither the simple nor the direct one supposed some decades ago.

A further area of life-history studies in the red algae, namely, that of *Porphyra,* has recently become of wide interest. The extensive cultivation in Japan of species of *Porphyra* make it one of the world's most used red algae, and one in which fuller knowledge of life history in relation to improved culture is of considerable economic importance. Drew in England and Kurogi in Japan demonstrated a decade ago that the well-known membranous *Porphyra* thallus is but one phase in the life history of the alga, and that a shell-boring, minutely filamentous stage occurs that for many years had been known under the name *Conchocelis rosea.* Although much work has been done in the past decade, and cultivation of *Porphyra* through use of *Conchocelis* has been put into practice, the full life history is still not completely worked out. Cytological evidences remain contradictory, and there seem to be a number of variations in the life histories within the genus. Thus, Kurogi has found four different kinds of "gametophyte" plants, some of which produce "neutral" spores that repeat the *Porphyra* stage, some that produce only carpospores that develop into the *"Conchocelis"* phase, and some that produce both kinds of spores (Figure 11-6).

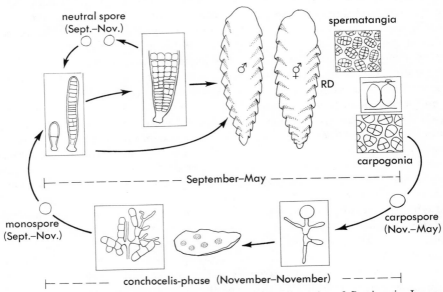

FIGURE 11-6. Diagrammatic life history of a cultivated species of *Porphyra* in Japan.

More recently, Drew has demonstrated that *Bangia fuscopurpurea,* another genus closely related to *Porphyra,* also produces an alternate *Conchocelis* phase in shells, but seems to do so only in certain geographic regions. Thus, in the British Isles, spores from *Bangia* always develop into free-living *Bangia* filaments, while plants from Naples, Italy, produce spores that form the *Conchocelis* phase.

As a result of these and other life-history studies that are rapidly being announced, Chapman and Chapman have formulated a classification of life histories in the algae that includes thirteen different categories for which representatives may already be recognized. They have adopted a revised terminology as follows: The three Svedelian cytological types (haplont, diplohaplont, and diplont) are classified according to morphological types, grouped first as to whether they are monobiontic (with only 1 kind of individual plant) or dibiontic (with two kinds of individuals). These are in turn broken down into monogenic, digenic, and trigenic types, depending upon the number of phases or generations in the life cycle. The digenic and trigenic types are further categorized as to the isomorphic or heteromorphic, dimorphic or trimorphic nature of their generations. Accordingly, *Codium*, in their terminology, is a monobiontic, monogenic diplont; *Gracilaria* and *Prasiola* are dibiontic, trigenic, dimorphic diplohaplonts. *Laminaria* is a dibiontic, digenic, heteromorphic diplohaplont.

Such categorization of the many variations of life history in the algae tends to obscure the salient features of the entire assemblage and has met considerable objection, although it does stimulate the search for new data that may further our understanding.

Firstly, as to these salient features, one should note that whereas many types of life history occur in the marine algae, the majority of benthic freshwater algae (which are, of course, Chlorophyta) are of one type — the haplont. In these a more or less extensive haploid vegetative stage is followed by a diploid, unicellular, resting stage (zygospore). This is a morphologically simple life history, but a specialized one closely dependent upon the environmental conditions of the habitat, which is generally subject to much greater periodic extremes than is the marine habitat.

Furthermore, despite the variety of kinds of life histories in the marine algae, we may recognize three common characteristics among these seaweeds, namely, the Laminariales, the Desmarestiales, and a large majority of the Florideophycidae, which are the most highly organized and specialized forms living today: 1) These are dimorphic algae; 2) The diploid phase is dominant; 3) The sequence of somatic phases is obligatory. In her masterly review of algal life histories, Drew has pointed out that each of these three characteristics should be considered as an important evolutionary achievement.

Dimorphy presents many fundamental evolutionary problems, for the diversity of somatic phases in the various types of life histories points to the probability of multiple origins in the different phyla, although for none of these do we yet have sufficient evidence. Nevertheless, we have now reached a point at which it may be desirable to classify separately the types of life history in these different major groups.

In considering the widespread dominance of the diplophase, to different degrees in different life histories, and in the highly developed Fucales even to the point of exclusion of the haplophase entirely, one is led to recognize evolutionary sequences in that direction. It seems evident that this dominance of the diplophase has been associated with evolutionary advance both in vegetative elaboration and in methods of reproduction.

An evolutionary development toward the obligatory sequence of haploid gametophyte and diploid sporophyte may also be recognized by considering various life histories, especially those of simpler algae. It may be seen as a progression: from conditions in which a haploid plant repeatedly reproduces itself by haploid spores without resorting to meiosis *(Ulothrix);* through stages in which a diploid plant produces both diploid spores and haploid spores (formed after meiosis) *(Ectocarpus);* and finally to the obligatory sequence in which the only spores are those produced after meiosis *(Laminaria).*

REFERENCES

Chapman, D. J., and V. J. Chapman. 1961. Life histories in the algae. *Ann. of Bot.,* n.s., 25: 547–561.

Chihara, M. 1962. Life cycle of bonnemaisoniaceous algae of Japan (2). *Sci. Rpts. Tokyo Kyoiku Daigaku, Sec.* B, 11: 27–53.

Drew, Kathleen M. 1955. Life histories in the algae, with special reference to the Chlorophyta, Phaeophyta and Rhodophyta. *Biol. Rev.,* 30: 343–390.

Fan, K. C. 1959. Studies on the life histories of marine algae, 1. *Codiolum petrocelidis* and *Spongomorpha coalita. Bull. Torrey Bot. Club,* 86: 1–12.

Feldmann, J. 1952. Les cycles de reproduction des algues et leurs rapports avec la phylogénie. *Rev. Cytol. et Biol. Veg.,* 13: 1–49.

Friedmann, I. 1959. Structure, life history and sex determination of *Prasiola stipitata* Suhr. *Ann. Bot.,* n.s., 6: 571–594.

Fritsch, F. E. 1935–1945. The structure and reproduction of the algae. Cambridge University Press. vol. 1 (1935), xvii + 791 pp.; vol. 2 (1945), xiv + 939 pp.

Harder, R. and W. Koch. 1949. Life history of *Bonnemaisonia hamifera (Trailliella intricata). Nature,* 163: 1060.

Kornmann, P. 1938. Zur Entwicklungsgeschichte von *Derbesia* und *Halicystis. Planta, Arch. für Wiss. Bot.,* 28: 464–470.

Magne, M. F. 1960. Sur le lieu de la meiose chez la *Bonnemaisonia asparagoides. Compt. Rend. Acad. Sci.,* 250; 2742–2744.

———————— 1961. Sur le cycle cytologique du *Nemalion helminthoides. Compt. Rend. Acad. Sci.,* 252: 157–159.

Papenfuss, G. F. 1955. Classification of the algae. In: *A century of progress in the natural sciences, 1853–1953.* San Francisco: Calif. Acad. Sci. pp. 115–125.

———————— 1957. Progress and outstanding achievements in phycology during the past fifty years. *Am. J. Bot.,* 44: 74–81.

Svedelius, N. 1931. Nuclear phases and alternation in the Rhodophyceae. *Bot. Centralbl.,* 48: 38–59.

———————— 1942. Zytologisch-Entwicklungsgeschichtliche Studien über *Galaxaura. . . . Nova Acta Reg. Soc. Sci. Upsaliensis* iv, 13(4): 1–154.

12

Calcareous Algae and Fossils

NEGLECT AND MISCONCEPTIONS

In the days of lace cuffs and powdered hair, the "collectors' cabinet" often displayed a diverse array of imperishable calcareous objects from worm tubes and mollusk shells to echinoderm tests and walrus tusks. Often arranged among bits of coral were branched or nodular stony calcareous structures, which, in the early classification of marine curiosities, were considered some kind of inorganic, stalactite-like material. Linnaeus considered them living and treated them as coral-like animal forms, as did many subsequent students of "zoophytes." Lamarck coined the name "nullipore" to distinguish these forms, without visible pores, from the porous corals, but it was not until 1837 that the stony crusts, pebbles, and branched nodules were finally recognized as plants. We now know them as members of the red algal family Corallinaceae and call them crustose corallines. Another group in the same family consists of forms with erect, free branches made flexible by the presence of noncalcified joints between the stony segments. These are the articulated corallines. Together they are the most prevalent of calcified marine plants (Table 3) and are so widely distributed that they form part of the marine flora of every maritime nation of the world.

In the glacial fjords of Norway or Greenland one finds thriving beds of nullipores. Crustose corallines cover wave-dashed rocks from Kamchatka to Chile, and from Newfoundland to Kerguelen. Delicate, flake-like forms live on the leaves of turtle grass in Cuba and on eel grass in Japan. The jointed corallines dwell no less successfully in the cold, clean tide-pools of Vancouver Island than beside sewer outfalls in southern California. The dainty janias are equally prominent in spongy algal turfs on the reef flats of East Africa and of Micronesia. Despite the ubiquity of these plants, they have been relatively little studied and remain among the least-known organisms of the sea.

Study of the coralline algae has been neglected by botanists for three principal reasons. The crustose forms are commonly bulky and weighty, and they can neither be pressed nor conveniently mounted and filed on herbarium sheets. The articulated forms, likewise, are ill adapted for herbarium filing, for

TABLE 3
Principal Genera of Living Calcareous Marine Algae

	approx. no. species	tropical	temperate	calcification heavy	light
CHLOROPHYTA					
Siphonales					
Halimeda	21	x		x	x
Penicillus	6	x			x
Rhipocephalus	2	x			x
Udotea	15	x			x
Tydemannia	2	x			x
Dasycladales					
Acetabularia	21	x			x
Bornetella	3	x			x
Cymopolia	2	x			x
Dasycladus	5	x			x
Halicoryne	2	x			x
Neomeris	10	x			x
PHAEOPHYTA					
Dictyotales					
Padina (most species)		x			x
RHODOPHYTA					
Nemalionales					
Liagora	60	x			x
Liagoropsis	1	x			x
Dermonema	2	x			x
Trichogloea	6	x			x
Trichogloeopsis	1	x			x
Actinotrichia	1	x			x
Galaxaura	"70"	x		x	x
Cryptonemiales					
Rhodopeltis	3	x	x	x	
Peyssonelia	35	x	x	x	x

TABLE 3
Principal Genera of Living Calcareous Marine Algae

	approx. no. species	tropical	temperate	calcification heavy	light
Archeolithothamnium	15	x		x	
Phymatolithon	2		x	x	
Clathromorphum	2		x	x	
Lithothamnium	100	x	x	x	
Mesophyllum	10	x		x	
Epilithon	5		x	x	
Metamastophora	5		x		x
Lithophyllum	100	x	x	x	
Tenarea	3		x	x	
Porolithon	15	x		x	
Crodelia	1		x	x	
Dermatolithon	15	x	x	x	
Hydrolithon	7	x		x	
Melobesia	25	x	x		x
Metagoniolithon	4	x		x	
Mastophora	3	x		x	x
Lithothrix	1		x	x	
Amphiroa	17	x	x	x	
Pachyarthron	1		x	x	
Cheilosporum	5	x	x	x	
Calliarthron	8		x	x	
Bossiella	8		x	x	
Corallina	25	x	x	x	
Jania	15	x	x	x	
Arthrocardia	8		x	x	
Duthiea	1		x	x	
Serraticardia	2		x	x	
Yamadaea	2		x	x	
Gigartinales					
Titanophora	6	x			x

(Coastal bracket labeled **Corallinaceae** grouping all genera from Archeolithothamnium through Yamadaea.)

they are exceedingly brittle and ordinarily break at each joint into a worthless pile of fragments unless treated with glycerine or housed with utmost protection. The examination of structural and reproductive characters is hindered by the need to decalcify and prepare sections of the resulting soft tissues by embedding procedures. The extra time required to circumvent the special problems of handling have been afforded by few investigators, and we find many marine algal floras omitting the corallines entirely. Most herbaria have meager representations of specimens. This general neglect has resulted in long delay in the recognition of the importance of coralline algae in certain natural phenomena, particularly in that most extraordinary of all marine biological phenomena — the tropical "coral" atoll (Figure 12-1).

FIGURE 12-1. Part of an atoll in the Marshall Islands. The elliptical reef is seen dotted with small vegetated islets and there is a passage on the far side into the lagoon. Note the heavy surf on the seaward reef margins and the absence of surf in the lagoon. The porolithon ridge is clearly visible in the white surf in the lower right-hand portion of the picture.

During the last century a number of naturalists made visits to the coral reefs of the Indo-Pacific region and, from their observations, developed theories of atoll origin and growth. Charles Darwin, James G. Dana, Sir John Murray, Reginald A. Daly, and others interpreted the atoll from a geological or zoological standpoint and failed to recognize fully the importance of calcareous algae as controllers of reef development. It was not until Sir Edgeworth David's South Pacific Expedition of 1896–1898 that evidence was obtained to establish the plants in this relationship. Since then only an occasional marine botanist (notably Marshall A. Howe and W. A. Setchell) has written on the subject and expanded the knowledge of the role algae play in atoll formation. Accordingly, some long-standing misconceptions are still prevalent.

Some of the pertinent facts are these:

1) Nullipores have been found to be among the principal components of atoll reefs in a great majority of cases. In some instances, they are almost the only visible components, to the virtual exclusion of coral animals.

2) The principal cementing agent in the reefs is the nullipore.

3) Calcareous algae have been found actively growing at depths of 600 feet.

4) The seaward margins of actively growing atoll reefs are often covered by a rough pavement-like or porous growth of *Porolithon,* a kind of nullipore

(Figure 12-2) that forms a slightly elevated ridge known as the lithothamnium ridge, or more correctly, the porolithon ridge (Figure 12-1; 12-3).

5)   Borings to depths of several thousand feet indicate the consistent presence of great quantities of nullipore material throughout the fossil reefs.

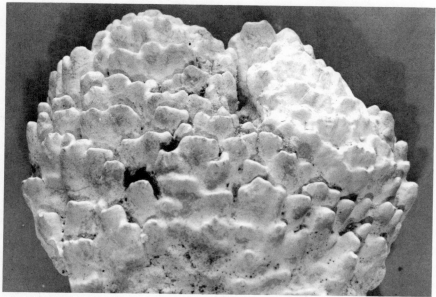

FIGURE 12–2. *Porolithon crasspedium,* a typical atoll reef alga in the tropical Pacific (reprinted from *Plants of Bikini* by W. R. Taylor, by permission of the University of Michigan Press, copyright 1950).

THE ATOLL

The most striking first impression of many atolls is of their enormous size. The vast lagoons of Kwajalein and Eniwetok stretch for 30 to 70 miles and are surrounded by comparatively minute dots and lines of vegetation-clad islets. But there are also small atolls such as Palmyra and Clipperton, only a few miles long or less, and some that still remain as reefs with scarcely any portion exposed except at low tide. All of these imply and exhibit growth. In fact, an atoll's development can be considered like that of a dynamic, living organism. It results from a vastly complex association of living things, all dwelling together in a marvelous balance, each plant and animal contributing to the life and growth of the whole atoll and to the delicate balance maintained between construction and destruction.

Although the origins of discrete, atoll-forming communities of plants and animals are related to the slow processes of sea-floor emergence and subsidence and to changing sea level, a small, still-submerged reef, such as may be found in the Pacific on a slightly underwater sea mount, can be taken as a point of departure in considering the process of atoll maturation.

FIGURE 12–3. Two views of a porolithon ridge on an atoll in the Marshall Islands. The ridge is cleft here by a narrow channel through which surfy water is forced. The favorable growth of the nullipores under these conditions is clearly evident (reprinted from *Plants of Bikini* by W. R. Taylor, by permission of the University of Michigan Press, copyright 1950).

When first such a small reef reaches and breaks the surface, a difference comes into effect with regard to optima for the growth of corals and nullipores under the influence of surf. The rigid, branched, brittle corals tend to break and fragment under severe surf action, while the massive, reef-forming nullipores (mainly species of *Porolithon*) are unaffected by the pounding. In fact, the stronger the surf, the better they grow (Figure 12-3), for one of the principal factors limiting their growth is the availability of oxygen for dark-hour respiration when photosynthetic pigments are inactive.

Accordingly, on the barely emergent reef the first organisms to grow above the water surface and to create surf also initiate conditions that tend to favor the growth of nullipores and to reduce the upward growth of coral. Here begins the formation of an atoll from a reef, for the nullipores grow into the breaking surf, developing upward and outward to form a rim slightly above sea level. This rim, which breaks the impact of the waves on all sides, provides a relative calm over the inner part of the reef. Within this slightly confined area, carbonic acid, resulting from the solution of respiratory carbon dioxide produced by the plants and animals living there, tends to dissolve the solid calcareous materials. As this solution exceeds the deposition of sediment and of new, calcified plant and animal bodies, and as the sea level rises or the sea floor subsides, a lagoon is formed whose depth commonly becomes stabilized at about 200 to 300 feet in accord with an equilibrium of these several factors.

The rate of outward growth of the reef margin reflects differences in surf and in available growth nutrients due to prevailing wind and currents. As a result, the young, dynamic atoll usually takes on a somewhat elliptical shape that may be modified in time to asymmetry.

The reef margins are extended seaward in three ways: by the growth and cementing action of the nullipores; by the often profuse growth of corals on the outer front, or face, of the reef below the surf zone; and by the infinitely slow build-up of a prodigious talus slope of nullipore and coral fragments to the abyssal sea floor. Whenever the nullipore reef ridge dissolves down to a level that permits the sea waves to pour in over it, the increased supply of oxygen for nighttime respiration evidently encourages the growth of pavement algae *(Porolithon)* by which it may be built up again.

The seaward advance of the nullipore ridge, whose height above sea level is controlled by desiccation, leaves behind it a reef flat that stretches between the ridge and the central lagoon. From the reef margins and talus slope, storms cast upon this reef flat calcareous fragments of all sizes.

Until a pile of sand and rubble appears on the reef flat, all rain water is dissipated into the open sea. With sufficient material to confine it, however, the fresh water stays in the sand at sea level, floating on the salt water below it, and mixing only very slowly. As this lens of fresh water forms in the sand, seeds carried to the islet by wind and water sprout and penetrate to the water supply, and the island vegetation comes into being. Sea birds come, feeding on the fish of reefs and lagoon, roosting and nesting in the vegetation and converting the animal life of the sea into fertilizer for the land. Gradually a humus forms on what at first was only barren sand and beach rock.

Although calcareous red algae dominate the seaward margins of the atoll, calcareous Chlorophyta are characteristically common to the lagoons. The genus *Halimeda* is usually quite abundantly represented and contributes great quantities of its segments to the sandy lagoon deposits (Figure 12-4). These become compacted over antecedent reef-flat and talus-slope materials to provide, with subsidence of the sea floor, the enormously thick fossil strata such as were first revealed by drilling at Funafuti Atoll in 1898.

FOSSIL ALGAE

Such fossil remains of calcareous algae are now well known and admit, from the preservation of their structure and reproductive features, sometimes in extraordinary detail, remarkably certain identification with various assemblages of recent forms. Thus, a considerable array of fossil calcareous red and green algae are reliably recorded.

The study of fossil algae is still quite young and is being undertaken by few investigators. Until 1913 it had not received any appreciable attention by geologists or paleobotanists. Although some Dasycladaceae and Solenoporaceae had been described in the late nineteenth century, they were to a large extent misidentified with various animal and plant groups before being recognized as algae. Rothpletz, working from 1891 to 1913, may be considered the most important pioneer in the field. Madame Lemoine, who continues her work today in France, was the trail blazer in studies of fossil coralline algae with her classic work in 1911. Pia's monograph of fossil verticillate, siphonous algae in 1920 has provided the illustrations of fossil algae most widely used in textbooks. J. Harlan Johnson (1961) has brought together much of our knowledge of fossil calcareous algae.

Johnson considers the calcareous algae as comprising the oldest fossils known, of extending all the way from Precambrian to Recent, and of being of much more geological importance than is generally recognized. Whereas the marine coralline red algae, which first appear in the late Mesozoic era are the most important rock builders today, a similar, extinct red algal group, the Solenoporaceae, occupied this position during the Paleozoic and most of the Mesozoic. The extinct red algal family Gymnocodiaceae had widespread and abundant rock-forming members during Permian times in Europe and Asia.

The most important fossil green algae are all marine forms assignable to the extant families Codiaceae and Dasycladaceae. They appear from the Cambrian to the present, but by Mississippian times began frequently to occur in sufficient abundance to be rock builders. By the Permian they were widely important in the formation of bedded limestones and reefs, and their abundance evidently increased through the Jurassic and declined in the Cretaceous. Many of the Dasycladaceae seem to have a time range limited to about the length of a geological period and to hold considerable promise as indicator fossils.

FIGURE 12–4. Two forms of *Halimeda* characteristic of atoll lagoons. Note the stony segments that contribute large quantities of calcareous sand to the lagoon deposits. Numerous species of *Halimeda* occur throughout the tropical world (reprinted from *Plants of Bikini* by W. R. Taylor, by permission of the University of Michigan Press, copyright 1950).

Apart from the calcareous algae, a prominent fossil record of the silicious diatoms has been investigated, to a considerable extent due to the commercial development of deposits of diatomaceous earth. In the vicinity of Lompoc, California, marine Tertiary strata of this material are over 1000 feet thick and are contributing enormous tonnages to industrial production of filtering and scouring compounds. The silicious frustule of the diatom is commonly so well preserved that the fine structure can be studied in detail. Some seventy extinct genera of diatoms have been described, nearly one-third of the total for the group. The occurrence of diatoms is well established for the Jurassic, but records for earlier periods are questioned by some workers. They were abundant by the late Cretaceous, and during this period many genera occurred that have retained their identity down to the present.

Fossil algae other than these calcareous and silicious forms, that is, the remains of fleshy types, present especial problems. In most cases it is impossible to determine anything of the nature of the cell contents or of reproductive characteristics by which assignment to any division or class can be admitted. Many workers who have attempted to deal with fossil algae evidently have been unfamiliar with the parallel morphological evolution in various algal divisions, and have made assignments on untenable grounds. Accordingly, a large body of

FIGURE 12–5. A fossil Miocene alga of the Cystoseiraceae from San Juan Capistrano, California.

unreliable information exists with regard to the systematic position of fossil examples of many of the simpler types of algae, and of larger fleshy forms. In addition there are numerous form genera supposed by some to represent algal remains, but whose organic origin is even doubted by others.

Although fleshy brown, red, and green algae are poorly represented in the literature of paleobotany, several forms have been known since the early nineteenth century. In recent years large numbers of them have been found in Miocene diatomite deposits in southern California, having been preserved quite perfectly under anaerobic conditions in deep marine basins. Ten genera and 22 species of these have been described by Parker and Dawson (1965); of these, 3 genera and 13 species were referred confidently to the Cystoseiraceae (Figure 12-5). In the same paper *Julescraneia grandicornis* (the largest brown-algal fossil known) was recognized as a member of the Lessoniaceae, intermediate between *Pelagophycus* and *Nereocystis*. These Miocene deposits continue to offer opportunity for the study of excellent preserved material of an elaborate benthic flora that may lead to significant evolutionary interpretations.

REFERENCES

Dawson, E. Y. 1963. Rim of the reef. *Smithsonian Rpt. for 1962:* 365–373.

Johnson, J. H. 1961. Limestone building algae and algal limestones. Boulder: Colorado School of Mines. 297 pp.

Parker, B. C., and E. Y. Dawson. 1965. Non-calcareous marine algae from California Miocene deposits. Nova Hedwigia 10: 273–295.

Pia, J. 1920. Die Siphoneae Verticillatae vom Karbon bis zur Kreide. Wien: *Abh. Zool.-Botan. Gesell.* 11(2): 1–236.

Taylor, W. R. 1950. Plants of Bikini.... University of Michigan Press. xv + 227 pp.

13

Marine Algal Physiology

Marine algal physiology had its beginning in the inquisitive minds of such observers as England's Dawson Turner, who before 1800 puzzled over the peculiar adaptations to diverse habitats that he noted among seashore algae of Britain, and conducted simple experiments with living plants in an effort to understand their functions. Kützing, in 1843, was the first to review seaweed physiology as a subject of scientific investigation, and at that time introduced the study of algal masking pigments by extracting what he called "phykokyan" and "phykoerythrin" from blue-green and red algae. Interest in these varicolored pigments led to the classical studies of Engelmann, who from 1882 to 1884 correlated the absorption spectra of various algae with oxygen production at different wavelengths in the visible spectrum, and introduced evidence that the masking pigments as well as chlorophyll are active light absorbers for photosynthesis. He ingeniously used motile, aerotactic bacteria as oxygen indicators. His work has led in turn to vastly expanded investigations of pigment analysis and photosynthesis in the algae, some of which have had far-reaching consequences.

Although a number of marine algae have been investigated specifically or incidentally over the years from various physiological points of view, a few have become famous as physiological subjects. The large-celled, multinucleate forms, *Valonia* and *Halicystis*, with their massive vacuoles, have been widely used since 1925 in studies of permeability, ion accumulation, and bioelectric phenomena. Since 1931 the unicellular, uninucleate green alga *Acetabularia* has become so well-established a subject of studies of nuclear-cytoplasmic interactions that it is familiar to most students of elementary biology. The establishment in the 1920s of techniques for obtaining bacteria-free cultures of unicellular algae has made these organisms widely useful to physiologists of many special disciplines. Extensive algal culture collections are being maintained in several institutions. Although earlier experimental successes were with fresh-water forms such as *Chlorella,* increasing success in the culture of such marine unicells as the brine flagellate, *Dunaliella,* is now making possible their extensive utilization as experimental subjects.

The physiology of an alga is essentially the sum of biophysical and biochemical processes developed as evolutionary adaptive responses to its environment. Cell and thallus morphologies are expressions of these processes that cannot be separated from the ecological factors that influence them. Thus, every environmental factor and every interrelationship elicits physiologic responses that vary with the degree of stress imposed. In the marine environment, some of these factors and interrelationships are of exceptional interest, and are the focus of attention of plant physiologists working with marine algae. The most widely investigated of these are light and photosynthesis.

LIGHT RELATIONSHIPS

In a consideration of any photoreaction, the light receptor is fundamental. In the marine algae these are the red, yellow, green, and blue pigments, which combine to provide a particularly striking diversity of color. Since Kützing first provided names for some of the special ones more than a century ago, over 40 different pigments have been described and analyzed as occurring in the algae.

It was long ago recognized that there was some correlation between the color of a seaweed and its morphology. Lamouroux devised in 1813 the first color-based classification of marine algae, and this was modified by Harvey in 1836 to arrange the three major benthic algal groups in much the same way as they are known today: the green algae, the brown algae, the red algae. Without realizing it, these early systematists introduced a biochemical character into the classification of algae, and this has proved in more recent times to be one of profound significance.

The pigments of algae are now recognized under three major categories: the chlorophylls, the carotenoids (carotenes and xanthophylls), and the phycobilins. A gradual correlation of pigment analyses with systematics based upon morphology and reproduction has demonstrated that each algal phylum contains special pigments or mixtures of pigments not found in the others (Table 4). Thus, the Rhodophyta contain the phycobilin, r-phycoerythrin, and the xanthophyll, lutein, both of which are absent in the Phaeophyta, while the latter contains a predominance of β-carotene and the xanthophyll, fucoxanthin. Fucoxanthin is absent and β-carotene is of minor occurrence in Rhodophyta.

TABLE 4

Distribution of Chlorophylls, Biliproteins, and Carotenoids among Principal Algal Groups with Marine Representatives

		Rhodophyta	Cyanophyta	Pyrrophyta	Phaeophyta	other Chrysophyta	Bacillariophyceae	Xanthophyta	Euglenophyta	other Chlorophyta	Siphonales
Chlorophylls	a	+	+	+	+	+	+	+	+	+	+
	b	−	−	−	−	−	−	−	+	+	+
	c	−	−	+	+	?	+	−	−	−	−
	d	±	−	−	−	?	−	−	−	−	−
	e	−	−	−	−	?	−	−	−	−	−
Biliproteins (phycobilins)	Phycocyanin	+	+	−	−	−	−	−	−		
	Phycoerythrin	+	+	−	−	−	−	−	−		
Carotenes	α-Carotene	±				±	±			±	±
	β-Carotene	+	+	+	+	+	+	+	+	+	+
	ε-Carotene						+				
Xanthophylls	Aphanicin		+								
	Aphanizophyll		+								
	Astaxanthin								+	+	
	Diadinoxanthin			+			+				
	Diatoxanthin						+				
	Dinoxanthin			+							
	Flavicin		+								
	Flavoxanthin					+					
	Fucoxanthin				+	+	+				
	Lutein	+	±		+	+			+	+	+
	Myxoxanthin		+								
	Myxoxanthophyll		+								
	Neoxanthin								+	+	+
	Oscilloxanthin		+								
	Peridinin			+							
	Siphonein										+
	Siphonoxanthin										+
	Taraxanthin	+									
	Violaxanthin				+					+	+
	Zeaxanthin	±	+							+	+

Similarly, other major groups are fundamentally distinguished by pigment chemistry (as well as by differences in food reserves and flagellation of reproductive cells). Although the Rhodophyta and the Cyanophyta are the only groups of benthic algae containing phycobilins, the pigments of the two are distinct, and there are other differences so basic that these plants are not generally recognized as showing direct phylogenetic connection. Within the Chrysophyta, recent pigment analyses have suggested biochemical distinction of four separate phyla. Such major changes in algal classification, however, are not yet acceptable to all systematists and have prompted fresh assaults on details of submicroscopic structure and of reproduction in these enigmatic organisms.

Apart from questions of phylogeny and classification, to which pigment studies are making their contributions, physiologists since Engelmann have continued their interest in the photosynthetic role of the accessory, or masking pigments of marine algae. Two approaches have been used in attempts to determine which pigments are active in photosynthesis and the extent of their activity: 1) efficiency measurements, in which light absorption and photosynthesis are measured quantitatively; 2) action-spectrum determinations, in which relative rates of photosynthesis under equal incident-light intensities are obtained and correlated with cell or thallus absorption.

Much of our knowledge of the chlorophylls is based upon studies of these pigments after extraction from the living plant in organic solvents. It has been known for some years, however, that the molecular state of these dissolved chlorophylls is not the same as that of functional chlorophylls, as evidenced by the fact that extraction results in a marked downward shift of 10 to 20mμ in the position of the absorption maxima. Increasing attention is, therefore, being given to the *in vivo* properties of the chlorophylls in an effort to understand the nature of the early photochemical steps in photosynthesis. Careful studies of the absorption spectra and photosynthetic properties of intact algae and of broken algal cells in suspension have been carried out on a number of fresh-water forms and such marine algal genera as *Ulva, Gigartina, Iridaea, Porphyra, Smithora,* and *Callithamnion.* From these data it has been concluded that there are *in vivo* at least two forms of chlorophyll *a*, a monomer and a dimer of different photosynthetic excitability, and that these occur together in varying proportions in each of the plants studied.

Wherever photosynthesis occurs in algae (as well as in higher plants) it is always associated with the presence of chlorophyll *a*, although chlorophylls *b,c,d,* or *e* may also be present. It is manifestly evident from many experiments of the types mentioned above, however, that energy absorbed by other (so-called accessory) pigments can be used as effectively in photosynthesis as that absorbed by chlorophyll. It has now been demonstrated with fluorescence experiments that energy absorbed by such pigments is actually transferred to chlorophyll *a*.

When Haxo and Blinks in 1950 determined action spectra of photosynthesis in several benthic algae and compared them with the absorption spectra of intact thalli, an interesting red algal anomaly became evident. In green *Ulva* and brown *Coilodesme* the action spectra and absorption spectra were for the most part closely parallel (Figures 13-1; 13-2). Similar sets of curves for several Rhodophyta, however, differed markedly, showing maximum photosynthesis rates in the spectral regions absorbed by phycobilins, but little activity in the regions of maximum chlorophyll absorption (Figure 13-3). They concluded that in red algae chlorophyll *a* plays only a minor role as a primary light absorber in photosynthesis, but that the phycobilins are of major importance in this respect. Subsequent extensions of these studies, however, have clarified this apparent anomaly, and it is now generally held that although these accessory pigments are highly efficient absorbers for photosynthesis, their participation in the process is effected by transfer of energy to the active form of the uniquely photocatalytic chlorophyll *a*.

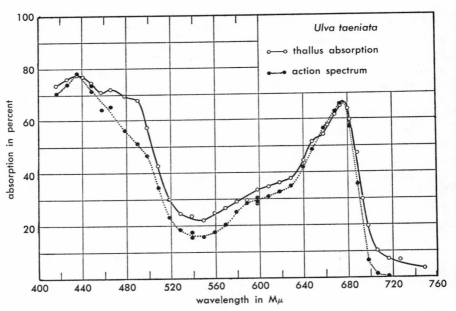

FIGURE 13-1. Absorption and action spectra of the green alga *Ulva taeniata* (after Haxo & Blinks).

A great deal of attention is now being focused on photosynthetic enhancement, or the "Emerson Effect." This is observed as an increased photosynthetic efficiency when one or more accessory pigments are activated in combination with chlorophyll *a*, compared with the activation of these pigments separately. Many of the marine algae, in which the several pigments show overlapping absorption bands, exhibit this phenomenon.

The functional significance of these accessory pigments is recognizable among those benthic algae whose descending sequence of occurrence into deeper waters (green, brown, and red algae, respectively) shows a correlation with the quality of ambient light. Thus, the red pigments of Rhodophyta of deeper waters, where green, blue and violet light prevails, seem specially adapted for its efficient absorption. On the other hand, there are many exceptions to be investigated, for a number of green algae are found at unexpectedly great depths *(Caulerpa),* and some Rhodophyta of distinctly red color *(Opuntiella)* are found in shallow or intertidal waters.

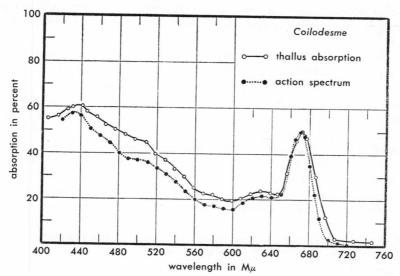

FIGURE 13–2. Absorption and action spectra of the brown alga *Coilodesme californica* (after Haxo & Blinks).

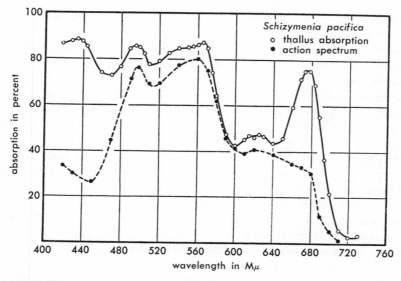

FIGURE 13–3. Absorption and action spectra of the red alga *Schizymenia pacifica* (after Haxo & Blinks).

The zonation of algae of shallow waters and those of sea caves points to the importance of light *intensity* as well as *quality*. Some sea-cave dwellers can grow under daylight intensities as low as 5 lux, while most intertidal algae can survive long exposure to direct sunlight (100,000 lux). Algae characteristic of shaded lower-littoral situations or of the sublittoral, however, show morphological damage or death even after short exposures to high light intensity, particularly if it is of the shorter wavelengths below 550mμ (*Polyneura, Callophyllis, Antithamnion, Microcladia*).

Biebl has pointed out an intriguing light problem in that various marine algae are sensitive to short-wave ultraviolet light (below 320 mμ) but that this sensitivity shows no regular correlation with their color or habitat.

New fields of investigation in the light relationships of benthic algae have opened up with the improvement of marine laboratory facilities for the culture of macroscopic plants. One of these is the study of photoperiodicity. Powell, at Friday Harbor, Washington, has studied *Constantinea rosa-marina* throughout the year, both in laboratory culture and by Scuba observations in its natural habitat at depths of 4 to 14 meters in Puget Sound. This plant shows annual development of new photosynthetic blades which are sloughed off after release of reproductive bodies at the end of a season of growth. He has found that growth of a new blade is normally initiated by short day-length in October, but that this growth can be suppressed indefinitely in the laboratory by providing continuous light. On the other hand, new vegetative development can be initiated in these suppressed plants by subjecting them to a daily 14-hour dark period (10-hour day).

Rhythmic light relationships to sporulation and gametogenesis in benthic algae are yet to be investigated adequately and will be of special interest in natural areas in which seawater temperatures show little annual variation. Several studies have been made on lunar or tidal rhythms, however, especially with regard to release of spores and gametes in various brown and green algae (*Sargassum, Nemoderma, Dictyota, Monostroma, Ulva, Halicystis*). *Ulva lobata*, in California, shows a 14-day periodicity correlated with low tides, particularly the spring tides. Several of the plants studied retain lunar periodicity in the laboratory. A correlation with increased light intensity at low water is suggested by *Monostroma*, in which infratidal as well as intertidal plants release swarmers according to a lunar-day periodicity.

It is evident that the deeper waters of many areas are subject to great variations in light intensity from seasonal differences in solar radiation, in turbidity and overshadowing. The algae of these waters apparently endure long periods during which the light intensity is below the compensation level. A partial explanation of this sustaining power may be found in their reserve-food storage products. It has been observed in many red algae of deep waters that the stipe appears whitish and is densely packed with starch. This floridean starch may sometimes occur in the blade, as in *Constantinea*, which has concentrations higher than for the starch in potato tubers. Such reserves are not confined to deep-growing algae, however, and the conditions of their utilization evidently vary widely.

Floridean starch, discovered by Kützing in 1843, is only one of numerous unusual reserve substances of marine algae that have since attracted the attention of algal biochemists. Apart from a number of kinds of algal starches, are the polysaccharides known as 1:3-linked glucans of which the ubiquitous laminarin of brown algae has long been studied with regard to its concentration according to such factors as season, depth, current, and nutrient availability. A wide seasonal variation in laminarin content has been measured in *Laminaria* and *Eisenia,* evidently linked with metabolic activity. Thus, a Scottish *Laminaria* blade may contain a peak content of laminarin at the end of the growing season in late Fall (10 to 20 percent of dry weight) and a declining content to zero during January through March.

The study of Arctic and Antarctic algae, which are subjected to long winter periods of darkness or of illumination below the compensation point, is of special interest. It has generally been accepted that these photosynthetic plants are sustained during the times of low light by respiration of storage products. In intertidal *Fucus,* for example, an adaptation for survival by efficient use and conservation of reserve foods has been shown. When kept in darkness for long periods, the respiratory rate shows a steady decrease until, after 5 months, it may be only 25 percent of the initial rate. Wilce, however, studying the occurrence and seasonal growth of deep-water brown algae in the Arctic has recently reported many of these plants growing at such great depths that only for a very brief time in summer are they photosynthesizing at a rate above the compensation level. Several of his observations suggest strongly that these plants, to a large extent, are living heterotrophically: 1) abundant food reserves are present; 2) juvenile plants are in growth; 3) adult plants show production of reproductive structures — all of this *before* the appearance of new light after the dark winter. Presumably, a source of dissolved organic material is present in these very cold waters, derived from the sub-ice and summer diatom blooms of the region.

One further type of physiological response to light, and one little investigated in marine algae, is that involving reactions to the direction of incident light. This may be a phototactic response, as is observed in movements of positively phototactic zoospores and gametes of *Ectocarpus* and the negatively phototactic zoospores and spermatozoids of *Chorda* and *Fucus,* respectively. Or it may be a phototropic response, as in the initiation of polarity in the germlings of Fucales and Dictyotales by the formation of a first crosswall at right angles to the direction of incident light (or in the plane of polarized light).

A few investigations of phototaxis have been made on unicellular marine plants, mainly with regard for the photoreceptive pigment involved. One of the earliest of these was a study in 1932 of the response of *Dunaliella* to different wavelengths of light. More recently, action spectra obtained for several dinoflagellates *(Gonyaulax, Peridinium,* and *Prorocentrum)* have been interpreted as indicating that the photoreceptor is a carotenoprotein. (It is now established that the eyespot of motile algae is not a photoreceptor.) Current studies are being made on the high-tidepool flagellate *Platymonas subcordiformis,* which shows phototaxis varying with light intensity, light quality, and the concentration of the cations Ca, Mg, and K. That negative phototaxis in this alga can be reversed by the action of the specific metabolic inhibitor 2,4-dinitrophenol, has provided indirect evidence that flagellar activity may be dependent upon high-energy phosphorylation.

TEMPERATURE RELATIONSHIPS

It has long been observed that intertidal marine algae tolerate extremes of temperature variation during exposure. *Fucus vesiculosis* survives temperatures of − 40°C. for many months in Arctic regions, while *Bangia fuscopurpurea* may remain viable on dry rocks insolated to 40°C. In recent years a number of experiments have been conducted to determine the various temperature sensitivities of seaweeds. Marked differences have been found in thermal tolerance of intertidal as well as infratidal algae in different geographic areas.

It is now evident that resistance to frost and to high temperature is correlated with resistance to desiccation. Thus, *Bangia* can survive 24 hours of subjection to 42°C at a relative humidity of 17.2 percent, but cannot tolerate even 35°C for such a period in seawater. Similarly, freezing results in physical abstraction of water from the protoplast and increases its resistance to low temperature.

As might be expected, infratidal algae have proved to be far more temperature sensitive than intertidal ones. None of 43 species tested at Naples, Italy, and Roscoff, France, survived freezing. (Their upper limits were mostly at about 27°C.) Some, however, survived near-freezing, low temperatures of − 2°C but could not survive 27°; while others tolerated 27° but were killed at 5°C. These investigations are providing a new tool in phytogeography for the interpretation of past migrations of cold-sensitive and heat-sensitive floras into new areas.

Other experiments are being devised to investigate in the algae the nature of reaction to the stress of marked temperature change. In a group of benthic algae of the Baltic Sea, photosynthesis was measured after they had been subjected to 3 hours of temperature shock by an 18°C increase. They showed a marked depression in photosynthesis, far below the compensation point, that lasted for many days. That such depression is due to the effect of temperature on various fundamental metabolic processes is evident from recent correlative research on other types of algae. Thus, temperature is known to have an important influence on the rate of uptake and distribution of carbon assimilated in photosynthesis. In certain blue-green algae, both low and high temperatures were found to impose a marked depression on carbon assimilation, but an even greater depressive effect on nitrogen assimilation. Measurements of respiration in such seaweeds as *Plocamium, Delesseria,* and *Fucus* show rapid increases when the temperature rises to the 20 to 30°C range. From these, the lethal effect of high temperature is seen to be due at least partly to the fast depletion of reserve foods and to an increase in respiration so that much more light is required to allow photosynthesis to keep up with respiration. Thus, the light compensation point for certain algae at 10°C. may be 250 to 300 lux, while at 16°C it rises to 350 to 400 lux. This suggests how in cold seas, even with low light intensity, net photosynthesis may be high.

Apart from such direct effects of temperature on metabolism, are the indirect effects on the seawater medium already alluded to in Chapter 1. The principal of these are the influences of temperature on the solubility of CO_2 for photosynthesis and of O_2 for respiration. In the case of O_2, the solubility coefficient is reduced by increased temperature. On the other hand, CO_2 levels in seawater increase with increasing temperature and are generally higher in the tropics than at high latitudes.

Yentsch has stated that the growth of marine phytoplankton is probably never seriously arrested by the lack of inorganic carbon. This is probably true also for a large number of benthic algae, especially under conditions of high calcium carbonate presence in which the dissociation of bicarbonate allows constant replenishment of CO_2 as it is removed ($CO_2 + H_2O \leftrightarrows H_2CO_3 \leftrightarrows H + HCO_3^- \leftrightarrows H + CO_3$). Nevertheless, Tseng has found that natural seawater (at least in tank culture at La Jolla, California) does not always provide a sufficient amount of carbon dioxide to saturate the seaweed enzyme system for photosynthesis (as in the benthic alga *Gelidium cartilagineum*). His work suggests that the availability of free CO_2 in the water medium, in response to temperature (and pH), may be limiting to photosynthesis.

Available oxygen for respiration may be more critical, for seawater is usually saturated only in areas of intense agitation. That increased temperature not only reduces the solubility of O_2 but also increases the rate of respiration, suggests a further explanation for the occurrence of most larger marine algae in areas of low temperature and a high degree of oxygen saturation.

Some influences of temperature on reproduction have been alluded to in Chapter 1. It is widely recognized that in temperate regions marine algae commonly mature to fertile condition during the warmer seasons of the year. Setchell's observations pointed to the narrower temperature range that many of these plants use for effective reproduction rather than for vegetative development, but the nature of the limits imposed have been little investigated experimentally.

RESPONSES TO OSMOTIC CHANGES

One of the most remarkable characteristics of an intertidal area, especially along an arid coast, is the ability of certain algae to survive extreme desiccation during long exposure (Figure 13-4). A number of plants have now been tested experimentally for this capacity. The high intertidal *Bangia fuscopurpurea* and *Urospora penicilliformis* can remain alive after 21 days of exposure to air drying at room temperature. On the other hand, algae characteristic of infra-

FIGURE 13–4. *Endocladia muricata* on a bare rock, subject to desiccation during full exposure to the sun for 6 hours or more between tides in southern California.

tidal habitats rarely survive even an hour of such exposure. Intertidal algae often show a relationship between resistance to exposure and the moisture content of the air. *Porphyra perforata*, for example, will survive 14 hours of exposure at 60 percent relative humidity, but not at 48 percent. *Ulva rigida*, from the same intertidal locality, tolerates 14 hours at 90 percent relative humidity, but dies at 83.9 percent. Some of the intertidal forms, such as *Fucus* and *Pelvetia*, not only survive extensive exposure, but require it, for they will succumb after short periods of constant submergence, evidently from oxygen deficiency during darkness.

That such differences in tolerances are not determined merely by the habitat, but are genetically controlled, has been indicated by photosynthesis experiments with three species of *Fucus* from successive intertidal levels. Each of these was air-dried for 5 hours and the photosynthetic efficiency subsequently measured and compared with controls. *Fucus platycarpus*, from the highest level, retained 97 percent efficiency; *F. vesiculosus* and *F. serratus,* from successively lower levels to near low water mark, retained only 72 percent and 42 percent, respectively, and took several hours to recover.

The ability to withstand drying is physiologically equivalent to an ability to withstand changes in the concentration of the seawater. Such changes are commonplace in the intertidal zone, and in shallow waters subject to fluctuation of a strong halocline, abrupt increases in salinity may occur during ebb tide due to evaporation; or, decreases may occur, instead, as a result of rainfall. Biebl has found that most intertidal algae can tolerate concentration ranges of 0.1 to 3.0 times that of seawater, and some can tolerate both distilled water and salinities up to 136°/₀₀ for 24 hours. Infratidal algae, however, have a narrow range of tolerance between 0.5 and 1.5 times the concentration of seawater. He has indicated several means by which intertidal red algae avoid plasmolytic damage in hypertonic concentrations of seawater: 1) possession of small cells with dense contents and cell walls that swell and contract in harmony with the expansion or shrinkage of the cell contents as water is taken in or withdrawn; 2) possession of so high an intracellular osmotic value that harmful plasmolysis cannot occur; 3) survival by unknown mechanism of periods of plasmolysis without possession of an especially high internal osmotic value; 4) possession of both a high internal osmotic value and great tolerance to plasmolysis. In addition, some intertidal forms (*Pylaiella* and *Elachista*) are shown to have an osmoregulatory mechanism for accumulating salts against a diffusion gradient, thereby either preventing plasmolysis or reversing it.

RESPONSES TO pH

Although most algae in the sea are bathed in a neutral or slightly alkaline medium (*p*H 7.5–8.4), those occurring in places that become tide pools at low water may be subjected to considerable variation in *p*H due to their own photosynthesis. Thus, the photosynthetic abstraction of CO_2 from bicarbonates in such confined bodies of water may cause a rise in *p*H to 9 or 10. At this level, however, some plants, such as *Ulva,* may still be unharmed. Of a wide variety of marine algae tested for resistance to different *p*H values, most are found able to survive 1 to 3 days or more within the 6.8 to 9.6 *p*H range.

The physiological effects of *p*H have been little investigated in the marine algae, although in a few fresh-water forms variation in *p*H is known to affect the optimum respiratory rate as well as the rate of uptake of carbon in photosynthesis.

The internal acidity of marine algal cells has been studied more extensively. Aqueous extracts of algal tissues have shown a somewhat acid condition to prevail without correlation with color or tissue character: 6.6–6.8 for *Antithamnion* and *Sphacelaria;* 5.0–5.2 for *Dictyosiphon* and *Codium;* 4.0–4.2 for *Polysiphonia* and *Odonthalia.*

The aseptate, multinucleate cells of *Halicystis* and *Valonia* are so large that clear vacuolar sap can be withdrawn directly into a tube containing a *p*H indicator. Accurate *p*H values have been obtained in this way for cell sap of *Valonia* (*p*H 6.0) and *Halicystis* (*p*H 5.1).

Of particular interest in this respect is the notoriously acid brown seaweed, *Desmarestia*. Marine algal collectors who encounter this plant quickly learn of its injurious and discoloring effect on other specimens with which it is brought into contact. When it is crushed or broken its acid is damaging even to itself and causes discoloration. Extracts of many different *Desmarestia* species have been tested for *p*H and found to give values of 1.8, 1.1, or even 0.78. Eppley and Bovell recently succeeded in locating the acid in the cell vacuoles, by staining with a *p*H indicator dye, and found in *Desmarestia munda* a concentration of 0.44 N sulfuric acid. Other workers have confirmed that the acidity of *Desmarestia* is due mainly to sulfuric acid and not to malic acid as reported earlier. The insulation of the acid in the vacuole, apart from the neutral cytoplasm, is of interest, for this explains the plastid discoloration and other acid damage observed in injured plants.

MINERAL NUTRITION IN THE SEAWATER ENVIRONMENT

Seaweed-ash analyses long ago revealed the major "essential" minerals and many of the trace elements needed for growth, and the list has been confirmed over the years, as methods of detection of nutrient needs have been refined. Because of the oceans' mineral abundances and the constant flow of fresh medium around the cells of marine algae, most of these essential and trace elements are in inexhaustible supply. Nitrogen and phosphorus in the sea, however, are in short supply, and the major importance of these has been confirmed most dramatically by oceanographic studies (Figure 13-5). These have shown a close correlation between the growth of phytoplankton and the availability of phosphates and nitrates, which provide the principal fertility of the seawater. A similar correlation is observed in the decrease in growth of European rockweeds and oarweeds with the summer decrease in PO_4 and NO_3 in the sea. Notwithstanding the importance, studies of nitrogen and phosphorus assimilation in benthic marine algae have been few. Nitrogen investigations have been confined mainly to the widely tolerant *Ulva* and *Enteromorpha*, while *Acetabularia* has been a principal subject in the study of inorganic phosphate metabolism. A major hindrance is the difficulty of culturing larger algae under bacteria-free conditions.

Nitrogen fixation by marine blue-green algae, especially for intertidal species of *Calothrix* (Figure 13-6), has been demonstrated by M.B. Allen.

The accumulation of nitrate in the vacuoles of *Valonia* and *Halicystis*, to concentrations 500 to 2000 times that of seawater, is a phenomenon of energy expenditure against a concentration gradient not clearly understood.

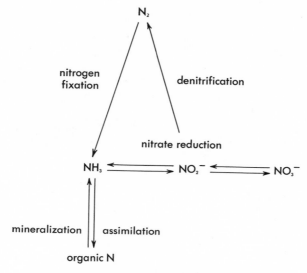

FIGURE 13–5. The nitrogen cycle (after Allen).

Other major cations have been investigated more extensively in seaweeds, particularly calcium, because of its conspicuous deposition in numerous marine forms (Chapter 12, Table 3). Nevertheless, there are yet few physiological or biochemical studies of the calcium deposition process.

Deposition of carbonate in algae is either in the form of calcite or aragonite, but never in a mixture of the two, as is common among invertebrates.

There is a geographic difference in the amount of $CaCO_3$ dissolved in seawater, and this is correlated with the distribution of calcareous algae. Thus, the "calcareous seas" are those tropical waters saturated or supersaturated with $CaCO_3$ as opposed to polar seas, which show less than 90 percent saturation. It is in the former that we see the enormous formation of reef limestone.

Although it has widely been assumed that $CaCO_3$ deposition is a cell-surface phenomenon resulting from carbon dioxide extraction from water during photosynthesis, studies of a number of calcareous marine algae are now suggesting that metabolic processes other than photosynthesis are involved in the precipitation. Evidences are accumulating from a number of approaches: studies of the isotopic fractionation of C^{12} and C^{13} in the organic tissues and mineralized parts of calcified algae; the metabolic incorporation of $MgCO_3$ in algal calcite; the isotopic composition of oxygen in carbonaceous algal skeletons; and the secretion of coccoliths by the golgi apparatus within the cells of coccolithophorids. The intriguing and unexplained facts remain, however, that many noncalcified algae live under precisely the same conditions side-by-side with $CaCO_3$ depositors, and that many calcareous forms (for example, articulated corallines, *Halimeda*) have heavily calcified segments separated by uncalcified tissues. Thus, it is evident that calcification is not necessarily cor-

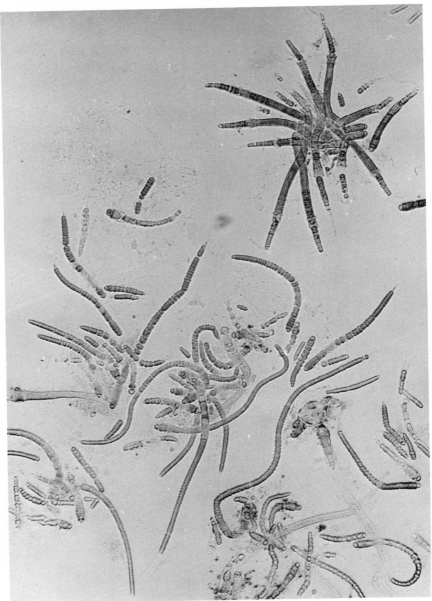

Figure 13–6. A typical nitrogen-fixing species of marine *Calothrix*. Note the clearly evident sheaths (after Allen).

related with photosynthesis in many of these plants. Recent observations by the writer in the eastern Pacific suggest that calcification may be a character of survival value evolved in the tropics by such plants as Corallinaceae under conditions of severe animal grazing.

Another area of special physiological interest in marine algae is the accumulation of a number of elements in concentrations far above any understandable functional need. Thus, one finds in the alga's protoplasm the essential mineral nutrients of functional systems, including phosphorus for various metabolic processes, magnesium for chlorophyll, nitrogen and sulfur for proteins, and iron for enzymes, but in addition, and almost universally among marine algae, a high concentration of potassium. Many seaweeds accumulate potassium to concentrations of 20 to 30 times the amount found in seawater, and it is to this quality that their traditional use as fertilizer for the land may be attributed. The potassium is often in the form of KCl, which in some kelps in the process of drying may be exuded in almost pure crystalline form. The location and concentration of potassium is best known in the cell sap of *Valonia* and *Halicystis*. In the former, a concentration of 0.5–0.6 molar is obtained of KCl, but the sulfate is excluded. *Halicystis ovalis* shows a 30-fold concentration, but *H. osterhoutii* shows partial exclusion of K by maintaining concentrations only about half that of seawater.

Whereas potassium is commonly accumulated, it has been shown in several marine algae that sodium may be actively excreted. Furthermore, several experiments with *Porphyra* and *Hormosira* have indicated a connection between an influx "pump" favoring potassium accumulation and an efflux "pump" effecting excess sodium excretion.

Another accumulation phenomenon in kelps of economic importance has been that of iodine. *Laminaria* may concentrate up to 30,000 times the seawater dilutions of iodine, which range from 0.03 to .07 parts per million. The green alga *Bryopsis* may accumulate iodine to a similar extent, and various other green and red algae are reported to have notable quantities. The concentration in *Laminaria* is such that iodovolatilization is effected at low tide, and free iodine may be detected experimentally (or by an acute sense of smell) in the surrounding air. Although iodine is usually distributed throughout the thallus, certain red algae show an accumulation in specialized cells. Studies with radioactive iodide show extremely rapid uptake. *Laminaria* may remove I^{131} from seawater equal to 30 times its own volume in an hour.

These abilities of marine algae to accumulate certain elements from very small dilutions in seawater have in recent years been given a practical significance in the study of uptake of radioactive wastes. Surface absorption of Sr^{90} and Y^{90} by various seaweeds has been measured, and the Ce^{144} and Sr^{90} uptake by marine phytoplankton. Uptake of Ru^{106} has been studied in *Porphyra*, Co^{60} in *Rhodymenia*, and Zn^{65} in a number of benthic algae.

ESSENTIAL TRACE ELEMENTS, MICRONUTRIENTS, AND GROWTH SUBSTANCES

Extensive investigations of minor elements in mineral nutrition have been pursued with fresh-water algae and with a few marine phytoplankton in recent decades, but few studies have been made on the benthic marine algae, largely because of culture difficulties.

Quantitative measurements of Co, Cu, Fe, Mn, Mo, Pb, Ni, and Zn in several Atlantic benthic algae showed no clear correlation with the occurrence of these elements in the natural seawater. Several of these are known to be necessary for the growth of specific fresh-water algae, but few tests have been made on marine forms. Manganese has been shown necessary for the growth of *Ulva, Bangia,* and *Ulothrix,* and boron, in excess of natural seawater concentrations, has been demonstrated to stimulate growth of germlings of *Ulva.* Boron also seems to increase photosynthesis in *Ulva* and *Fucus.*

Perhaps the most interesting current work on marine algae in this context is that with vitamins. Several investigations have demonstrated that various marine flagellates and diatoms, and the red alga, *Goniotrichum,* require B vitamins as growth factors. A considerable number, including dinoflagellates, require vitamin B^{12} and thiamin, while the dinoflagellate, *Oxyrrhis marina,* requires both of these plus biotin.

These organic micronutrients, without which growth cannot occur, are of a different character from the *growth substances,* which change the form and rate of growth without being absolutely limiting. A number of these latter substances have been investigated during the last three decades with respect to their influence on marine algal growth.

Auxins have been detected in *Fucus, Macrocystis, Laminaria, Desmarestia,* and *Valonia* in concentrations up to 0.5 micrograms per kilogram.

A considerable number of experiments have been performed on the growth responses of marine algae to Indolyl acetic acid, Indolyl butyric acid and other growth substances. Among these, the green algae *Ulva, Enteromorpha, Rhizoclonium, Codium,* and *Acetabularia,* and the brown algae *Ascophyllum* and *Fucus,* have shown increased growth by 15 to 53 percent resulting from varying concentrations of IAA. *Rhizoclonium heiroglyphicum* showed growth stimulation by 37 percent during 16 days of IAA concentration of 10^{-6} to 10^{-3} M, while at the same time IBA at 10^{-9} M increased growth by 53 percent. *Bryopsis plumosa* showed rhizoid stimulation in seawater containing 100 mg/liter of IAA, but concentrations of IAA above 0.1 mg/liter have been injurious to *Laminaria agardhii.*

Japanese workers with economic species of *Porphyra* have found that 0.01 mg/ liter of gibberellin produces a 28 percent increase in growth of thallus sections. Growers of *Ulva* sporlings have seen development favored by kinetin and IAA. On the other hand, neither gibberellic acid nor kinetin has any effect on vegetative growth or cap formation in *Acetabularia.* Other inconsistent findings are accumulating, and it is clear that the mechanism of action of growth substances in the marine algae is far from understood.

PNEUMATOCYST GASES

A subject long of interest to students of seaweed physiology has been that of the gas content of air bladders of brown algae. Early investigations of *Nereocystis leutkeana* in 1916 revealed that beside nitrogen, oxygen, and carbon dioxide, carbon monoxide was present in concentrations from 0.4 to 12.2 percent. This was later confirmed by a number of workers, although not such high concentrations of CO were found. This respiratory poison has since been found in *Pelagophycus porra* and *P. giganteus* in quantities ranging from 0.2 to 2.4 percent. Analyses of vesicles of European *Sargassum linifolia* and *Fucus virsoides*, and of *Egregia menziesii*, *Macrocystis pyrifera*, and *Fucus evanescens* on the Pacific Coast, however, have revealed no carbon monoxide.

The origin and function of CO in kelps is unknown. Some have considered it to be a respiratory by-product; others say it is the result of some kind of microbial fermentation. The inside of the air bladders, however, has been shown to be sterile, and the respiratory relationship has not been confirmed. A possible clue to the interpretation of this phenomenon is found in the ability of certain green and blue-green algae to perform carbon-monoxide fixation.

REFERENCES

Allen, Mary Belle. 1962. Nitrogen fixing organisms in the sea. In C.H. Oppenheimer (Ed.), *Symposium on Marine Microbiology*. Springfield, Ill.: Charles C Thomas. Chap. 8.

Haxo, F. T., and L. R. Blinks. 1950. Photosynthetic action spectra of marine algae. *J. Gen. Phys.*, 33: 389–422.

Lewin, R. A. (Ed.) 1962. *Physiology and Biochemistry of Algae*. New York: Academic Press. 929 pp. (Note that the book contains a large number of references on various physiological subjects.)

Smith, G. M. (Ed.) 1951. *Manual of Phycology*. Waltham, Mass.: Chronica Botanica (Ronald). Chap. 14. xi + 375 pp.

14

Spermatophytes;
Mangrove Associations;
Salt Marshes

SPERMATOPHYTES

The marine flowering plants, commonly known as the "sea grasses," all belong to two closely related families of aquatic plants, the Hydrocharitaceae and the Potamogetonaceae. In the first of these are three marine genera: *Halophila, Thalassia,* and *Enhalus.* In the second, there are eight genera: *Phyllospadix, Zostera, Posidonia, Halodule (Diplanthera), Cymodocea, Syringodium, Amphibolis,* and *Ruppia.* Some 45 species have been described in all, but many of these remain poorly understood, and a few are known only from a single collection (Figure 14-1).

The marine angiosperms for the most part live in areas seldom visited by terrestrial botanists, and, since they usually do not lend themselves to inclusion in marine algal floras, they have generally been overlooked except by a very few specialists. Furthermore, most species live well submerged, and seldom if ever are uncovered by low tides. Some occur in waters too deep and murky for shore collecting, yet too shallow for a ship's dredge. Such habitats will probably yield additional species when they have been more thoroughly explored, just as happened in Pacific Central America in 1959, when the writer found two undescribed species in a series of shallow dives in muddy bays.

FIGURE 14–1. *A–D, Halophila*: *A*, part of a leafy plant; *B*, a male flower; *C*, a female flower; *D*, young fruit. *E, Syringodium filiforme,* showing terete leaves and part of a rhizome. *F–J, Halodule (Diplanthera)*: *F*, part of a leafy plant with a rhizome; *G*, a leaf tip; *H*, a female flower; *I*, a male flower (anther); *J*, a young fruit.

The majority of the genera and species of sea grasses are of strictly tropical distribution. All of the genera of Hydrocharitaceae are characteristically tropical, and, in the Potamogetonaceae, only *Zostera* and *Phyllospadix* are typically of temperate range. *Posidonia* is of warm-temperate to subtropical distribution. *Ruppia* is essentially cosmopolitan and exceptional in occurring both in purely marine habitats and in brackish or inland alkaline waters.

Several points of geographical distribution of the tropical sea grasses are especially notable.

1) There is almost complete oceanic segregation of the species of the Old World from those of the New World.

2) About three-quarters of the species occur only in the Old World. The center of distribution appears to be in the Indo-Malaysian region. A second area of important occurrence is in the Caribbean Sea. This distribution, according to Ostenfeld, den Hartog, and others, indicates that the sea grasses are old plant types that originated not later than early Tertiary while the Panamanian isthmus was still open. Distribution between Indo-Malaysia and the Caribbean evidently occurred before the Panama land barrier arose, and subsequent speciation in the two areas has provided for several vicarious pairs of closely related species such as: *Thalassia hemprichii* and *T. testudinum; Syringodium isoetifolium* and *S. filiforme; Halodule uninervis* and *H. beaudettei.* The effectiveness of land barriers to sea-grass dispersal is evidenced by the fact that *Halophila stipulacea* did not occur in the Mediterranean until after the opening of the Suez Canal, through which it then quickly moved to establishment along the coasts of Greece.

3) The west coasts of Africa and the west coasts of tropical America are markedly deficient in sea grasses. Although several species are now known to occur in both these areas, they are sparsely represented. There is evidently a marked connection between the presence of tropical sea grasses and the occurrence of abundant coral-reef formations. This, in turn, is related to the occurrence of large tidal amplitudes that inhibit coral and coralline-algal reef development.

The coasts of North America have a good representation of both the temperate and the tropical sea grasses (seven genera), while South America, except for the Caribbean coast is almost without these plants. The more important and abundant of the North American marine phanerogams are *Zostera, Phyllospadix,* and *Thalassia,* which will be taken up in turn.

Zostera

The most widely distributed sea grass in America is *Zostera marina,* the eel grass, which occurs on the Pacific Coast from Port Clarence, Alaska, to Baja California and Sinaloa, Mexico. On the Atlantic it ranges from southwest Greenland to South Carolina. It is generally a plant of shallow lagoons and bays, but may occur at depths as great as 50 meters. In areas of its abundance it supports a great variety of marine animal life and serves as the staple winter food for sea brant. Canada geese and black ducks also depend upon it to a considerable extent. Because of these interrelations, great attention attended its sudden disappearance by "wasting disease" on the Atlantic Coast in 1931–

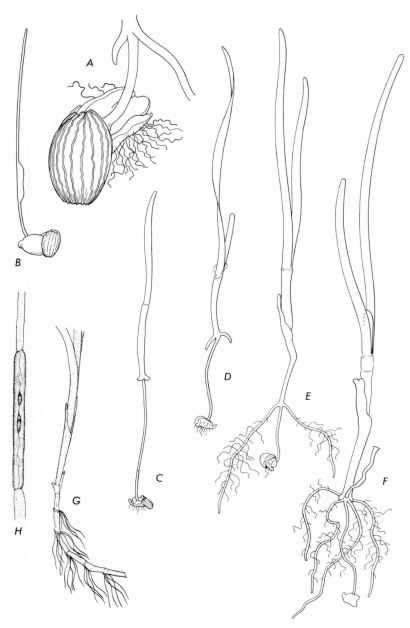

FIGURE 14–2. *Zostera marina*: *A,* seed and lower part of a young seedling showing costate testa, protruding flattened portion of radicle with root hairs, caulicle, and first pair of secondary roots; *B–F,* stages in development of seedlings; *G,* lower part of an older plant showing rhizome and roots from nodes; *H,* a spathe with ripening fruits partly evident (*A–F* after Setchell).

1932. Such decline resulted in reduction of wintering populations of Atlantic brant in some areas to as little as 2 percent of earlier years. (See Chapter 3 for comments on a possible causative organism, *Labyrinthula.*)

Setchell has provided several accounts of the morphology and phenology of *Zostera* in America, especially with regard to seasonal periodicity of growth and anthesis in response to temperature.

The seed of *Zostera* is more or less cylindrical, about 1 millimeter wide and 2 to 3 millimeters long. Its seed coat is marked with 16 to 25 ribs. Upon germination the testa splits longitudinally and allows the enlarging embryo to protrude. The radicle produces abundant root hairs, while the caulicle elongates through several centimeters of muddy substrate and carries up the plumule enwrapped by the cotyledon (Figure 14-2). The cotyledonary sheath ruptures along one side as the leaves expand and project beyond it. Meanwhile, adventitious roots appear from opposite sides of the first node and develop root hairs as they elongate. Further growth involves development of a rhizome by elongation of the internode and loss of the first leaves. Adventitious roots develop from each node, and from time to time lateral buds are initiated at the nodes. Depending upon environmental conditions, 1 to 2 years may be required to develop a plant to the stage shown in Figure 14-2,*F*).

The next stage of growth, which follows a period of quiescence, involves extensive development of the rhizome and its leafy branches, some of which become erect and produce the elongate fertile branches with 20 or more spadices enclosed within spathes. The fertile shoots are ephemeral and perish at the end of the season, while the prostrate shoots persist but become fragmented.

The flowers are imperfect, each consisting of either a pistil or a stamen. They are borne alternately in two rows in a series of about 12 on a spadix, and exhibit proterogyny. The style branches protrude first from the boat-like spathe, and only after these have fallen do the anthers project themselves. The ripening of seed is successive in the spadices upward in the fertile axis. From 500 to 1000 seeds may be produced on a luxuriant plant in a season, but most of these, falling into the mud, are grubbed up and swallowed by fish and water fowl. A few become favorably buried in the substrate by being carried into the cavities and tunnels of mud-burrowing organisms of the *Zostera* association.

Phyllospadix

The two Pacific coast species of this genus are unusual among sea grasses in being adapted to intertidal conditions often of considerable violence. They are the "surf grasses" which form emerald-green masses at or just below low water and are exposed generally to strong wave action and foaming surge. They are the cumaphytes or "surge plants," and are firmly fastened to rocky substrates by short, condensed rhizomes that often form a tough mat under a thin layer of shifting sand.

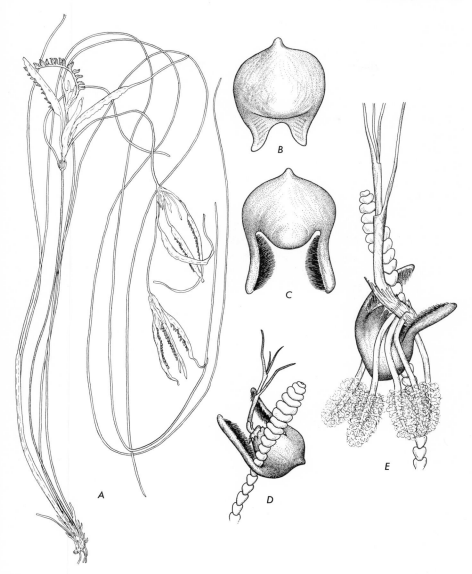

FIGURE 14–3. *Phyllospadix torreyi*: *A,* mature fruiting spadices; *B,* a young fruit; *C,* a mature fruit with exocarp worn away; *D,* germination of seed after attachment to a coralline; *E,* young plant with developing roots.

Sterile, leafy plants of *Phyllospadix* are usually encountered and are identified by leaf characters. *P. torreyi* has narrow, thick leaves 0.5 to 2 millimeters wide with inconspicuous nerves, while *P. scouleri* has broader, flat leaves 2 to 4 millimeters wide, with three distinct nerves.

Flowers are borne on dioecious plants in two rows on the side of a flattened spadix, and the whole inflorescence is enclosed by a spathe. In *P. torreyi* the flowering stems are 20 to 30 centimeters long and with two or three pairs of spadices (Figure 14-3). In *P. scouleri* the flowering stem consists of a peduncle only 1 to 6 centimeters long, supporting a solitary spadix.

Staminate plants are usually less numerous than pistillate ones, in the proportion of 1:12 or less. Pollination commonly occurs at time of flood following a low tide. The pollen is extraordinary in being filamentous, about 5 μ in diameter and 1000 μ long. It is often released by the first flood waves after a period of exposure, to be cast about among the more abundant pistillate plants. The pollen may at times move with the water to contact submerged stigmas, or may come to the surface, be deposited by receding waves, and refloated.

The manner in which young *Phyllospadix* plants gain a foothold as seedlings in the surfy environment is an interesting adaptation of the mature fruit. The fruits remain in serial position in the spadix until they are fully ripe. When freed they have a pulpy exocarp which becomes gradually worn away as the ripe, drupe-like fruit is dashed about in the surf. This leaves a dark, horny mesocarp. The mesocarp has two projecting, incurved arm-like structures that bear inwardly-pointing, stout, fringing bristles. By means of these bristly arms the fruit is able upon occasion to become fastened to the branch of an articulated coralline growing on otherwise bare or smooth rock (Figure 14-3,*D*). It clings so tightly by these retuse bristles that it may germinate in position and send out a quantity of stout roots from each segment of the developing seedling rhizome (Figure 14-3,*E*). Root hairs are produced in abundance, attach themselves to whatever they contact, and tend to collect sand that forms a sandy patch about the developing plant. A tussock gradually takes shape and may reach a half-meter in diameter.

Thalassia

The Caribbean turtle grass, *Thalassia testudinum*, is the most abundant marine phanerogam in the tropical western Atlantic region. It occurs in the United States, with only minor discontinuity, from Sebastian Inlet, east Florida, around the whole arc of the Gulf of Mexico to southern Texas. It occurs in a variety of loose substrates from mud to sand and broken shell wherever these materials are maintained in position by relatively calm water. In quiet lagoons a dense intertidal growth may occur, while in open water beds may be found at depths of up to 30 meters. The plants evidently tolerate salinity variations from 10°/$_\circ\circ$ to 48°/$_\circ\circ$, with optimum range of 25°/$_\circ\circ$ to 38.8°/$_\circ\circ$.

Thalassia develops its erect, leafy shoots from a creeping rhizome buried 5 to 10 centimeters in the substrate. New shoots arise successively from near the apex of the rhizome. The erect shoots consist of a short stem bearing a small group of four to five exposed, ligulate leaves with sheathing base. The leaves have a median main nerve and four to six smaller, lateral vascular bundles on either side. Between the vascular bundles a number of rather con-spicuous air spaces are arranged longitudinally in the leaf.

Thalassia is dioecious. Staminate flowers are long-pedicelled with a three-petaloid perianth and six stamens. Pistillate flowers are nearly sessile in the spathe and have a beaked, six- to nine-celled ovary. In Florida, flowering may occur from May through July. Phillips points out that when flowering is observed, only one kind of flower is noted. He cites several instances in which 5 to 15 percent of the plants observed were either staminate or pistillate, accord-ing to their flowers, but were not mixed. He also suggests that in view of the generally sparse production of flowers that vegetative reproduction is probably of greater importance in the maintenance and spread of *Thalassia* plants than is seeding. Careful observations on dissemination and growth of seeds and of vegetative fragments have, however, not yet been made. The peculiar stalked, oval, pointed fruits may float for long distances and roll about in the surf before opening to discharge seeds.

MANGROVE ASSOCIATIONS

Aside from the marine phanerogams that grow wholly submerged, there is a group of seed plants closely associated with the intertidal marine environ-ment, but only partly submerged. The tidal woodland, or mangrove, occurs in muddy tidal waters throughout most of the tropical world, and into temperate latitudes in some areas, depending upon oceanic currents and the presence of favorable temperatures. Mangroves of some 30 species occur as shrubs or trees belonging to several different plant families. Like the sea grasses, most of the species are Old World ones. Only four species, in the broad sense, occur in America, while southeast Asia has 23. Three of the American mangroves are widespread on both East and West Coasts: *Rhizophora mangle* (Rhizophoraceae), *Laguncularia racemosa* (Combretaceae), and *Avicennia nitida* (Verbenaceae).

Mangrove plants characteristically grow in quiet lagoons and estuaries, and are provided with an intricate growth of prop roots that support the vegetative portions of the plants 1 to 2 meters above the mud bottom. Ordinarily the leafy parts hang down to the level of high tide, so that in areas of considerable tidal amplitude the most conspicuous feature at low water is the thicket of arching masses of prop roots standing in the mud.

The mangroves support a unique algal vegetation consisting mainly of the red algal genera *Bostrychia, Caloglossa, Catenella,* and *Murrayella.* The overhanging leafy branches provide protection from excess light and desiccation at low tide, so that the prop roots commonly support a rich vegetation of these small algal species (Figure 14-4). The shade also sometimes allows the development of thick carpets or felts of algae on the mud. These usually consist of species of *Caulerpa, Cladophoropsis,* or *Vaucheria.*

Some of the best-developed mangrove algal floras are encountered in the West Indies, while some of the poorest occur in tropical Pacific Mexico.

FIGURE 14-4. Muddy bottom of a sheltered cove bordered with mangroves in Bermuda. The *Rhizophora* stilt roots are covered between tide marks with shaggy *Bostrychia* coated with mud, while on the mud below are multitudinous small black snails (reprinted from *Marine Algae of the Eastern Tropical and Subtropical Coasts of the Americas* by W. R. Taylor, by permission of the University of Michigan Press, copyright 1960).

Børgesen has described the association in some detail as it occurs in the Virgin Islands. In a typical mangrove lagoon in that region the uppermost and most prevalent of the algae is *Bostrychia tenella.* This is a bi-tri-pinnately branched, bushy, creeping form fastened by means of discoid haptera and forming a soft bolster 2 to 3 centimeters thick around the mangrove roots. Intermingled with it is *Catenella opuntia,* a decumbent, jointed form of cartilaginous consistency, and frequently, also, the delicate, membranous *Caloglossa leprieurii.* All of these plants are commonly exposed by falling tide, but are adapted by their chemistry and by the water-holding character of the spongy mass of intergrown branches, to survive considerable desiccation. Furthermore, they are seldom found except on well-shaded roots and those protected from drying currents of air. On the other hand, very heavy shading of the interior of the mangrove thicket, together with the relative stagnation of the water, is unfavorable, and poor or negligible growths occur. At lower levels, where there is little or only brief exposure, the plants are nearly all very finely dissected, richly branched, filamentous forms such as *Murrayella, Polysiphonia, Ceramium,* and sometimes *Bryopsis,* and the delicate *Caulerpa verticillata.*

The world distributions of the algae associated with mangroves, often referred to ecologically as the Bostrychietum, has been long studied and extensively documented by Erika Post of Kiel. Some of the species of *Bostrychia*, *Caloglossa*, and *Catenella* are widely distributed in nearly all tropical mangrove habitats, while others are evidently localized or of exceedingly discontinuous distribution. Some have achieved peculiar ecological adjustments, such as *Bostrychia flagellifera*, known from several mangrove habitats in Australia, but found on lava rocks under reduced salinity in Japan and New Zealand. *Murrayella* is a characteristic mangrove inhabitant in the Atlantic American tropics, but does not occur in the Pacific. Its nearest relative, *Murrayellopsis*, is a remarkable plant known only from depths of 6 to 11 meters in California and northwest Mexico as the nesting plant of the ocean goldfish, *Hypsipops*.

SALT MARSHES

In the temperate regions of the world the quiet, muddy shores of marine lagoons and estuaries are not clothed with heavy brush and tree vegetation, but with a low marsh flora consisting of such plants as *Spartina*, *Limonium*, *Puccinellia*, *Spergularia*, and *Salicornia*. These halophytes often are subject to partial inundation, but are seldom completely submerged for more than a brief time. They, like the mangroves, are terrestrial plants rooted within tidal reach. The channels of the salt marshes, however, are the habitats of numerous algae. Some of the commonest ones are cosmopolitan or widespread, boreal green algae of the genera *Ulva*, *Enteromorpha*, *Rhizoclonium*, *Percursaria*, and *Ulothrix*. *Vaucheria* is often abundant, and there may be a variety of blue-green algae on the mud. A *Bostrychia-Catenella* association may occur, and there may be various fleshy red algae attached to shells or debris in the shallow waterways. Some of the especially interesting marsh algae are the marsh fucoids that live in several areas of the north Atlantic and Baltic. They are modified forms of species of *Pelvetia*, *Fucus*, and *Ascophyllum* living either free on the marsh, rising and falling with the tide, or embedded in the mud. They evidently arise as loose-lying plants by vegetative budding from fragments of normal plants. A free-living form of the southern fucoid, *Hormosira*, occurs in New Zealand on mangrove marshlands.

REFERENCES

Chapman, V. J. 1958. *Salt Marshes and Salt Deserts*. London: Leonard Hill. 392 pp.

den Hartog, C. 1964. The taxonomy of the sea-grass genus *Halodule* Endl. (Potamogetonaceae). *Blumea*, 12: 289–312.

Dudley, W. R. 1893. The genus *Phyllospadix*. In: *The Wilder Quarter-Century Book*. Ithaca: Comstock. pp. 403–420.

Phillips, R. C. 1960. Observations on the ecology and distribution of the Florida seagrasses. *Florida State Bd. of Conserv. Marine Lab.*, *Prof. Papers* (2): 1–72.

Post, Erika. 1936. Systematische und pflanzengeographische Notizen zur Bostrychia-Caloglossa-Assoziation. *Rev. Algol.*, 9: 1–84.

Setchell, W. A. 1929. Morphological and phenological notes on *Zostera marina* L. *Univ. Calif. Publ. Bot.*, 14: 389–452.

15

Ecology and Geographic Distribution

ENVIRONMENTAL FACTORS

Some of the major characteristics of the marine environment have already been presented, and also some of the ways in which the environmental factors that influence the distribution of algae have been investigated experimentally. It is now feasible to reiterate in tabular form these principal factors, although in many cases the influence of one factor depends upon another, and the importance varies with the species of plant in question.

A. Physical factors
    1. light
        a. intensity (varying with latitude, tidal exposure, cloud cover, shore shading, biological overshadowing)
        b. quality (varying with water depth, transparency, tidal amplitude)
        c. periodicity (daily; seasonal)
    2. substrate
        a. solidarity (bedrock, cobble, gravel, sand, mud)
        b. texture (penetrability or suitability for attachment)
        c. porosity (water-holding capacity)
        d. position

      a'. with regard to water availability (tidal flooding, wave wash, splash, spray, seepage, tidepool retention)
      b'. with regard to wave shock or disturbance
      c'. with regard to ice action or cobble scour
   e. solubility and erosibility
   f. color (with regard to intertidal heat absorption, radiation and reflection)
   g. chemical composition
  3. temperature
   a. seawater temperature
      a'. annual variation
      b'. duration of maximum and minimum
      c'. diurnal variation
      d'. stratification; thermocline position with respect to tides, mixing of nutrients, etc.
   b. air temperature during intertidal exposure
      a'. annual variation
      b'. duration of maximum and minimum
   c. direct heat of insolation (complete exposure; tidepool exposure)
  4. relative humidity (with respect to algae subject to exposure)
   a. seasonal variation in conjunction with exposure
   b. duration of minimum coincident with maximum exposure temperature
  5. rain
   a. seasonal extent coincident with tidal exposure
   b. maximum duration
  6. pressure (mainly significant with regard to effect of tidal amplitude on attached seaweeds bearing air vesicles)
B. Chemical factors
  1. salinity
   a. annual variation from runoff
   b. tidal fluctuation of the halocline
   c. maximum concentration from evaporation during exposure
  2. availability of dissolved oxygen during dark-hour respiration
  3. availability of nitrogen, phosphorus and other essential metabolic substances
  4. availability of free carbon dioxide for photosynthesis
  5. pH (mainly significant in confined pools subject to marked increases during active photosynthesis)
  6. pollution
   a. by natural marine organisms
   b. by waste products of human activity
C. Dynamic factors
  1. water movement
   a. surf

b. ocean currents

c. tidal fluctuation and currents

d. maximum severity of annual storms or hurricanes

e. upwelling

f. extent of surface chop vs. calm

2. tidal exposure (period and amplitude)

3. tidal rhythm (with respect to release of reproductive bodies)

4. wind (with respect to coincidence with exposure)

D. Biological factors

1. grazing pressure

2. fungal and microbial activity

3. competition for substrate

4. protective cover against desiccation during exposure

5. light restriction by overgrowth (either by macroscopic or microscopic forms)

6. availability of host plants or animals for obligately epiphytic, endophytic, epizootic, endozootic, and parasitic algae.

ZONATION

In every littoral environment it may be observed that a number of the above-named factors are present and active along a gradient from higher to lower values. The adaptation of the different plants to the varying conditions — such as of light, temperature, exposure, and salinity — along these gradients results in a more or less distinct zonation of the plants. Where the gradients are abrupt, such as those on nearly vertical rock surfaces subject to a marked tidal range, the zonation is clear-cut (Figure 15-1), and one can easily identify limits of tolerance to desiccation, high light intensity, or the like, by the outlines of the girdle formed by the individual species. Where there is a broad intertidal area of irregular configuration, the zonation may be spread so widely as to be indistinct (Figure 15-2).

Zonation with respect to tide levels is that most commonly noted and has been treated in a large volume of literature. Each geographic area, however, has its tidal peculiarities. Periodicities and amplitudes vary widely on different coasts. Tidal amplitudes may range from a few centimeters in some areas to several meters in others. Some regions exhibit semidiurnal fluctuations in which two high tides and two low tides occur daily. Others show a single high and low level during 24 hours. In California, for example, with its semidiurnal tides, the significant very low tides (the springs or "minus tides") occur during summer just at or before sunrise, while during the dry autumn they occur in midafternoon.

The zonation is by no means confined to the intertidal region, for under favorable conditions a distinct banding of vegetation can be observed all the way to the limits of light penetration. Even when the zonation is indistinct,

FIGURE 15–1. An example of sharp zonation on a nearly vertical surface in the high intertidal zone of Puget Sound, Washington. A dark marine lichen zone is evident above a sharp upper band of small barnacles followed by a girdle of *Fucus* and a second barnacle zone.

FIGURE 15–2. Irregular lateral zonation on a rocky shore in southern California.

and the slope of the bottom quite gentle, the occurrence of the various major components of the vegetation can be plotted with depth and found to conform clearly (Figure 15-3).

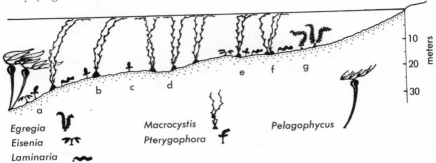

FIGURE 15–3. Diagram of a typical southern California kelp bed.

It is readily seen that the large number of interrelated factors that effect zonation, and the diverse responses of plants to these in different geographic areas, provide a multitude of aspects of zonation in various parts of the world. On this account there have arisen several conflicting sets of terminology of the zonate littoral environment around which there remains much difference of opinion. Perhaps the most satisfactory set of terms for the basic littoral zonation is that proposed by the Stephensons in 1949 after many years of studies of intertidal regions throughout the world. It is a simplified grouping of belts based both upon the tides and on the occurrences of certain widely important plants and animals. It is almost universally applicable for rocky shores (Figure 15-4).

A study of intertidal zonation can be conducted easily and effectively on almost any well-exposed rocky shore by recording a set of transect observations. The transect is laid out by means of a measured line provided with convenient interval markers, beginning with the upper limits of the supralittoral fringe and extending to low-water mark or below. Tide levels can be determined, with respect to the predicted values in a tide table, by measurement with a surveyor's transit and pole. The occurrence and frequency of the various kinds of plants are then spoken into a portable tape recorder and the record transcribed and plotted in the laboratory to give a profile of the various distributions with tide level.

Neushul recently perfected a system for doing the same kind of zonation profile in the sublittoral. The transect line is laid out under water using underwater breathing apparatus and depth gauge, and the botanist observes, identifies, and records on a portable underwater tape recorder. It is necessary only that one first become sufficiently acquainted with the flora of an area by advance study in order to be adept at recognizing the principal species at a glance as the transect is taped. In this manner an entire underwater region can be surveyed and mapped by direct observation as was done for the first time at Friday Harbor, Washington, in 1963.

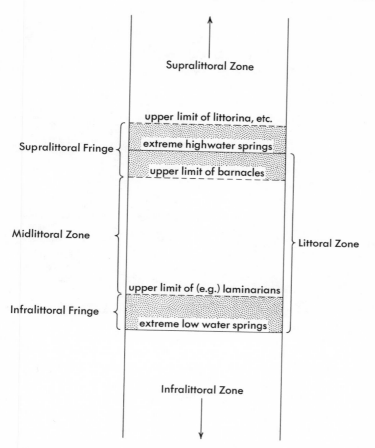

FIGURE 15-4. A terminology for littoral zonation according to Stephenson, 1949.

GROWTH FORMS

Whereas many of the evolutionary responses to the environment have been physiological or morphological at the cellular level, others have had their expression in external morphology. Accordingly, we observe in various ecological situations growth forms that are a reflection of various combinations of factors. An elaborate terminology has been devised to designate these morphological types: cumatophytes (surf inhabiting); herpophytes (small creeping algae); metarrheophytes (living in currents); galenophilic psammophiles (species living in calm, sandy situations) (Figure 15-5); leprydophytes (encrusting forms); tranophytes (rock penetrating forms), and, of course, epiphytes, endophytes, and so forth. The terminology has been extended, too, to include physiological adaptations, so that most of the ecological characteristics of a

FIGURE 15–5. A community of galenophilic psammophiles (mainly *Penicillus* and *Thalassia*) living on a calm sand bottom in a protected Florida bay (reprinted from *Marine Algae of the Eastern Tropical and Subtropical Coasts of the Americas* by W. R. Taylor by permission of the University of Michigan Press, copyright 1960).

plant can be expressed in a few words. As an example, we can consider *Sporochnus peduncularis,* which is an annual brown alga characteristically found in deep water only during the summer, the rest of the year being passed as a microscopic stage. It grows attached to rocks in areas subject to a narrow temperature amplitude in the medium temperature range, where the light is of quite uniform intensity and quality, though dim. Its habitat shows little salinity variation and is prevailingly calm. In ecological terms such a plant is described as an epilithic, stenomesothermic, stenophotic, sciophilic, stenohaline, galenophilic, aestival eclipsophycean of the inferior infralittoral.

It is evident from the fact that many growth forms may be found within the same local environment, especially in the intertidal region, that plants have solved the problems of survival in many different ways. We have, thus, in a given locality a community of plants or an association living under the same gross environment, but in which the plants themselves modify the environment greatly for one another and create in the aggregate a variety of microhabitats. Often these microenvironments become sharply defined, and we find one alga showing adaptive response to the presence of another, perhaps characteristically growing in its shade.

A conspicuous instance is that of epiphytes, of which there are many and diverse forms. Tokida has recorded 126 genera and 285 species of epiphytes on members of Laminariales alone. An algal collector soon recognizes in the field that some epiphytic algae are characteristically associated with a particular host or bearing plant, and that some are never found elsewhere than on this host. These are known as obligate epiphytes, in which one plant has evolved such close ecological relationship with another that no alternate habitat fulfills its need.

Studies of such obligate epiphytes, and of the great and common diversity of other epiphytes, especially among the floridean red algae, have led to a remarkable theory of the origin of some of the numerous parasitic forms of Florideophycidae, of which 40 genera are known (Figure 15-6). These parasites

FIGURE 15-6. Various examples of floridean parasites: *A, Ceratocolax hartzii,* on *Phyllophora* (after Rosenvinge); *B, Harveyella mirabilis* on *Rhodomela* (after Newton); *C, Erythrocystis saccata* on *Laurencia* (the penetrating base in median optical view); *D, Onychocolax polysiphoniae* on *Polysiphonia,* in median optical view (after Pocock); *Choreocolax polysiphoniae* on *Polysiphonia,* as seen in transection (after Newton).

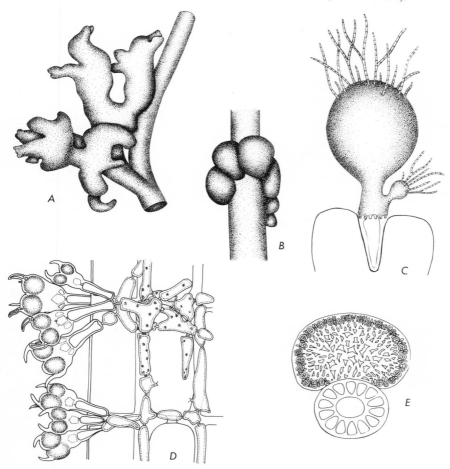

represent the most highly evolved relationship between two dissimilar algae. There are two types of floridean parasites: those that are closely related phylogenetically to the host on which they grow (adelphoparasites) and those that show no particular relationship (alloparasites). It is remarkable that nearly 90 percent of the total are adelphoparasites belonging to the same family or order as their host.

According to the hypothesis of Sturch, elaborated by Fan, these many adelphoparasites originated from epiphytes by successively more effective penetration of host tissue by haustorial, intrusive basal cells, and by absorption of metabolic materials through secondary pit connections. Major support of this hypothesis is provided by the following observations:

1) the floridean groups to which the majority of the parasites belong have a high capacity for development of secondary pit connections

2) the ease with which these interconnecting pits may be formed between an epiphyte and a host depends in part upon close relationship as evidenced by biochemical similarity

3) the survival of an epiphyte that has formed this intimate connection may yet be possible even if a loss of photosynthetic ability is suffered by mutation.

It might be expected that in an epiphyte that successfully undergoes these changes subsequent evolution would reduce the plant in such a way as to eliminate the photosynthetic blade (or its counterpart), except insofar as the production of reproductive organs is required. Such an ultimate result is evidenced in many floridean parasites that consist externally of little more than warts or nodules. On the other hand, some have not yet undergone extreme reduction of the thallus or loss of pigments and exist in a hemiparastic stage, seemingly part way along this evolutionary line (Figure 15-5,*C*).

ECOLOGICAL SURVEYS

During recent decades a number of efforts have been made in various parts of the world to survey the intertidal flora and to relate the occurrences to the diverse ecological factors indicated earlier in this chapter. Rocky-shore localities have usually been chosen because of relatively rich development of the flora and the usually well-marked zonation. Some of these regional ecological studies, such as Feldmann's on the south coast of France and Waern's for the Swedish Baltic, have been conducted in elaborate detail and are documented with numerous illustrations of the algal vegetation types. Others, such as Williams' study of the jetty flora of Cape Lookout, North Carolina, survey the vegetation of a single restricted habitat.

Perhaps the most ambitious intertidal ecology project ever undertaken by an individual was that of T. A. Stephenson. He began in South Africa in 1939 a series of studies that extended, before his death in 1961, to include investigations for North America from Nova Scotia to Florida and from Vancouver Island to San Diego. His work treated the whole biota of each region, including much data on the algae, although his point of view was primarily that of a zoologist.

Two outstanding ecological studies have recently appeared for North America treating especially of benthic marine algae. These will be summarized here as contrasting examples of the kind of work currently being done by some of the most intrepid adventurers of biology. The first of these, a study of the algal ecology of Labrador and northwest Newfoundland, is an example of a regional study of an intertidal and sublittoral marine flora by a single individual. The second, the ecology of the Pacific American bladder kelp, is an example of a large-scale study, by a biological team, of a specific algal community of economic importance.

Algal Ecology of Labrador and Newfoundland

To study the development of the marine flora of the inhospitably cold, subarctic northwest Atlantic region, Robert T. Wilce traveled by open boat with the Eskimos, often through floating ice and bitter weather, exploring 1500 miles of rugged coastline. During two ice-free seasons, for a total of 8 months, he observed and recorded the characteristic algal inhabitants of mud flats, protected shallows, tide pools, and variously exposed coasts, all diversely affected by the salient limiting factors of moving ice, reduced salinities, and seasonal land run-off.

Wilce observed for the first time in the subarctic the "seeding in" and subsequent development of a number of annual algae *(Ulothrix, Enteromorpha, Mono-stroma, Spongomorpha, Pylaiella, Chordaria, Elachistea,* and *Porphyra)* which, by their rapid summer growth lend striking periodic change to the appearance of the shore vegetation during the short ice-free season. Some other annuals *(Chaeto-morpha, Dilsea)* begin growth late in autumn or even after the freeze-up, develop slowly under the winter ice and mature early the following spring, subsequently to become epiphytized and torn from the rocks.

He observed a number of biennials (such as *Ahnfeltia, Polysiphonia, Rhodomela*), which begin their second year in a condition denuded of smaller branches, but vigorously regenerate new growth of contrasting appearance.

Mud-flat habitats in the subarctic Atlantic are marked by a paucity of species, but by many individuals. The habitat is severely affected by low air temperatures during emersion throughout all but a few weeks of the year, and by the devastating movement of prevalent masses of ice. Consequently, only a few annual species succeed, and these (dominantly *Vaucheria*) do so as a dark green slippery turf.

Protected shallows at the heads of quiet inlets are significantly affected by reduced salinity and by the early formation of ice that may be up to 4 meters thick during winter. In such habitats there is a dearth of species. Most are small annuals, but large populations of remarkably tolerant *Fucus* occur.

Moderately exposed coasts contain the richer populations of algae in these subarctic regions. The intertidal populations are largely restricted to tide pools and sheltered crevices, while the principal development occurs at depths of 10 to 30 meters below low tide level. The grinding and scouring of the ice is a primary factor, and it is only in mid-summer that a dense clothing of annuals *(Chordaria, Petalonia, Scytosiphon)* covers the rocks.

Fully exposed coasts are typically subjected to severe forces of surf and ice, and support meager populations of algae except in deep water. Intertidal vegetation is almost restricted to late-appearing annuals.

Contrasting Ecology in Costa Rica

In contrast to Wilce's records of the conditions of life in the subarctic, which severely limit the diversity and extent of algal populations, are some recent observations by the writer in Pacific Central America, which show a similar effect of depauperation achieved in a very different environment.

The rocky shores of Pacific Costa Rica exhibit some of the world's most reduced algal populations. Several factors, in addition to the prevailingly high and unfavorable temperatures, combine to disfavor the seaweeds. A large tidal amplitude prohibits development of fringing calcareous reefs with their varied algal habitats. It also provides for such intense insolation and desiccation during periods of low water that almost nothing survives intertidally except in the shade of trees overhanging the shore. The frequent extensive exposure also makes the algae subject to unfavorable fresh-water influence during the rainy season. The height of high water, in conjunction with the low transparency of the water during this season of heavy sedimentation, provides limiting conditions of low illumination for all but a few tolerant species. To these severely restricting factors are often added the denuding effect of heavy animal populations (for example, fish, crabs, echinoderms) which graze the sparse, fleshy food supply almost to obliteration. Under such conditions, very often only calcareous crustose algae remain as a conspicuous component of the flora.

Ecology of Macrocystis

Just before World War I the United States became sharply aware of its great Pacific Coast kelp resources for fertilizer and chemicals. Surveys of the beds were made and commercial harvesting was developed during the next 3 decades. By 1950, however, some of the most productive beds had declined or even disappeared, and the finger was being pointed at the great ocean outfall sewers of the cities of southern California as a prime cause of the loss. The California State Water Pollution Control Board instituted in 1957 an ecological survey program of the continental shelf of southern California to investigate the status of the biota and possible effects of pollution. During the past few years the kelp investigation phase of this program has been provided with more than $200,000 of which a large part has been spent on observational and experimental ecology of *Macrocystis* itself.

The advent of self-contained underwater breathing apparatus made many of the field aspects of this work possible (Figure 15-8), and at Scripps Institution, La Jolla, a diving team, including several trained botanists and zoologists, was organized to undertake this difficult and hazardous investigation.

Aerial surveys of the beds were made and compared with old maps to determine areas of decline. Hundreds of man-hours were spent on the bottom in the beds studying density, attachment, regeneration, grazing pressures, associated plant and animal species, light intensity, and the like. During many of the dives botanists of the team collected representative samples of the plants associated with *Macrocystis* for the preparation of a flora of the kelp association. Other samples were cultivated under controlled conditions in an effort to assess ecological factors. Zoologists investigated such problems as the effects of invertebrates attached to the kelp blades or living around them, the feeding habits of kelp-associated fishes and herbivorous invertebrates, the effects of kelp harvesting on the total biota of the beds. Natural factors affecting kelp deterioration were extensively documented, including storm damage, sand movement, water turbidity, high temperatures, and fungal and bacterial diseases. The great quantity of data has not yet been fully digested, although voluminous publications have appeared and further studies continue to be made not only in the temperate northeastern Pacific, but in Argentina, Peru, New Zealand, and other areas of *Macrocystis* occurrence.

The Giant Bladder Kelp grows attached to the ocean floor by means of a large, mounded, or spreading holdfast from which arise numerous leafy stipes supported by pear-shaped pneumatocysts (Figure 15-7). The tangled bundle of stipes and blades spread out at the surface as a canopy that appears to a diver below like a vast, golden-brown roof supported by many pillars.

The aggregated plants form beds that in California occupy some 100 square miles of sea bottom in depths mainly of 20 to 60 feet. Although from the surface the beds look very much alike, the differences in appearance of kelp beds from the sea floor are striking, and the composition of associated algal species varies from place to place in accord with differences in substrate, exposure, upwelling, temperature, and other factors.

The kelp bed at La Jolla, California, undoubtedly the world's best-known, is diagrammed in Figure 15-3. The inner boundary is usually at a depth of about 30 feet and is bounded by *Egregia laevigata*, which extends into shallow water. On the outer edge, the bull kelp, *Pelagophycus,* is commonly found. Both of these plants may grow intermixed with *Macrocystis,* but within the bed usually occur only as scattered individuals.

The undergrowth present in a kelp bed may be divided generally into those species that are stalked and tree-like and those that lie along the bottom. Of the larger and more conspicuous stalked forms, *Eisenia* and *Pterygophora* form what may be called an intermediate layer of vegetation, for their heavy, erect stipes commonly hold the fronds well off the bottom and above the mixed growth of smaller plants there. This tree-like vegetation is usually sparse except in open patches or "glades" in the kelp bed.

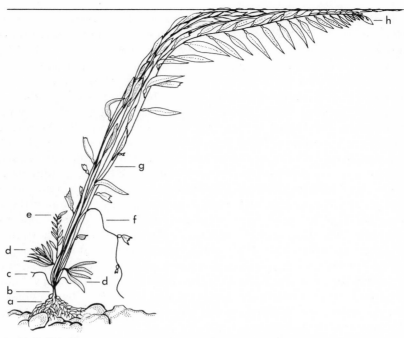

FIGURE 15-7. Diagrammatic representation of a young adult *Macrocystis* plant, 2 to 3 years old: a, holdfast; b, primary stipe; c, stubs remaining from first fronds; d, sporophylls; e, developing young frond; f, deteriorating senile frond; g, bundle of intertwined stipes; h, growing point of mature frond in the canopy (after North).

Several other large brown algae with broad, leathery fronds, such as *Laminaria, Agarum,* and *Desmarestia,* are frequent to occasional in the beds. In the case of *Laminaria farlowii,* the individual blades may reach a length of 15 feet and lie out along the bottom like large, undulate strips of leather.

Red algae comprise the greatest number of species in the bottom community and are often present in a bewildering array of forms. The most ubiquitous of these are the jointed Corallinaceae that grow even in the deep shade of the canopy. Crustose calcareous algae occur as pink layers on the bottom rocks and often cement together pebbles, shells, and sand to form nodules or even areas of rough "pavement."

The plants of the bottom community vary greatly in size, and many of the smaller, filamentous, or delicate forms remain invisible to the diver except on days of most brilliant sunlight and clear water. The changes in the aspect of the bottom upon the occasion of such favorable illumination are remarkable, for many plants and animals appear that cannot be seen at all under light of different spectral quality.

Some species present within a kelp bed, and most of those inhabiting the inner margins, extend shoreward into the lowest intertidal zone. Others are strictly shade forms that extend toward the other extreme into the lesser-known deep zones where light limits the distribution of attached plants. The common inshore forms include *Eisenia, Cystoseira, Zonaria, Dictyopteris, Codium, Plocamium, Lithothamnium,* and *Corallina.* Those plants that exist normally at the lowermost limits of plant distribution are exemplified by *Maripelta rotata* and *Phyllophora clevelandii.* Only a few species, such as *Laminaria farlowii,* are found growing almost exclusively with *Macrocystis* under the canopy itself and not extending past either margin of the bed.

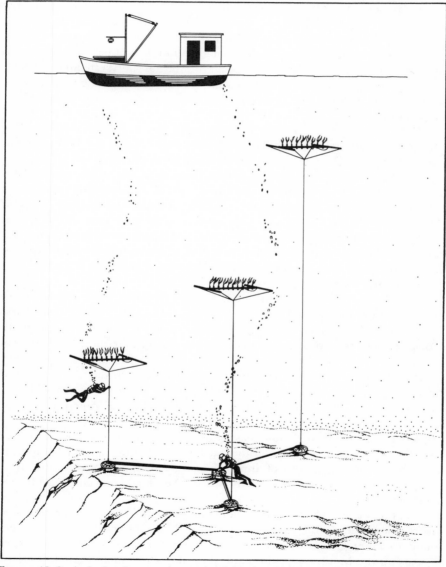

Figure 15–8. A device for experimental cultivation of *Macrocystis* or other algae and study of their development without the necessity of their removal to the laboratory (after Neushul).

GEOGRAPHIC DISTRIBUTION

Whereas a great many physical, chemical, dynamic, and biological factors interact in a given environment and affect the composition of a flora there, a relatively few factors can be recognized as influencing the occurrence of the major types of marine floras throughout the world. We have already seen how temperature, with regard to the distribution of winter sea ice, and to the availability of metabolic gases in warm seas, is of profound importance. Thus, the ice conditions inhibit the occurrence of great numbers of perennial intertidal algal species that might otherwise occur in the far northern and southern regions, while the presence of Laminariales in such a temperate region as the northern Gulf of California is prohibited by a brief period of very high summer temperature.

Tidal amplitude is another overwhelming factor, for, notwithstanding other circumstances, a large tidal amplitude may control the occurrence of whole formations of plants upon which much of the diversity of a flora may depend. Thus, tidal amplitude controls to a large extent in the tropics both the occurrence of sea-grass communities and of reef-building corals and coralline algae. The extraordinary contrast between the marine floras of Atlantic and Pacific Panama may be attributed in large part to this factor.

The position and flow of major oceanic currents, and the occurrence of wind-influenced upwelling, have also been pointed out as major determining factors. These provide for such contrasts as are seen in the algal floras of Pacific Baja California and Florida.

With these considerations in mind, one can recognize those regions of the world in which the greatest number of species of benthic algae occur. These are the south Australian region, the Japanese region (Figure 15-9), the South African region, the northeast Pacific Coastal region, and the Mediterranean region.

In tropical areas we find the richly diversified floras in the far west-central Pacific, in the Caribbean, and along south India. These are in marked contrast to the relatively impoverished floras of Pacific Central America, tropical west Africa, and the Red Sea.

As a nation, the United States has the northern hemisphere's most diversified algal floras, for, with its shores on the Pacific, the Atlantic, and the Caribbean, it combines the vegetations of three diverse regions. Only the continent of Australia, with about one-third of the world's benthic algae, boasts a broader assortment.

On the Pacific Coast, a rich flora, dominated by many Laminariales, Gigartinales, and Corallinaceae, extends without interruption from Puget Sound to Point Conception, California. It reaches a peak of extraordinary diversity in the Monterey Peninsula, California, where more than 400 species are reported. This is about equal to the entire flora of northeastern North America. At Point Conception, the southwardly moving California Current veers

FIGURE 15-9. A low-tide scene along southern Hokkaido, Japan, near the Tsugaru Kaikyo in one of the richest marine algal regions of the world. Seaweed gatherers are seen in the background. In the foreground is a great diversity of red algae.

offshore and is replaced by an eddy system in the Santa Barbara Channel. Here the dramatically warmer character of the marine climate introduces several tropical elements as many boreal ones drop out, and a warm-temperate flora builds up to maximum diversity in the vicinity of the Mexican boundary.

The Atlantic Coast is similarly marked by the effects of a powerful current system, the Gulf Stream, which profoundly influences the character of the algal flora. In the Maritime provinces and northern New England a flora occurs that, for the most part, ranges northward and may be termed dominantly subarctic. At Cape Cod, a point of division occurs between this assemblage and a southern flora adapted to warmer waters. Some of the subarctic elements do not grow south of Cape Cod, while others extend into Long Island Sound. The flora south of New Jersey continues to be boreal in character, but at Latitude 34° 45' in North Carolina the tropical element contributed by the Gulf Stream becomes strongly marked, especially in summer and in the deeper waters of offshore reefs. This warm influence is especially strong in Bermuda (at North Latitude 32° 20'), where a flora characteristic of Jamaica and of tropical South America occurs far out of latitudinal range.

From North Carolina to Florida the tropical element rapidly increases, although distributions are discontinuous due to long, unstable stretches of sand and mud inhospitable to algae. A strictly tropical flora occurs in southern Florida, in the Keys and the Dry Tortugas. The tropical element dominates the northern Gulf of Mexico, although a number of eurythermal species are added there.

The flora of the Gulf of Mexico was formerly thought to be an impoverished one, determined entirely by muddy shores and brackish water. Humm has shown recently that this conception is true only of strictly shoreline localities, and has arisen from fragmentary and fortuitous beach-drift collections. Dredging and diving operations have revealed a well-developed flora around the west coast of Florida. Even the coast of Texas, consisting of 400 miles of sand beach without natural rocks other than oyster reefs, has yielded 116 species to date.

REFERENCES

Chapman, V. J. 1957. Marine algal ecology. *Bot. Rev.,* 23: 320–350.

Dawson, E. Y. 1952. Circulation within Bahia Vizcaino, Baja California, and its effects on the marine vegetation. *Am. J. Bot.,* 39: 425–432.

Dawson, E. Y., M. Neushul, and R. Wildman. 1960. Seaweeds associated with kelp beds along southern California and northwestern Mexico. *Pacific Nat.,* 1(14): 1–81.

Doty, M. S. 1946. Critical tide factors that are correlated with vertical distribution of marine algae. . . . *Ecology,* 27: 315–328.

Fan, K. C. 1961. Studies of *Hypneocolax,* with a discussion of the origin of parasitic red algae. *Nova Hedwigia,* 3: 119–128.

Feldmann, J. 1937. Recherches sur la végétation marine de la Mediterranée, La Côte des Albères. *Révue Algol.,* 10: 1–339.

Humm, H. J., and H. H. Hildebrand. 1962. Marine algae from the Gulf coast of Texas and Mexico. *Publ. Inst. Mar. Sci.,* 8: 227–268.

North, Wheeler J. 1959. Annual report, 1958–1959, kelp investigations program. *Univ. Calif. Inst. of Marine Res.* (59–10): 15 pp. (mimeographed).

——————— 1963. Kelp habitat improvement project. Final report. *Univ. Calif. Inst. of Marine Res.* (63–13): 123 pp. (mimeographed).

Pocock, Mary A. 1955. South African parasitic florideae and their hosts. 3. Four minute parasitic florideae. *Proc. Linn. Soc. London,* 167: 11–41.

Stephenson, T. A., and Anne Stephenson. 1949. The universal features of zonation between tide marks on rocky coasts. *Jour. Ecology,* 37: 289–305.

Tokida, J. 1960. Marine algae epiphytic on Laminariales plants. *Bull. Fac. Fish., Hokkaido Univ.,* 11: 73–105.

Waern, M. 1952. Rocky-shore algae in the Oregund archipelago. *Acta Phytogeogr. Suecica,* (30): xvi + 298 pp.

Wilce, R. T. 1959. The marine algae of the Labrador peninsula and northwest Newfoundland (ecology and distribution). *Nat. Mus. Canada, Bull.* 158: 1–103.

Williams, L. G. 1949. Marine algal ecology at Cape Lookout, N.C. *Bull. Furman Univ.,* 31(5): 1–21.

16

History of the Study of Seaweeds

SURVEY OF IMPORTANT DEVELOPMENTS

The written record of the study of marine plants begins in the third century B.C. with the Greek naturalist Theophrastus, who gave descriptive accounts of certain conspicuous and useful seaweeds and grouped them along with terrestrial plants in his classification of trees, shrubs, undershrubs, and herbs. After Theophrastus, however, with the exception of the mention of a very few sea plants by Pliny and by Dioscorides in the first Christian century, the marine algae received no advancing inquiry for some 1800 years.

By 1601, seaweed collections had accumulated in Europe from a century of widespreading explorations of the seas of the world. Many of the more curious forms were gathering in collectors' cabinets, and some of those resembling parts of higher plants were being given names such as *Abies marina, Cupressa marina, Myrica marina, Quercus marina.* Clusius in that year recorded and illustrated some of them in his *Rarorum Plantorum Historia,* but for the most part scattered them indiscriminately throughout his book. At about the same time, John Gerard in England was assembling an account of sea plants, which he placed largely together simply as a marine group but named in such a way as to show the beginning of a generic concept of the seaweeds. Such names as *Fucus* and *Conferva* were coming into frequent use.

Seventeenth-century works, such as that of Kaspar Bauhin in 1671, generally contained a miscellaneous lot of attached marine organisms, including plants, sponges, corals, bryozoans, and the like. Some accounts of these biological mixtures continued, especially involving calcareous algae, until the late eighteenth century.

During the period from 1680 to 1747 the various systems of plant classification devised by Morison, Boerhaave, Ray, Ludwig, and Tournefort show a gradual realization of the natural distinction of cryptogams from the flowering plants and a trend to segregate them into a separate group. Finally, Linnaeus, in 1747, set aside the twenty-fourth section in his classification of plants as "Cryptogamia" and there placed the groups Filices, Musci, Algae, Fungi, and Lithophyta. Under the section "Algae" were arranged what we know as liverworts, lichens, algae, and a few miscellaneous groups. Some coralline algae and calcareous greens were placed in Lithophyta. Otherwise, however, three principal genera — *Fucus, Ulva,* and *Conferva* — were established under the algae, providing a basis for the beginning of special treatments of these plants.

The first to enlarge upon Linnaeus' lead was Hudson, who, in his Flora Anglica (1762), gave descriptions and synonymies of a large number of species of the Linnaean genera *Fucus, Ulva,* and *Conferva,* which now came to embrace most of the seaweeds. Soon after these works of Hudson and Linnaeus, which treat the algae more or less incidentally, Samuel Gottlieb Gmelin published in Saint Petersburg his monumental *Historium Fucorum* (1768), the first special treatise on marine plants.

The elaborately illustrated work of Gmelin evidently generated considerable interest in the collection and preparation of seaweed specimens. Algal herbaria began to be assembled all over Europe. It took a quarter-century for the new students of algae to gather their materials and to prepare to engage the problems of algal classification, but by 1795 we find advanced concepts appearing on all sides.

In that year Goodenough and Woodward presented their *Observations on British Fuci* to the Linnaean Society in London and criticized the systems of classification of their predecessors who had failed to take any account of fructification in the marine plants. In the same year Stackhouse, working with British seaweeds, divided them among six genera, while Dr. Albrecht Roth of Bremen in his *Catalecta Botanica* segregated the algae into nine (although he dealt mainly with fresh-water forms). At this time, two large illustrated works on marine plants of the world were being prepared: *Icones Fucorum,* by Esper of Nuremberg, and the four-volume *Fuci,* by Dawson Turner in England. In 1802 Turner, writing his *Synopsis of the British Fuci* seems to have looked farther into the future than any of the others, perceiving that an elaborate classification would have to be devised to accommodate the great diversity of the world's seaweeds once the perplexities of their fructification could be understood. He decried Stackhouse's piecemeal establishment of new genera on fragmentary evidence.

Stackhouse, however, carried on his description of genera, and in 1809 greatly amplified his system by the arrangement of 38 genera in his *Tentamen Marino-cryptogamicum.* For some obscure reason, Stackhouse published this account in the Mémoires of the Imperial Society of Naturalists of Moscow, and, since it was during the time of the Napoleonic wars, the paper did not become immediately available to other workers in Europe. Almost all copies were subsequently destroyed in the burning of Moscow, and those that remained did not become generally known to the world for many decades. Thus, though Stackhouse was the real father of generic segregation of marine algae, he never received credit for his most significant work, and by the time it came to light, the genera of later investigators had become so firmly established by usage that it was no longer feasible to give way to them.

Lacking knowledge of Stackhouse's work, J. V. F. Lamouroux in France published in 1813 his *Essai sur les Genres de la Famille des Thalassiophytes Non Articulées.* This work embodied an important advance toward a natural system of classification, for he divided the seaweeds into orders, divisions, and genera upon both reproductive and structural characters. For the first time the colors of green, brown, and red algae were employed in classification.

With Lamouroux's work, the knowledge of marine algae had reached a vantage point from which the whole field could be surveyed in order to place the world's exceedingly diverse forms of algae into groups that could be continually amplified and supplemented as new discoveries of species were made. This stage of taxonomic development may be considered the "Linnaean Age of the Algae." Subsequently the science of phycology began a much accelerated advance.

The 3 decades following Lamouroux's *Essai* saw world-wide exploration for seaweeds. The French round-the-world expedition of the Coquille provided Bory de Saint Vincent with material for a sumptuous imperial report. Montagne, in Paris, began in 1834 a series of floristic works on the algae and other cryptogams of French exploring expeditions to tropical America, the south Polar regions, the Indian Ocean, and Polynesia. The imperial Russian expedition under Lütke explored Pacific North America and in 1840 brought material for publication of the grandest algal treatise of all time: Postels and Ruprecht's *Illustrationes Algarum,* in which parts of the giant west-American kelps are shown in natural size and color. The British Antarctic voyages provided a wealth of algal material from the cool, rich southern-hemisphere regions of New Zealand and Australia.

As new collections from all the world were brought in and reported in Europe, a most distinguished algal center was forming in Sweden. C. A. Agardh, Professor of Botany at Lund University, began in the first years of the nineteenth century a systematic compilation of the algae known from Sweden, and soon expanded it to embrace the world. His son, J. G. Agardh, developed this program more fully than his father, and published studies and synopses throughout a long life that reached into the twentieth century. The Agardhs recognized the systematic value of the red algal cystocarp and contributed materially to the expansion of studies of that group by their extensive use of it in taxonomy. The elder Agardh, as early as 1824, was arranging the algae into orders and making studies of reproductive structures, despite such inter-

FIGURE 16–1. William Henry Harvey in about 1840.

pretive handicaps as led him to consider the zoospores of *Tetraspora* a metamorphosis from plant to animal.

William H. Harvey of Dublin (Figure 16-1) was making his first critical studies of algal systematics at this time, and in 1836 developed the concept of divisions (phyla) by recognizing the brown algae (Melanospermae), the red algae (Rhodospermae), the green algae (Chlorospermae), and the diatoms and desmids (Diatomaceae).

J. G. Agardh presented in 1842 a division of the algae into groups somewhat like Harvey's, and he continued for 65 years to elaborate and refine their systematics. Unfortunately, his ponderous Latin works were mostly without illustrations and were of use only to advanced specialists. Furthermore, Agardh evidently seldom left his laboratory for fieldwork, and depended almost solely upon his world-wide herbarium specimens for his interpretations of marine plants.

Harvey was of a different sort. That remarkable algologist of the mid-nineteenth century excelled both as a field collector and as an illustrator. He traveled and collected widely in Britain, South Africa, Ceylon, Australia, Polynesia, and Atlantic America, so that his taxonomic interpretations were soundly supported by wide knowledge of the plants in nature. During a lifetime of only 55 years he produced more than a dozen volumes of magnificent colored illustrations to accompany his writings, and these despite miserably cold working conditions in Dublin, frequent illness, and, finally, fatal tuber-culosis.

Another algal artist, who began his work in 1833, was the prodigious German schoolteacher, F. T. Kützing. He took upon himself the stupendous task of illustrating all of the algae of the world available to him. He succeeded, before the Franco-Prussian War made free scientific interchange impossible, in drawing some 7000 species. He was a poor man, who often made drawings on the backs of his school children's exercise papers, and since he saved his meager salary to publish at his own expense, the edition of his classic, 20-volume *Tabulae Phycologicae* was so small that it disappeared decades ago from the used-book market. One curious occurrence was Kützing's publication of an account of 73 new species of marine algae in a brochure for the graduation exercises of his Nordhausen high school in 1863. All but a handful of these were discarded by those who attended the ephemeral affair, and the existence of this publication did not become generally known to science for the greater part of a century.

Contemporary with Harvey, Kützing, and J. G. Agardh was Gustav Thuret, a Belgian working with Bornet in Paris, who made memorable dis-coveries of reproduction in the algae (see Chapter 7). Rabenhorst at this time was beginning his systematic studies in Leipzig and initiated what became the great European cryptogamic-flora series.

The last quarter of the nineteenth century saw the accumulation of a large number of papers by relatively numerous authors. Areschoug made important morphological and life-history studies in Sweden (1878, 1880). Berthold did likewise at Naples in 1881. Bornet and Thuret extended their earlier studies in Paris and published some of the finest illustrations of all time. Schmitz, in Germany, produced from 1883 to 1889 a new system of treatment of the red algae with his studies of the auxiliary cell and of the development of the gonimoblast. Numerous critical workers were examining the brown algae and probing the reproductive process there. Reinke (1878) and Falkenberg (1879), working with *Zanardinia* and *Cutleria*, and Kuckuck (1891) and Oltmanns (1899), working with *Ectocarpus*, all made observations that contributed to the subsequent demonstration of the remarkable alternation of heteromorphic generations in many of the Phaeophyta.

The enormous growth of algal literature in the nineteenth century led G. B. de Toni to begin in 1889 the compilation of Latin synopses of all the algae of the world. The *Sylloge Algarum* was continued for 35 years and became a master reference index for all systematists and taxonomists in the field. It is still widely used.

Farlow (Figure 16-2) published his *Marine Algae of New England* in 1879, and Kjellman (1883), wrote a major flora on the *Algae of the Arctic Sea*, but there were otherwise rather few extra-European regional floras presented during this period.

Figure 16–2. Williams Gibbs Farlow in 1891.

The early twentieth century saw the rapid development of modern systematics in the algae. Sauvageau continued his prolific studies of life history and morphology in the brown algae. Yamanouchi's (1906) analysis of the life history of *Polysiphonia* stimulated numerous studies in the Rhodophyta, the most prominent of which were those of Svedelius and Kylin in Sweden and of Oltmanns in Germany. From 1906, Svedelius published steadily for half a century, and Kylin developed during this same period the scheme of arrangement of the Rhodophyta now generally followed. He spent 27 years, following a major collecting trip to Pacific America in 1922, making comparative anatomical studies on a large number of liquid-preserved specimens. He first summarized his work in 1937 in his *Anatomie der Rhodophyceen*, but this became generally unavailable to workers because of World War II and the destruction of the German stocks. Kylin's life work on the genera of the red algae was finally completed by his widow 7 years after his death in 1949 (see Chapter 10).

As the systematic arrangements of the seaweeds became well established and the great index of de Toni was assembled, a new stimulant to floristic accounts was felt, for it was now possible, within reasonable limits, for an algologist to identify and systematize major world collections. Thus, from 1900 to 1930 a number of local European floras appeared not only for Denmark,

France, Britain, Sweden, Norway, and Italy, but also for many areas throughout the world. Some of the important floras of this period were the following: Madame Weber van Bosse's *Marine Algae of the Siboga Expedition* (East Indies): Bφrgesen's *Marine Algae of the Danish West Indies,* (and of the Canary Islands); Setchell and Gardner's *Marine Algae of Northwest North America* (and of the Gulf of California); Okamura's *Icones of Japanese Algae;* Jonsson's *Marine Algae of Iceland;* Howe's *Marine Algae of Peru;* Taylor's *Marine Algae of Florida;* Skottsberg & Kylin's *Antarctic and Subantarctic Marine Algae.* This attempt to cover the major parts of the world with floristic accounts has continued to the present, and has now reached the point at which in some cases extensive revisions of earlier seaweed floras have been undertaken by several authors: Kylin, for West Sweden; Dawson, for the Gulf of California; Taylor, for northeast North America and for tropical and subtropical Atlantic America; Dawson, Acleto, and Foldvik, for Peru.

The great expansion of anatomical and morphological studies of marine algae stimulated by Schmitz, and by Falkenberg, Svedelius, Sauvageau, Kylin, and others had produced by 1930 an overwhelming literature in numerous languages through which students could make their way only with great difficulty. Oltmann's two-volume treatise in German on the morphology and biology of the algae, completed in 1923, was getting out of date, and there was no synopsis of the subject in English. At this critical time, F. E. Fritsch, of the University of London, with extraordinary linguistic ability and a facility for writing in shorthand, undertook a review of the world's algal literature and prepared *The Structure and Reproduction of the Algae* (1935, 1946). This has been reprinted several times and remains today the most useful and inclusive reference work on the subject.

Whereas Fritsch alleviated the difficulties of dealing with the literature on morphology and reproduction, the problem of taxonomy and phytogeography of the algae grew, and there is still today, 4 decades after the last volume of de Toni's *Sylloge Algarum,* no index of the world's algae. Consequently, it has been increasingly difficult for a student to cope with the large number of new species, new combinations, and geographical records of the algae of the world.

To provide a stop-gap aid in this circumstance, the writer published in 1962 a catalog of new taxa in marine algae since de Toni. There proved to be some 4000 entries. He also prepared a catalog of the literature and distributions of all Northeast Pacific marine algae, but most other parts of the world lack such a ready synopsis. Silva, of Berkeley, is currently preparing a world list of algal names *(Index Nomina Algarum).* In addition to listing tens of thousands of names already in the literature, this catalog is expanding at the rate of about 1000 per year from current publications. Silva also continues to compile annually the bibliography of world algal literature (see Appendix A).

Another marked advance in the review and compilation of algal literature in a special area within phycology has been accomplished by Lewin as editor of a major review book, *Physiology and Biochemistry of the Algae* (1962).

A HUNDRED YEARS OF MARINE BOTANY
IN THE UNITED STATES

It is remarkable that the first treatise on the marine algae of the United States was the most sumptuous ever to have appeared. It was in the first years of the Smithsonian Institution that W. H. Harvey (Figure 16-1) was invited to prepare an illustrated account of all the seaweeds of North America known to the mid-nineteenth century. It was published in quarto with hand-colored figures, and provided a stimulus to the study of American marine vegetation that was sustained for decades.

Harvey completed the *Nereis Boreali-Americana* in 1858 and continued his study of American algal material in Dublin through a friendship with the Harvard botanist, Asa Gray, formed during his visit to the United States and Gray's visit to Ireland. As a favor to Gray he accepted the study of a special collection of Japanese algae from the United States Exploring Expedition of 1853–1856 and presented an unfinished, preliminary manuscript in 1859. Gray shelved this, however, after extracting the diagnoses of new species. It was forgotten during the Civil War, and was not published until 100 years later upon its discovery in the Farlow Herbarium of Harvard University. This circumstance spans an interesting history.

William Gibbs Farlow (Figure 16-2) entered Harvard University during the Civil War, completed his M.D. in 1870, and was appointed assistant in botany to Asa Gray to put in order the cryptogamic collections. His interest in algae was sparked, and he wrote his first paper on Cuban seaweeds the next year. In June 1872, he carried algal collections to Europe to study with Agardh at Lund, and upon his return he plunged into studies of all manner of cryptogams. He was a specialist in fungi and ferns, but he was also the first resident marine botanist in America and built the first great cryptogamic herbarium in America at Harvard. It came to be known as the Farlow Herbarium and Library.

Among Farlow's correspondents, and his principal collaborator on the first American seaweed exsiccata, the *Algae Exsiccatae Americae Borealis,* was Dr. C. L. Anderson, a physician and amateur botanist of Santa Cruz, California. Anderson was the first resident student of seaweeds of California, and through his collaboration with Farlow at Harvard, Eaton of Yale, and J. G. Agardh of Lund, he stimulated interest in algae on the part of many seaside residents who contributed specimens and data to the early efforts to record the marine plants of California. Some of these were Mr. Cleveland of San Diego, Dr. Dimmock and Mrs. Bingham of Santa Barbara, Miss Lennebacker of Santa Cruz, Mrs. Bush of San Jose, and Miss Westfall, Mrs. Weeks, and the Misses Bayles of Pacific Grove.

Another contemporary of Farlow and of Anderson in California, working summers at the new Hopkins Seaside Laboratory and writing in 1893 on the sea grasses, *Phyllospadix* and *Zostera,* was William R. Dudley, founder of Stanford University's Dudley Herbarium.

Figure 16–3. Frank Shipley Collins in 1898.

Whereas Farlow occupied a place of eminence in the greatest university in America at the time, there appeared in 1879, nearby in Massachusetts, another algologist, named Frank S. Collins (Figure 16-3). He was a bookkeeper and ticket clerk in the Malden Rubber Shoe Company, and became interested in seaweeds through a friend of his wife who prepared "sea moss" novelty cards. He began to collect and study seaweeds for a hobby and, although entirely self taught, became the most expert and productive amateur marine botanist America has yet known.

Collins early became interested in the distribution of sets of dried algae as reference specimens, and contributed to such classical European exsiccatae as those of Wittrock and Nordstedt, and of Hauck and Richter. He finally undertook in 1894, with Isaac Holden and W. A. Setchell, the enormous task of issuing 100 sets of the 51-volume *Phycotheca Boreali-Americana*. During 25 years he handled over 200,000 specimens, and at the same time wrote 86 botanical papers in his spare time. Most notable of these were his *Marine Algae of Jamaica*, *Marine Algae of Bermuda*, and a monograph of the *Green Algae of North America*.

Collins' collaborator on the *Phycotheca*, W. A. Setchell (Figure 16-4) was a student of Farlow, a man of wide botanical interest and of great self-con-

Figure 16–4. William Albert Setchell in 1931.

fidence. Setchell did his doctoral studies on a New England kelp, and, after some years of work at Yale University on Atlantic Coast seaweeds, was offered an instructorship in botany at the University of California in Berkeley. With audacious confidence he announced that he would accept the position, but only as professor and head of the department. Setchell moved to Berkeley, remained head of Botany at the University of California for 40 years, and built it into one of the outstanding botanical centers of the world.

On the West Coast Setchell soon plunged into a variety of projects and took the lead in algology over the only other professional marine botanist there, de Alton Saunders. He planned from the outset a major marine flora of the Pacific Coast of North America and began in 1899, on an expedition to Alaska, to develop it. He was soon joined in the program by a schoolteacher on Whidbey Island, Washington, N. L. Gardner, who, after nearly 2 decades of collaboration by mail, at length assumed professional standing as a second algologist in the department at Berkeley.

At the turn of the century, as Farlow passed into retirement, as Collins came to dominate phycology on the Atlantic Coast and Setchell on the Pacific, a new marine algal center began to form in an unlikely place at the University of Minnesota. Miss Josephine Tilden, professor of botany, as a result of summer seaweeding acquired a piece of property on the wild, wooded, west coast of Vancouver Island, where some of the finest marine algal habitats in the

FIGURE 16–5. Marshall Avery Howe in 1898.

world occur. There, in 1899, near the logging town of Port Renfrew, she founded the Minnesota Seaside Station. For several years, before Washington's Friday Harbor marine laboratory became established in that general region, Miss Tilden conducted summer marine botany classes in a log cabin on the Canadian shore. In later years she took groups of students on even more extended algal collecting trips, to Hawaii and New Zealand. Tilden is also known for her synopsis of the blue-green algae of North America and for a huge bibliographic effort, the "Tilden Algal Index."

During this early twentieth-century period another and greater marine algal center began growth in New York. Marshall A. Howe (Figure 16-5), a graduate of the University of Vermont, went to California in 1892, where he spent 5 years studying cryptogams preparatory to taking a Ph.D. at Columbia University. As a result of contact with Anderson and with the rich seaweed flora of Monterey, he became interested in marine algae, and wrote his first paper on the reproduction of marine plants. He became associated with Nathaniel Lord Britton in the early development of the New York Botanical Garden, and in 1901 joined its staff for the remainder of his life. For 35 years Howe worked in the most industrious and meticulous manner to build during his life the finest algal herbarium in America. Under his curatorship the algal collections rose to over 78,000 specimens, and in addition he filed nearly 60,000 hepatics. Howe was a more careful worker than any of his contemporaries, and left both a splendid record of reliable published works and the best-documented algal reference collection of his time.

Collins died in 1920, and his collections were purchased for the New York Botanical Garden. Howe had written *The Marine Algae of Peru* and the algae section of *The Bahama Flora*. On the West Coast, Setchell and Gardner were in the midst of their major work on the *Marine Algae of the Pacific Coast of North America*. It was through Setchell, as dynamic teacher and counselor of youth, that a new generation of marine botanists was developing. Among his many students during this decade were Kathleen Drew, who became world-famous and honored as an investigator of red algal life histories; and Yukio Yamada, now dean of Japanese algologists and founder of the Hokkaido Institute for Algological Research.

During this time of Setchell and Gardner's intense activity on their monograph of Pacific Coast marine algae, Kylin made an extended visit from Sweden to America (1922) and collected algae at the principal marine stations of the Pacific Coast — La Jolla, Pacific Grove, and Friday Harbor. His subsequent anatomical study of this Pacific material was offensive to Setchell, who never recognized him as a friend; yet Kylin, in deference to the work of the California team, and particularly that of Gardner, withheld description and report of a major part of his California material until several years after Gardner's death in 1936.

In 1924 a young cytologist from the University of Pennsylvania, William Randolph Taylor (Figure 16-6), undertook a special project for the Carnegie Institution of Washington on the marine algae of the Dry Tortugas of Florida. This experience led him into a lifelong specialty of benthic algae which he enjoys today. Taylor moved in 1930 to Ann Arbor, Michigan, and began an intense career of teaching and research on the algae, aiming from the start at a major marine flora of the tropical and subtropical Atlantic coasts of America. He completed this 36 years after his first collection in Florida, while building a great algal herbarium and library at the University of Michigan, training a number of the world's professional marine botanists, and writing some of the most important floristic accounts of algae in the English language.

Although Taylor's work was primarily concerned with the algae of the Atlantic Coast, and most of his summers were spent in his own cottage at Woods Hole, Massachusetts, he embarked upon Pacific algal studies in 1934 upon the invitation of Captain Allan Hancock to join an expedition to the Galapagos Islands. He subsequently participated in another cruise and produced in 1945 the first major algal work for the region from Baja California to Ecuador.

Meanwhile, a new group of algologists was replacing the Setchell and Gardner team in the West. Gilbert Morgan Smith had come to Stanford University and was working on a marine flora of the Monterey Peninsula. In 1935

FIGURE 16-6. William Randolph Taylor in 1960.

Setchell retired at Berkeley and the next year Gardner died. Setchell fell ill for a time and did not return to his laboratory until 1939. World War II was shaping up, but three new students appeared in marine botany: George Hollenberg and Maxwell Doty with Smith, and the author, Yale Dawson, the last student, assistant, and "nephew" of "Uncle Bill" Setchell. The war years were fruitful ones for phycology despite handicaps and restrictions. Dawson completed the *Marine Algae of the Gulf of California,* and Doty, the *Marine Algae of Oregon.* Hollenberg contributed special studies of southern California seaweeds, and Smith completed his magnificently illustrated *Marine Algae of the Monterey Peninsula.*

As World War II engulfed Europe, G. F. Papenfuss, studying in Sweden with Kylin and Svedelius, found himself caught between warring nations and unable to return to his native South Africa. He made his way across Soviet Russia and Siberia, embarked for Hawaii and ultimately for California. At war's end he established himself at Berkeley and at length received his huge South African collections. Setchell had died in 1943 and algology was in need of a new program there. Papenfuss set energetically to work, attracted and trained numerous students, and has seen the publication by several of these (Wagner, Scagel, Eubank-Egerod, Hommersand, Norris, Fan, Sparling, Silva, Abbott) of some of the finest morphological studies on record. Papenfuss continues his studies at Berkeley on the seaweeds of South Africa, and has been joined by his former student, P.C. Silva, who now is in charge of the algal herbarium and is advancing the colossal *Index Nomina Algarum.*

The author, meanwhile, in 1945 joined the Allan Hancock Foundation in Los Angeles, and proceeded to develop a new herbarium there, especially in connection with studies of Pacific Mexican marine algae. During 18 years that collection grew to some 40,000 specimens, and 30,000 more were deposited in other herbaria. Several major floristic studies grew out of that effort, especially those of Pacific Mexico, the Marshall Islands, Viet Nam, and Peru.

Atlantic and Gulf coast marine botany has been dominated for several recent decades by the work of Taylor, but there are others now who are advancing studies of those regions. Harold Humm developed an algal study center at Duke University, and has improved the knowledge of the seaweeds of west Florida and the Gulf of Mexico. Robert Wilce, a student of Taylor, is in Massachusetts where the study of the seaweeds of the United States began. Hommersand is in North Carolina; Zaneveld in Virginia. Marine laboratories all over the nation are now offering courses in marine botany, and with the new emphasis on marine science sparking the minds of youth, the next hundred years should see advances never dreamed by Harvey and Farlow.

We have reached a point of fairly comprehensive knowledge of the kinds and distributions of seaweeds of the United States, and can now proceed to more critical studies of anatomy, reproduction, growth, and physiological behavior, subjects that have as yet been only touched upon. Leaders for this new era in marine botany are already among us, equipped with scuba, the controlled-environment culture room, the electron microscope, and a pervading curiosity about plant life of the sea.

REFERENCES

Papenfuss, G. F. 1955. Classification of the algae. In: *A century of progress in the natural sciences, 1853–1953.* San Francisco: California Acad. Sci., pp. 115–224.

Prescott, G. W. 1951. History of phycology. In: G. M. Smith, *Manual of Phycology.* Waltham, Mass.: Chronica Botanica (Ronald). pp. 1–9.

17

Utilization of Marine Algae

The American layman's usual experience with marine algae is in accord with the implications of the word "seaweed," as a useless or even noxious plant of the sea. Seaweeds may have appeared unsightly to him, littering a lovely beach; they may have entangled his fishing line; they may have fouled the bottom of his boat, or even caused him swimmers' itch. More than likely, he does not realize that he uses seaweed products virtually every day of his life, and that our marine algae are an enormous natural resource that has in recent decades become fundamental to numerous industries. It is the aim of this chapter to point out briefly some of the historical uses of marine plants in various parts of the world and to show how some simple uses of the wild vegetation have evolved into important industrial productions and marine agricultural practices that touch the lives of millions of people.

MARINE ALGAE AS FOOD

A great many kinds of seaweeds are edible and have entered as marine vegetables into the diets of human beings from ancient times. The earliest records are those of the Chinese, who mentioned such food plants as *Laminaria* and *Gracilaria* in their "materia medica" several thousand years ago. From earliest times, however, aboriginal man must have experimented along sea shores with marine algae for food, and some of the results of this experimentation have evolved into established custom. The utilization of *Porphyra* is an interesting example.

Porphyra is a widespread plant in the North Pacific. It grows in the northeast from the Gulf of Alaska to California, and is reported by anthropologists to have been used for thousands of years by the American Indians, ever since they came from Siberia. Because of the Indians' aversion to salting their food, they used *Porphyra* to supply the salt needed for their bodies.

The ancient inhabitants of Japan ate *Porphyra* as a healthful supplement to their rice diet. Its use became so widespread, not only in Japan, but in China, that cultivation of the plant was begun at an early date. The oriental demand for "nori," as *Porphyra* is known in Japan, has grown steadily, so that the production of the seaweed as a farm vegetable has reached huge proportions. Some details of this cultivation will be described and illustrated below.

Other widely used food seaweeds of the orient from ancient times are kombu and wakame, consisting of the stipes and blades of various species of *Laminaria* and *Undaria*, respectively, gathered from natural beds mainly in the cold waters around the island of Hokkaido, Japan (Figure 17-1). These dried marine vegetables found their way into commerce long before the Christian era.

The most diversified dietary use of seaweeds was developed by the Polynesians and reached its peak in Hawaii, where, during the nineteenth century at least 75 species were separately named and used regularly as food in that island world. The Hawaiians called them "limu" and considered them a necessary staple of their daily diet. There is far less quantity and quality in Hawaii than in the rich submarine environments of Japan, but each kind was carefully collected for specific purposes. Some species (as a kind of *Porphyra*) occurred in such small quantity and limited habitat that they were choice delicacies served only to nobility. In fact, the nobility introduced measures that anticipated by centuries the seaweed-cultivation practices in other areas of the world. Certain kinds of limu were transplanted to royal limu gardens where they were protected and tended. The marine fish ponds of Hawaii were frequently used for this purpose. The introduction of glass into the Hawaiian Islands in the early nineteenth century was a great boon to the limu-collecting activities, for glass-bottomed "look boxes" provided a marvelous advance over unaided underwater vision.

The use of seaweeds for food in European areas was never so extensive as in Japan, Hawaii, the Philippines, Malaysia, or Indonesia, but several species nevertheless achieved significance. *Rhodymenia palmata*, known in Scotland as dulse, in Ireland as dillisk, and in Iceland as sol, has been widely used for food for 12 centuries. In more recent years it has been marketed in British Columbia.

FIGURE 17–1. *Undaria* being collected and dried in Hokkaido, Japan, for the making of wakame.

Perhaps the best-known and most widely used food alga in western Europe in recent centuries was Irish moss, or carragheen *(Chondrus crispus),* which was cooked with milk, seasoned with vanilla or fruit, and made into a highly palatable dish known as blancmanges. Use of this alga was carried by colonists to America, and for decades supplies of the raw seaweed were imported to Boston before it was noticed that some of the world's best growths of *Chondrus crispus* occur in that precise area along the New England coast. The jellying qualities of Irish moss, a result of an etherial sulfate in its cell walls, gave the alga an early food use. The extract, now known as carrageenin, has become the basis of a considerable phycocolloid industry which will be described below.

Seaweeds generally are not of very high nutritive value, for some of the carbohydrates are not easily digested by human beings due to a lack of suitable enzymes in the alimentary tract. One might roughly compare the seaweeds with lettuce and celery in this respect. Their value as food lies more in the way they stimulate appetite, provide necessary salts in available organic form, and furnish a number of important vitamins and trace elements. A general improvement of health may for other reasons accompany a diet supplemented with seaweeds. For example, the suppression of hay fever in the orient is considered a corollary of the custom of eating various kinds of seaweeds containing large amounts of potassium chloride, a known alleviative of that distress.

MARINE ALGAE AS FODDER

Whereas the orientals developed wide human uses for marine algae, the Europeans profited by extensive use of these plants for stock feed. In Iceland and Scandinavia, in the British Isles, and along the coast of France, stock has long been driven or allowed to wander to the seashore at low tide to feed on seaweeds. Some kinds of algae, such as *Rhodymenia palmata* and *Alaria esculenta,* are favorite foods of goats, cows, and sheep, and in Scotland and Ireland the stock actively hunt the shores at low tide for particular algae, especially the former. They often are very selective of *Rhodymenia* and will nibble that species and leave alone others adjacent to it, or even overgrowing it. In some coastal areas of Ireland and Scotland, cattle and sheep are fed almost exclusively on *Rhodymenia* and *Alaria.* The milk does not have any taste of algae, nor is the meat inferior because of the seaweed diet. Such animals, that have for several generations been nourished on algae, show better ability to digest it than those not so habituated.

The shortage of grain in many parts of Europe during World War I led to considerable experimentation with the use of seaweeds as food for cows and horses. Stock-feed factories were established in France, Norway, Denmark, and Germany, and various methods of treating and reducing seaweeds to meal or powder were developed.

The favorable results in animal husbandry in Europe led to the industrial processing of the great Pacific-Coast kelp *(Macrocystis)* for animal rations. Seaweed-meal factories have been operating in Los Angeles for several decades, providing supplementary feeds for poultry, cattle, and hogs. The high mineral and vitamin-G content of kelp meal has made possible its use in supplanting dried milk in various poultry and other animal rations that, in addition to kelp meal, have such ingredients as dried fish, fish oils, molasses, ground oyster shell, sodium bicarbonate, and yeast.

FERTILIZER USES

The value of seaweeds in fertilizing the soil was discovered early in the history of agriculture in coastal Asia, and by the ancient colonizers of the coasts and islands of northwestern Europe. The seasonal casts of drift weeds provided the most convenient supplies in all these regions, and were not only used directly by introduction into the soil, but often piled on the farms to dry or partially to disintegrate before being worked in with spring plantings. In some areas of Britain, and especially along 400 miles of the coast of northwest France, the cutting of rockweeds for manure has been so intensively practiced that it became necessary to regulate it by laws that have now been in effect for nearly 100 years.

One of the remarkable small areas in which seaweed fertilizer has been the primary support of a population is on Arran Island, off Scotland. There the barren, rocky land was made fertile for the production of potatoes by the building of a soil in clefts of the rock from decades of hauling up kelps and rockweeds from the shore.

In the United States, long before the recognition of their potash content, seaweeds were employed for fertilizers by the thrifty farmers of New England. Not only the chemical fertilization, but also the water-holding capacity of fragments of the algae in the soil proved effective. These provided valuable small reservoirs of water in close contact with the roots of the cultivated plants. Furthermore, the bulky organic substances decay slowly in the soil and form humus.

As agriculture developed on a mechanized scale in the United States in the late nineteenth century, and chemical fertilization methods became widely adopted, the potash supplies from the Strassfurt mines of Germany became of increasing importance. By 1910, American farmers were practically dependent upon German potash supplies and more than $12 million worth was imported annually. At this time difficulties arose that threatened the availability of German potash, and the United States Congress initiated an investigation of fertilizer resources of its own, taking into account the extensive groves of kelp on the Pacific Coast. In 1912 a report was issued in which these kelp beds were mapped and their estimated productive tonnages given. When the German potash supplies were completely cut off during World War I, the harvesting and rendering of California *Macrocystis* was undertaken in earnest. During 1917 about 3600 tons of potash were produced, and harvesting and drying procedures were developed. During succeeding decades these developments contributed to the establishment of a permanent kelp industry despite the cessation of potash production from seaweeds at the close of the war (see algin industry below).

MEDICINAL USES

Medicinal applications of sea plants are almost as old as their food uses. From earliest times the Chinese used *Sargassum* and various Laminariales for treatment of goiter and other glandular troubles. *Gelidium* very early became employed for stomach disorders and for heat-induced illness. The gentle swelling of dried *Laminaria* stipes upon exposure to moisture gave them use as a surgical tool in the opening of wounds. Similarly, the orientals have employed the same technique in childbirth for expansion of the cervix.

Perhaps the algae used most widely and for the longest time for medicinal purposes have been the agarphytes, including *Gelidium, Pterocladia,* and *Gracilaria.* The name "agar-agar" is of Malay origin and means "jelly." This jelly was obtained by boiling up seaweed and cooling the resulting liquid. Agar early became useful for stomach disorders and as a laxative, and was once employed as a slenderizing dietetic. It was originally produced and marketed mainly in China, but the Japanese took over production in about 1662 and maintained a world monopoly until 1940. The most significant date in the utilization of agarphytes was 1881, when Robert Koch proved the value of agar in the cultivation of bacteria. Since that time it has become essential to the work of hospitals and medical research laboratories throughout the world.

Irish moss *(Chondrus crispus)* has had a long medical history in Europe in the treatment of diarrhea, urinary disorders, and chronic pectoral infections. In the early nineteenth century it was a popular remedy for consumption, and at that time the demands in the United States brought about the establishment of the moss industry at Scituate, Massachusetts. It is still used in Ireland for pulmonary distress, and modern industry (see below) has developed numerous medical and pharmaceutical applications.

The use of marine algae as vermifuges is an interesting story. Linnaeus knew the calcareous alga *Corallina officinalis* as a popular vermifuge from medieval times. In 1775, however, a Greek doctor discovered on the island of Corsica the vermifuge properties of a small red alga later known as *Alsidium helminthochorton.* This was considered the same vermifuge sea plant used by the ancient Greeks, and quickly became an article of commerce (Corsican moss) that outranked *Corallina.*

INDUSTRIALIZATION OF SEAWEEDS

Industrial utilization of seaweeds in Europe had its principal early development in the production of "kelp," a name that originally referred to the ash, rich in soda and potash, derived from burning marine plants. The term still retains much of its original usage in Europe, but in America it has come to apply to the large brown seaweeds themselves. Kelp production was begun sometime in the seventeenth century by French peasants, and spread to other parts of northwest Europe. Driftweeds were first used, but cutting was later resorted to. *Laminaria* and *Saccorhiza* in north Britain became of major importance, but *Fucus* and *Ascophyllum* were also widely used, and in some areas *Himanthalia* and *Chorda*. The kelp ash from these plants was widely bought by early industrialists for use in manufacture of soap, glass, and alum. During the eighteenth and early nineteenth centuries the demands became considerable, and enormous quantities of seaweeds were handled in areas of rich algal growth. In the British Hebrides some 20,000 tons of ash were produced annually, and this required the cutting and handling of 400,000 tons of wet weed by some 3000 crofters.

The kelp industry in Britain reached its peak in 1810, when barilla soda, a higher quality soda obtained from marsh *Salicornia* plants in Spain, became a competitor. A major decline set in, but by 1840 the industry revived as a result of the discovery of high iodine yield in seaweeds. It continued at a favorable level until 1873, when iodine from Chilean nitrate sources reduced the value of seaweed iodine. The kelp industry then declined steadily until, by 1930, it had virtually ceased in most areas. Only in Japan is iodine now produced in any commercial quantities from seaweeds.

In the United States the wartime demands for potash and acetone during 1917–1918 brought about a rapid industrialization of the Pacific-Coast *Macrocystis* beds. Mechanical harvesters were developed, and annual cutting of nearly 400,000 tons resulted. Even after the end of hostilities and the abandonment of these productions, the utilization of these seaweed resources for other purposes was soon to be realized. Inventions and discoveries made during the productive war years had, by 1926, led to uses for the versatile phycocolloids known as the algins, and a new industry came into being.

Algin is the general term designating the hydrophilic, or water-loving derivatives of alginic acid. The most commonly known algin is sodium alginate, but other commercially important compounds are the potassium, ammonium, calcium, and propylene glycol alginates, as well as alginic acid itself. With the exception of alginic acid and calcium alginate, the algin products offered commercially are soluble in water to form viscous solutions.

Algin occurs generally throughout the brown algae as a cell-wall constituent, and is especially prominent in Laminariales. In *Macrocystis* it constitutes about $2\frac{1}{2}$ percent of the plant, and the ease of quantity harvesting of *Macrocystis* has made it the chief raw material in the United States algin industry. The primary producer is Kelco Company of San Diego, California.

Macrocystis is harvested by a motor-driven barge (Figure 17-2) which is equipped with a mowing machine capable of cutting the kelp about 3 feet below the surface of the water and of elevating the cut material onto the barge. Some 300 tons of wet kelp can be handled in a single load, which is taken directly to the factory for washing and processing. The leached kelp is chopped, shredded, and placed in a soda-ash digester. The resulting pulp is diluted, alkalinized, and clarified by filtering or centrifuging, and is then treated with

FIGURE 17–2. The modern kelp cutter, *Kelmar,* loaded with *Macrocystis* and ready to return to the processing plant in San Diego, California. Courtesy of Kelco Company.

calcium chloride. This results in the precipitation of calcium alginate which, when treated with acid, is converted into alginic acid from which various kinds of alginates may be prepared for specific uses.

Algin has remarkable water-absorbing qualities that make it useful in numerous industries in which a thickening, suspending, stabilizing, emulsifying, gel-forming, or film-forming colloid is required. Thus, algin provides ice cream with a smooth texture by preventing the formation of ice crystals. In auto polishes it suspends the abrasive; in paints, the pigments; in pharmaceuticals, the drugs and antibiotics. As a stabilizing agent it serves in the processing of rubber latex and in the printing of textiles. As an emulsifier it is widely used in such products as water-base paints, French dressings, and cosmetics.

The algin industry has become so important to such a wide variety of industries that fluctuation in supply is significant, and when, a few years ago, a marked decline in the kelp beds along southern California occurred, the State undertook an extensive survey of kelp-bed ecology in an effort to guard against loss of this important resource. Harvesting methods are now carefully regulated, and to date more than a quarter-million dollars have been spent on kelp-bed research. Experimental studies are continuing on the relation of pollution to kelp survival and on kelp-bed grazing organisms. Current work involves the use of calcium oxide to combat the grazing of sea urchins in the beds.

Agar

Since the introduction of agar into bacteriology in 1882, the agarphytes have become increasingly industrialized and the technical uses of agar enormously expanded. A few of the medical uses have been mentioned above, but modern industry has developed such a multitude of applications that only a fraction of them can be noted here. Large quantities of agar are used as a food adjunct. Agar serves widely as a substitute for gelatin, as an anti-drying agent in breads and pastry, in improving the slicing quality of cheese, in the preparation of rapid-setting jellies and desserts, and in the manufacture of frozen dairy products. The use of agar in meat and fish canning has greatly expanded, and hundreds of tons are utilized annually. Agar has proved effective as a temporary preservative for meat and fish in tropical regions, due to the inability of most putrifying bacteria to attack it.

Early industrial uses of agar in the orient included sizing fabric, water-proofing paper and cloth, and making rice paper more durable. Modern industry has refined and expanded these uses to meet new needs in the manufacture of such items as photographic film, shoe polish, dental impression molds, shaving soaps, and hand lotions. In the tanning industry agar imparts a gloss and stiffness to finished leather. In the manufacture of electric lamps a lubricant of graphite and agar is used in drawing the hot tungsten wire.

TABLE 5

Systematic Arrangement of Useful Seaweeds and Seaweed Colloids, Showing Phycocolloids, Acids, and Salts Derived from Various Marine Algal Genera
(after Tseng)

Brown Seaweeds (Phaeophyta)
    kelps
        leaf kelps
            Laminaria
                laminarin
                fucoidin
                algin
                    alginic acid
                        sodium alginate
                        ammonium alginate
                        calcium alginate
                        chromium alginate
        giant kelps
            Macrocystis
                algin (as above)
    fucoids
        gulfweeds
            Sargassum
                algin (as above)
        rockweeds
            Fucus
                fucoidin
                algin (as above)

The increasing applications have called for wide expansion of the collection of agarphytes, and since Japan supplied most of the world's markets before World War II, when those supplies were cut off, a great amount of hurried research was conducted in an attempt to develop domestic agar supplies not only in the United States, but in South Africa, Australia, New Zealand, and Russia. The United States industry centered in southern California, where five companies were operating in 1944, using *Gelidium cartilagineum* mainly from Baja California, Mexico, but in part from local beds near Los Angeles. Some 166,000 pounds of agar were produced in 1943, but the high cost of hand harvesting of *Gelidium* caused the abandonment at war's end of collecting by individual divers in California. Japan again is the world's major supplier, but the harvesting of agarphytes is widely practiced in many parts of the world. Some of Japan's raw agar materials, for example, are now imported from Chile.

The place of agar in the scheme of phycocolloids according to Tseng is seen in Table 5. This classification has come into general use since it was published in 1945, and it has greatly aided in standardizing nomenclature in the field.

Red Seaweeds (Rhodophyta)
  agarphytes
    Gelidium (California, Japan, China)
      agar (gelose)
        agarinic acid
          sodium agarinate
          potassium agarinate
          calcium agarinate
          magnesium agarinate
    Gracilaria (Australia, South Africa, North Carolina)
      agar (as above)
    Pterocladia (New Zealand)
      agar (as above)
    Ahnfeltia (Sakhalin, Siberia, White Sea)
      agar (as above)
  carrageens
    Gigartina; Chondrus
      carrageenin
        carrageenic acid
          potassium carrageenate
          calcium carrageenate
  others
    Phyllophora
      agaroid
    Iridaea (Iridophycus)
      iridophycin
        iridophycinic acid
          sodium iridophycinate
    Gloiopeltis
      funorin

Carrageenin

Carrageenin is another phycocolloid of rapidly expanding industrial utilization, and in the United States it is currently produced in much greater quantity than is agar. Carrageenin resembles agar in a general way in being a carbohydrate ethereal sulfate, but it has a higher ash content and requires higher concentrations to form gels. It is produced mainly from *Chondrus crispus* (Irish moss), but also from several species of *Gigartina.*

In North America rich stands of *Chondrus crispus* occur in many places along the East Coast from Cape Cod to Newfoundland. Although Scituate, Massachusetts, was for over a century the center of collection, in recent decades the harvesting has moved north into Maine and Canada. The lower labor costs in Nova Scotia and Prince Edward Island, and a favorable alternation with seasonal agriculture, have made those areas prime producers.

The modern carrageenin industry on the East Coast actually grew out of an algin-production effort begun in 1937 by the Algin Corporation of America established at Rockland, Maine. Using a process of extraction under precise control developed by the French chemist, Victor Le Gloahec, the company was able to produce a high-quality product that found use in printing inks and surgical jellies, salves, and ointments. Some years later it adapted to carrageenin production and recently merged with a major competitor to form Marine Colloids, Inc., which has become the dominant producer of red-algal extracts in America.

In New England and Nova Scotia, Irish moss is collected from May to November by many hundreds of fishermen, vacationing students, and part-time agriculturists. Some of the best collecting is done after a storm, such as an Atlantic hurricane, when windrows of cast algae are piled along the beaches and can be loaded with pitchforks into trucks. Under more usual conditions, however, the mossers work with long-handled rakes scraping the algae off the submerged rock surfaces of shallow bays and inlets. The wet weed sells for up to $1.75 per hundred pounds.

Mossers often do their own cleaning and drying by speading the material in a thin layer on fields or on wooden racks. In Nova Scotia an abandoned airfield became the mossers' drying yard. The weed must be turned during the drying process and can survive only one wetting by rain without unfavorable bleaching and rotting. Mechanical dryers are now being installed in Maine and Canada, and mechanical harvesting procedures are being developed to exploit the seaweed beds in deeper waters than can be reached by the hand rakers.

Some 10-million pounds of seaweed are now being processed annually at Rockland, and raw materials of various red algae are imported from such places as Morocco, Portugal, India, Malaya, and Australia, to provide specific colloidal blends. These are now marketed under the trade name Gelcarin.

Some of the large-scale uses of these products are in stabilizing chocolate milk, egg nog, ice cream, sherbets, frozen specialties, whipped cream, and confectioners' syrups. Many types of puddings, frostings, and bakers' jellies employ it for aiding texture and emulsification. In creamed soups it replaces starch as a thickener.

Other phycocolloids

Three other phycocolloids are of relatively minor importance, but of value for specific purposes. Funorin, from *Gloiopeltis,* has long been used in Japan as the best material for sizing silk. It has become of sufficient value to merit the specific cultivation of *Gloiopeltis* in some areas of northern Japan.

Agaroid is the name applied to the agar-like extract of *Phyllophora* from the Black-Sea region of Russia.

Iridophycin is obtained from various species of *Iridaea* and is used to some extent in Japan in the sizing of finished cloths.

Nori

The most extensive industrialization of seaweeds at the present time is that of nori culture in Japan. The utilization of species of *Porphyra* for food in the orient has led to enormous expansion of this marine agricultural practice which now employs more than a half million persons.

In earlier times nori was cultivated by placing bamboo poles supporting a crown of brush in the muddy shallows of quiet bays along the coast, and by harvesting such *Porphyra* plants as came to grow on the twigs (Figure 17-3). This crude technique has been improved progressively by the use of fixed nets and has been brought to a high degree of perfection.

Modern methods call for the driving of thousands of bamboo poles into the mud at low tide during early autumn and the stringing of nets at a precise level with respect to the tides. Special kinds of rope suitable both for *Porphyra*-spore attachment and for ready hand-harvesting are used. From late November to March the *Porphyra* plants (sometimes more or less mixed with *Monostroma*) are harvested by picking or scraping them from the ropes by hand. The harvester (Figure 17-4) in his narrow boat moves up and down the rows of nets at low tide when they are favorably exposed. The water, and often the weather, is bitter cold at this season, and the harvester may be bundled to his ears except for the bare forearm which becomes modified by the cold-water work to a blood-red condition. When his wicker baskets are filled, they are taken to the mother boat, which transports the wet harvest to the processing yards. The fresh *Porphyra* is washed and then chopped into small fragments. These are stirred in a vat, from which measured amounts of the mixture are dipped by means of a small wooden container and poured over uniformly sized, stiff, porous mats. As the liquid drains away, the nori fragments are spread evenly over the mat, which is hung on outdoor bamboo racks to dry. The thin film of dry nori is then removed as a sheet from the mat (Figure 17-5), folded, and packaged for market. Various grades are sorted, depending upon purity of the *Porphyra* versus *Monostroma*. In some cases nearly pure *Monostroma* is used.

The three or four pickings each season yield about 133,000 tons of nori which makes nearly 2 1/2 billion dried sheets. The 300-odd miles of nets and their supporting poles are then removed and held for nearly 6 months for another season.

FIGURE 17–3. A, The ancient method of growing nori by planting bundles of brush. B, The modern method of preparing nori fields by driving bamboo poles into the mud for the support of nets.

FIGURE 17–4. A, The nori nets heavily laden with *Porphyra* and ready for harvest. B, Hand picking the *Porphyra* from the nets.

FIGURE 17-5. A, The nori farmers gathering, washing and loading baskets of fresh *Porphyra* into the mother boat within a plantation in Tokyo Bay. B, Dried sheets of nori being removed from the flexible drying mats.

Nori is so widely used, and the agriculture employs so large a number of workers (70,000 "fishermen" alone), that special research stations have been set up to study improvements in the program. Experiments have been conducted on the varied growth requirements in numerous *Porphyra* species occurring in Japan, and of the kinds of netting material best suited for attachment. More recently, life-history studies have been made in an effort to improve the effectiveness of "seeding" the beds (formerly accomplished by distributing fragmented *Porphyra* through the culture waters by means of motorboats.)

In 1950, while these experiments were progressing, Kathleen Drew, in Manchester, England, had discovered the relationship of *Conchocelis* to *Porphyra*, and that the former, a small, filamentous, shell-boring red alga, represented an alternate phase of the cultivated *Porphyra* plants. This fact opened a whole new field of investigation for nori culture, and Drew's work came to be considered so significant that upon her recent death a monument was erected in her honor on the shore of Tokyo Bay looking out to the nori fields.

Extensive investigations are now being conducted by Kurogi and other Japanese specialists on *Porphyra* life histories, and *Conchocelis* is already being cultivated commercially in oyster shell to provide means of artificial seeding as part of the agricultural procedure in promoting prime nori production.

REFERENCES

Chapman, V. J. 1950. *Seaweeds and Their Uses.* London: Methuen. 287 pp.

Chase, Florence M. 1941. Useful algae. *Smithsonian Report for 1941*: 401–452.

Kurogi, M. 1963. Recent laver cultivation in Japan. *Fishing News Internat.* July/Sept. 1963: 4 pp.

Tseng, C. K. 1944a. Agar: a valuable seaweed product. *Sci. Monthly,* 58: 24–32.

——————— 1944b. Utilization of seaweeds. *Sci. Monthly* 59: 37–46.

18

Field Collecting
and the Marine Plant Herbarium

COLLECTING PROCEDURES

The most effective learning experience in the beginning study of seaweeds is that which accompanies the collection of specimens in the field and their preparation for the herbarium. Recognition of the plants, both as they appear in nature and as pressed or preserved specimens, is accomplished by this practice of handling and distinguishing them, not by reading descriptions alone. It is intended here to point out some of the procedures that will enable the student quickly and efficiently to assemble a marine-plant study collection in which the specimens will be suitable for permanent scientific reference.

A great many marine algal herbarium specimens have been obtained fortuitously, without special planning or intentions, simply by the collection of material cast ashore in beach drift. It is possible, in fact, to find some algal materials on almost any shore, notwithstanding the state of the tide. Even on the broadest, cleanest beaches the cast of seaweeds after a storm may provide some of the most convenient and exciting opportunities for the marine botanist. Much material not otherwise obtainable is found in storm drift, and the sorting over of windrows of cast, before it has been dried, bleached, or infested with invertebrates, may be highly rewarding.

As a rule, however, the phycologist will best plan his field trips to the shore to coincide with the hours of falling tide, so that he may observe, collect, and record the plants in their natural habitats and life positions. It is, of course, best to select a tide during a period of the low-water springs, or "minus tides," in order to take advantage of maximum exposure of the intertidal zone. The most favorable timing is to arrive at the shore 2 hours or more before the time of low tide predicted by a tide table. This allows time to work the shore from high to low levels as the water recedes. The water is usually clearer on a falling than on a rising tide, and it is always better to observe and collect the exposed plants before they have been subjected to any appreciable desiccation. The collecting, thus, should be finished shortly after the time of low water.

The manner of collecting varies greatly with the degree of exposure. A broad reef, exposed at low water and with many tide pools, may provide convenient and comfortable collecting, while a shore pounded by surf may necessitate the most strenuous activity and agile movements in accord with the dangers of slippery rocks and powerful water. In cold waters, the collector will work in hip boots or hunters' waders. In warm waters, trousers should be worn to guard against cuts and scratches from barnacles or corals, and cord-soled shoes will aid movement over slippery rocks.

As the collector works from higher to lower levels, he may segregate materials from various habitats in plastic bags and carry them in a pail. Small or rare specimens, or fertile plants of critical interest, may be fixed in vials of preservative and kept with the material in respective bags. Many specimens can be removed from rocks with the fingers, but a spoon, a putty knife, or similar scraping blade is useful to secure complete holdfasts and to remove crustose forms from the rocks. Some crustose or low, mat-forming plants adhere so closely that they must be removed with the rock. For this purpose a geologist's pick or an alpinist's hammer may be used. A sharp blade may be needed in some areas for cutting coarse kelps to obtain the epiphytes on their stipes or holdfasts.

If one has arrived at the shore for low-tide work early enough, he will have time to explore carefully upper levels for varied and special habitats in which particular species will be found. The high, dark bands of marine lichens may be noted first in some areas. The damp walls and ceilings of sea caves or overhanging cliffs harbor special associations, as do high rock pools subject to spray and often to the accumulation of bird droppings. At somewhat lower levels rocks may be turned to reveal algal patches or mats partially embedded in sand. The tops of boulders may be covered with a film of blue-green algae scarcely recognizable except when wet and slippery. As one works down into lower levels of more abundant growth, the specialized habitats become more numerous. Some species will inhabit only the bottoms of small tide-pools subject to warming, others the shaded under-edges of submerged rocks. Some species will be found only under the protective cover of surf grass, or of coarser algae, and others fixed only to barnacles in areas subject to surf. Many of the larger algae will harbor epiphytes, sometimes of many species, and the red algae should be examined carefully for parasitic genera, of which there are especially numerous forms on the Pacific Coast. Exposures and habitats in some quite small areas may be so diverse that several days of low-tide work may be required to obtain a representative sampling.

In shallow bay waters and on broad reefs or flats, such as those of Florida, where collecting can be done in wading depth, a glass-bottom "look box" greatly aids the investigator by making readily visible the plant associations as one slowly wades along, exploring the shallows. All manner of shell, coral, and rock substrates should be examined, as well as sponges, tunicates, hydroids, submerged wood, floating woodwork, buoys, and the like. The collections made by such a wading botanist may readily be carried in a floating basket, consisting of a canvas-covered, inflated automobile tube drawn by a line. This same device, provided with an anchoring weight, serves in deeper waters in which the collector may use a face mask and snorkle for shallow diving. Perforated plastic bags are good underwater containers for such diving work.

Scuba diving has in recent years become commonplace in marine botanical investigations, but the proper procedures for safe work of this kind should be learned through careful instruction and adequate swimming-pool practice before undertaking fieldwork. In cold waters the diver will need a well-fitted, protective wet suit with hood and boots. In warm waters, regular shirt, trousers, weight belt, and shoes may be worn for comfortable exploratory walks on the bottom. One can conveniently survey large areas of shallow bay bottoms in quiet waters by pulling a skiff along overhead as he collects. He can, thus, easily go up and down the painter as materials need to be passed to a companion in the boat.

Although diving is becoming increasingly effective for all manner of aquatic biological work, the traditional service of the ship's dredge is still widely used for algal collecting in areas of cold, deep, rough, or turbid waters. Diving may often be impracticable because of poor visibility, lack of a safe compressed-air supply, or absence of companion divers. Under such circumstances, a dredge handled by a powered winch can be depended upon to bring up at least a sampling of the bottom vegetation, and, with good luck, a rich haul amply representative of the flora. The dredge may commonly break off only fragments of the plants, but sometimes scoops up a rock bearing the plants intact and in normal position. Furthermore, the dredge, although towed blindly, brings its catch into the light for careful sorting and analysis. The diver is handicapped by the loss of recognizable color, and often overlooks red algae on the bottom because of their extreme obscurity in blue light. Biological dredges of many sizes are available on the market, suitable for small launches as well as larger vessels. They are in service at virtually all the marine stations.

PRESERVATION AND PREPARATION

When collecting at any locality has been completed, the specimens should either be pressed directly as fresh material or be preserved as quickly as possible to prevent unnecessary deterioration. The latter is best accomplished at the shore or on shipboard by having at hand one or more 5-gallon, wide-mouthed tin cans with pressure lids. Seawater should be brought up in a bucket and mixed with commercial 40 percent formaldehyde to obtain approximately a 3 percent solution. Fresh water may harm some species, and a few will actually dissolve in it. The various plastic bags into which specimens have been separated may then be partially filled with the preservative and tied. These bags, together with bulkier materials, as well as small bottles or vials of specimens, may be placed in the can in preservative and provided with an appropriate label made from 100 percent rag paper that will not decompose in the liquid. A little borax added to the preservative will buffer it and prevent unfavorable increase of acidity. Such a tin of specimens may be closed and kept for months without deterioration of the specimens or significant loss of color, while the same specimens kept in glass jars exposed to light would be bleached and largely worthless in a few days. The tin, may, indeed, be sealed with solder and boxed for shipment with ease and without fear of damage to the contents.

Of utmost importance in the preparation of any collection is the provision of adequate field data in the field-collection notebook, and the careful preparation of labels. For this purpose, all pertinent observations on the character of the habitat, size, and aspect of the various dominant species, the major associations that may be recognized, and such factors as water temperature, substrate type, and exposure, should be recorded before leaving the field. These data should be incorporated in the permanent book of field notes in which a consecutive series of collection numbers is tabulated later as each species is recognized, sorted out, and recorded.

In some cases it will be found desirable to reduce the bulk of large or coarse specimens rather than to include them in the tins of preserved materials. Large kelps and coarse red algae may be rough-dried by laying them out in a shaded place and turning them several times as the dehydration proceeds. Before they are completely dried, they may be folded or rolled into a compact bundle for removal to the laboratory. Such rough-dried specimens can readily be soaked up again in water and made into herbarium specimens.

Sometimes there may be sufficient time and facilities at the shore to permit specimens to be prepared for the herbarium immediately after collecting. The procedure outlined below may be followed, except that for thin and delicate specimens it is not generally necessary to treat them with preservative first. On the other hand, coarse specimens should always be killed and sterilized before mounting to prevent mould and to allow for quicker drying. Another difficulty is encountered in the mounting of fresh specimens in seawater, namely, the retention of salt and the formation of crystals in the specimens. This is alleviated by adequate fixation of the specimens and later washing with tap water.

Upon return to the laboratory the preparation of preserved specimens may begin at once, although it is preferable to leave the material in preservative for a few days in order to allow for complete fixation. This applies particularly to those few species that, when fresh, are damaged by being immersed in tap water, but that are not harmed by the same treatment after having remained for a few days or weeks in the formalin-seawater solution.

A large, flat-bottomed, white enamel sink provides the most effective means for sorting specimens, but large, white enamelware trays may be used. A number of wide-mouthed jars should be arranged around the sorting area and some small rectangles of rag paper kept at hand for assigning serial numbers to the specimens as they are sorted and listed at the wet table preparatory to final entry in the field notebook.

The specimens from individual collecting bags may first be dumped into the sink and washed to remove the excess formalin. They should then be separated into the jars, each species receiving a number that is listed with a tentative identification on the field-data sheet. Of each of the species, especially the smaller or more delicate forms, appropriate portions should be selected and placed in small vials (4 dram shell vials) of formalin for future use in making preparations for microscopic examination. These wet-stack materials should receive the same field number assigned to the remaining material of each given species destined for herbarium mounting.

After segregation of all the species into separate containers, the drying may begin. Several methods may be employed, depending upon the nature of the specimens. Crustose algae that have been brought from the shore, along with pieces of their substrate, may be dried directly in the air and preserved in this dry state in small boxes of suitable size. Articulated, calcareous algae that are so fragile and/or so three-dimensional as to suffer badly from pressing should be treated in the same protective way. They should, however, preferably be soaked for several days or weeks in a formalin solution containing 10 to 40 percent glycerin before being dried and placed in the small boxes. The glycerin retains the flexibility of the genicula and prevents fragmentation. A similar glycerin procedure may be used for large algal specimens for which it is desirable to retain natural form and flexibility. After killing in formalin and soaking for several days in about 50 percent glycerin (with a little phenol), they may be hung out to dry, and then rolled up and kept in plastic bags for future examination or demonstration. Other than these special preparations, the seaweeds may be dried in a standard plant press.

Inasmuch as the algal specimens should ultimately be mounted on standard $11\frac{1}{2}$ inch by $16\frac{1}{2}$ inch herbarium paper, whole sheets or suitably sized pieces of this all-rag paper may be used for the next step, which is the backing of the specimen as it is floated out for drying.

Mounting may best be done in a flat sink, or in a broad, shallow tray large enough to accommodate a full-size herbarium sheet. (A plastic cafeteria tray serves well.) The sheet of paper to be used in each instance should first be given its collection number and then immersed in the water in the bottom of the tray. The water should be of the least depth suitable for floating out the particular specimen at hand and spreading it on the paper. After the plant has been spread out in a natural manner on its backing sheet in the water tray, the sheet should be lifted carefully from one side to allow the water to drain off gradually and to leave the specimen spread out and undisturbed. A device for effecting this drainage may be made from a piece of galvanized sheet metal, by bending down the corners to form short legs. These will permit the middle to be depressed slightly for spreading a specimen and to be released to allow the water to drain off evenly.

The sheet or card bearing the spread specimen is then placed directly on a dry felt in the press and covered either with a piece of cloth or a sheet of ordinary waxed paper. Cloth will serve best for drying coarse, succulent specimens, but waxed paper will prove more satisfactory for smaller forms and especially for very lubricous or mucilaginous ones. Exceedingly coarse specimens need not be spread on paper at all, but arranged between cloths, newspapers, or waxed paper in the press. After drying, they may be mounted on the herbarium sheets by means of straps or small spots of glue.

When the spreading has been completed and the last felt drier has been placed over a specimen, the press should be strapped with the application of moderate pressure. Small press stacks may conveniently be weighted with concrete blocks or rocks. It is necessary to prevent the specimens from shrinking or curling during the drying process and to accomplish the drying in the shortest possible time. This may best be done by frequent changing of the driers (at least once a day). The specimens should not be subjected to heat, as by placing the press in an oven; rather, they should be dehydrated by frequent replacement of the wet driers with warm, dry ones. In changing the driers, the first wet one on top should be removed and a dry one placed over the specimen. Then, by insertion of one hand beneath the next lower wet felt, while the other is placed on top, the whole layer may be lifted and turned upside down without disturbing the specimens or the waxed paper covering them. If this process is repeated quickly for each sheet, and the pressure promptly reapplied in the press, good specimens will result in which a large proportion will adhere to the paper satisfactorily by means of their own mucilage. Drying will usually take from 2 days for delicate specimens to a week for coarse ones.

A better and more time-saving method of pressing is now possible through the use of corrugated aluminum sheets cut to plant-press size. These corrugates are used as separators between the herbarium felts in the press, and when the press is placed in the warm-air draft of a fan, they permit the circulation of air throughout. This effects very rapid drying with no necessity for relieving the pressure in the press, and results in superior specimens.

Care must be taken to be sure the drying is complete before removal of specimens from the press, for otherwise shrinkage of the specimen, and consequent wrinkling and curling of the paper backing will result.

In the preparation of the marine plant herbarium it will be found necessary to provide for the storage of several different kinds of preservations. The fleshy species, which lend themselves to pressing and mounting on herbarium sheets, may be handled in the same way as are terrestrial plants. Those that have adhered well to backing sheets during the drying process may be mounted by pasting to standard herbarium sheets. Tin paste, standard herbarium paste, or Wilhold glue should be used. Rubber cement, staples, cellophane tape, and the like, are not satisfactory. Coarser specimens, which are dried free of backing, may be fixed to herbarium sheets by means of glue spotted sparsely here and there on the specimen, or by strips of gummed cloth. When the herbarium label, properly inscribed, has been affixed to the lower-right-hand corner of the sheet, the plant is ready for filing. If portions of the specimen have been retained in liquid preservative, this should be indicated somewhere on the sheet for future reference.

Liquid-preserved specimens usually may be kept in dilute formalin for months or a few years without damage, but for long periods of time, 65 to 70 percent ethyl alcohol is more satisfactory. A convenient short-term procedure is to keep the small portions of preserved material in 4-dram shell vials in the 1-gross boxes in which they are sold. They may be cross-referenced on the herbarium sheets by means of the field numbers written on the corks. The corked vials will need to be checked for preservative refill at least once a year. More permanent filing of wet-stack materials is accomplished by placing the vials within air-tight, pint jars provided with soft-plastic sealers under the lids.

Bulky specimens, especially calcareous forms and crustose species adhering to rocks, shells, and so forth, may best be kept in small boxes fitting into standardized cardboard herbarium trays. The trays may be numbered, and the labeled specimens referred to by means of cross-reference sheets in the herbarium file.

Specimens which are too small for convenient mounting on herbarium sheets may be placed in small packets affixed to the sheet, or, if exceedingly small and delicate, may be mounted whole on small rectangles of mica and stored in a packet. They can be reexamined at any time by adding a drop of water and a cover slip. A still better procedure is to mount the specimens whole on microscope slides and then to cross-index them in their permanent storage boxes. Inasmuch as the preparation of slides for study and reference is of great importance in phycology, it seems well to explain here an easy method suitable for the majority of cases.

Permanent slides may readily be made of most species and for most general morphological purposes by using the ordinary crystal-clear variety of Karo corn syrup. Material preserved either in formalin or alcohol may be prepared after washing with water. The specimen is first stained either with aniline blue or acid fuchsin on a slide by adding a little of a 1 percent aqueous stain, acidifying after about a minute, and then washing with a drop or two of distilled water. After washing away the acidified stain, and the excess water has been drawn off with blotting or filter paper, Karo syrup, diluted to 50 to 60 percent with distilled water, is applied and the slide left open to the air in a dust-free drawer overnight. The next day, after the first drop of dilute Karo has dried down so that excessive or permanent shrinkage of the cells of the specimen has been avoided, another drop of more concentrated Karo (about 80 percent) is added and the cover slip applied to complete the preparation, which is self-sealing. The Karo dries around the edges within a few days, and although the slide should not be allowed to stand on edge for a considerably longer period, it may otherwise be handled with ease. Shrinkage is not appreciable in small plants of a dense structure of minute cells, or in microtome or hand sections, and these may be mounted directly in 80 percent Karo. Very small bubbles usually will form gradually under the cover slip as the drying proceeds, but these rarely affect the usefulness of the preparation. In the writer's experience such slides have shown no appreciable deterioration after more than 20 years of storage.

Thin sections of marine algae are best made with a freezing microtome, and for this purpose the liquid-preserved materials in the wet stack will prove most useful. Either a sliding or a swinging microtome with CO_2 attachment may be used. A drop of water is put on the CO_2 platform and barely frozen. The small piece of alga is then oriented on top of the frozen drop and more water added and frozen to encase the specimen. As the sections are cut (using the razor-blade attachment instead of a knife), they are removed to a drop of water on a slide by means of a moist camel's-hair brush. For minute or very delicate sections, the blade holder is removed and the sections washed onto the slide with a drop of water. These may then be stained and run into corn syrup. Gum guaiacum solution may sometimes be used instead of water on the freezing platform for smoother cutting.

In the absence of a freezing microtome, good sections can be made by hand, after a little practice, with a single-edged razor blade. This is most easily accomplished by using dried specimens, for in the majority of cases such sections will expand in a drop of water to very nearly their normal size and shape. If they do not, a little heat usually helps. Stubborn cases usually respond to the addition of potassium hydroxide and heat. The most convenient cutting method is that whereby the specimen fragment is held with the index finger on a white card under a dissecting microscope of 6 to 10 power and sliced with the blade against the finger-nail for support and guide. If a large number of sections are cut in this way, some of them will have portions sufficiently thin to reveal the necessary details of cellular structure for identification. The cutting of fresh or liquid-preserved specimens by hand, especially those of soft texture, requires more care and skill.

In some instances it may be desirable to prepare permanent sections or whole mounts by the more traditional methods of alcohol dehydration. Various dehydration and paraffin-embedding procedures have been worked out for diverse groups of algae by Johansen (1940).

Calcareous algae, particularly crustose ones, are some of those presenting unusual difficulties to study and often require special sectioning procedures. The following method used by Mason (1953) is a satisfactory one. "Fresh or dried material may be used, but for histological purposes fresh material is preferable. Small thalli may be used whole, but larger plants should be broken into pieces a centimeter or less in diameter, since the rate of decalcification is inversely proportional to the size of the specimen. Dried material should first be boiled for 30 minutes. Fresh material may be placed directly in Pérényi's fixing and decalcifying solution. It is composed of 4 parts 10 percent nitric acid, 3 parts 70 percent alcohol, and 3 parts 0.5 percent chromic acid. Thin pieces may be completely freed of calcium and magnesium carbonate in from 4 to 6 hours, whereas thick pieces may require several days or even weeks. The solution should be changed at least twice a day. Complete decalcification is essential, since any trace of hard material will ruin both knife and specimen. After complete decalcification the material is rinsed in 70 percent alcohol and then placed in fresh 70 percent alcohol for 24 hours. It is then carried through 85, 95, and 100 percent alcohol and through 6 grades of xylol-alcohol to pure xylol at 24-hour intervals. It is next imbedded in paraffin. Sections 10 to 20 μ thick are satisfactory for general study. Delafield's haematoxylin has proved a satisfactory stain for most structures."

Since the paraffin-embedding procedure is relatively time-consuming, the writer has used a short-cut method for routine examination and identification. Specimens may be partially decalcified so that they still remain firm enough to cut. Moderately thick sections can then be made on the freezing microtome and the decalcification completed on the slide along with staining. From these sections certain reproductive features, or the critical cell forms and sizes, may be determined for taxonomy, despite the imperfections of the preparation.

In some calcareous algae, such as *Peyssonelia*, the plant remains sufficiently firm after complete decalcification to permit sectioning either by freezing microtome or by hand. In others, such as *Liagora*, decalcification will permit a small bit of the material to be placed on a slide and squashed out under the cover slip to reveal the cellular details of the filaments. The "squash technique" is useful for many of the soft-bodied red algae of filamentous structure in which significant details, especially of reproduction, are best seen when the entangled threads are spread out in a thin layer. Even fairly firm species may be squashed if a suitable softening agent is used. Although 5 to 10 percent KOH is often good, trial and error may show NaOH or HCl to serve better in some instances. Length of treatment also varies, from a few minutes to 24 hours. Permanent squash mounts may be made by using corn syrup.

An effective method of embedding small specimens of fresh algal material for herbarium storage is accomplished by carbowax mounting. (Carbowax [water-soluble polyethylene glycol] may be obtained from Union Carbide Chemicals Co., 30 E. 42nd Street, New York City, New York.) Washed, formalin-fixed or alcohol-fixed algal material is transferred to a bath of melted

Carbowax (about 56°C) for 30 to 120 minutes. It is transferred to a second bath for similar duration and then spread evenly on an herbarium-paper card. The card is quickly placed between two sheets of waxed paper and flattened while the Carbowax hardens. The resulting card provides permanent protection for the specimen, which can be rehydrated merely by placing the card in lukewarm water.

CLEANING AND MOUNTING DIATOMS

Diatoms may be cleaned and prepared for examination and permanent herbarium filing according to the following method. Formalin-preserved diatoms are washed four or five times with distilled water using a centrifuge and the supernatant fluid poured off after each spinning. Concentrated HCl is added and centrifuged once. The HCl is changed and the material boiled under a hood. Concentrated HNO_3 is added drop by drop until no more fumes are evolved. The acid is then gradually removed by pouring off some of the acid, adding distilled water, and centrifuging successively four or five times. The cleaned, acid-free diatoms are then removed in a drop or so of water and placed on a clean cover slip, which is heated to evaporate the water. A drop of Hyrax mounting medium is placed on a clean slide and heated. The cover slip with its diatoms is turned upside down onto the Hyrax and gently pressed down. After cooling, the mount can be ringed with nail polish.

REFERENCES

Johansen, D. A. 1940. *Plant Microtechnique.* New York: McGraw-Hill. 523 pp.
Mason, Lucile R. 1953. The crustose coralline algae of the Pacific Coast. . . . *Univ. Calif. Publ. Bot.,* 26: 313–390.
Sass, J. E. 1951. *Botanical Microtechnique.* . . . Ames, Iowa: 2nd ed. xi + 228.
Taylor, W. R. 1957. *Marine Algae of the Northeastern Coast of North America.* Ann Arbor: University of Michigan Press. (rev. ed.) ix + 509 pp.

Appendix A

General Information, Literature, and Research Facilities

Important Societies for American Phycologists
Phycological Society of America. Department of Botany, Washington University, St. Louis, Missouri. Annual membership: $9.00
International Phycological Society. Department of Botany, University of California, Berkeley, California. Annual membership: $4.00

Important Journals devoted entirely or in large part to algae
Botanica Marina, published by Cram, de Gruyter & Co., Hamburg 1, Germany
Phycologia, published by the International Phycological Society (see above)
Journal of Phycology; Phycological Newsletter, published by the Phycological Society of America (see above)
Révue Algologique, published by Musée National d'Histoire Naturelle, Paris V^e, France
Nova Hedwigia, published by J. Cramer, Lehre, Germany
British Phycological Bulletin, issued by the British Phycological Society, Marine Station, Millport, Isle of Cumbrae, Scotland
Phykos, journal of the Phycological Society of India, Division of Microbiology, Indian Agricultural Research Institute, New Delhi 12, India
Bulletin of the Japanese Society of Phycology, Phycological Lab., Faculty of Fisheries, Hokkaido Univ., Hakodate, Hokkaido, Japan
International Seaweed Symposia, Proceedings, published in connection with meetings every few years

Libraries containing extensive marine botanical literature

University of California, Berkeley, California (including Setchell library and private collections of P.C. Silva and G.F. Papenfuss)

Farlow Herbarium and Library, Harvard University, Cambridge, Massachusetts

New York Botanical Garden, Bronx Park, New York, New York

University of Michigan, Ann Arbor, Michigan (including private collection of Wm. Randolph Taylor)

University of Hawaii, Honolulu, Hawaii (including private collection of M. S. Doty)

Smithsonian Institution, Washington, D.C. (including private collection of E. Yale Dawson)

Library of Congress, Washington, D.C.

U.S. Department of Agriculture, Washington, D.C.

Philadelphia Academy of Natural Sciences, Philadelphia, Pennsylvania

Duke University Biology Library, Durham, North Carolina

Lloyd Library, Cincinnati, Ohio

John Crerar Library, Chicago, Illinois

Marine Biological Laboratory, Woods Hole, Massachusetts

Important Herbarium collections of marine algae

New York Botanical Garden, Bronx Park, New York, New York (large general collection)

University of California Herbarium, Berkeley, California (large general collection)

Chicago Natural History Museum, Chicago, Illinois (large general collection)

University of Michigan, Ann Arbor, Michigan (large marine collection strong in Atlantic materials)

Smithsonian Institution, Washington, D.C. (large general collection)

Allan Hancock Foundation, University of Southern California, Los Angeles, California. (large marine collection, mostly Pacific Ocean)

University of British Columbia, Vancouver, Canada (marine collection mainly of northeast Pacific)

University of Minnesota, Minneapolis, Minnesota (general collection)

Philadelphia Academy of Natural Sciences, Philadelphia, Pennsylvania (general collection and large collections of diatoms and Cyanophyta)

International bookdealers who handle appreciable stocks of out-of-print phycological literature

Wheldon & Wesley, Ltd., Lytton Lodge, Codicote, near Hitchin, Herts, England

Paul Lechevalier, Paris 6, France

Antiquariaat Junk (Dr. R. Schierenberg), Lochem, Netherlands

A. Asher & Co., Amsterdam-C, Netherlands

Andr. Fred Høst & Son, Kobenhavn-K, Denmark

Stechert-Hafner, Inc., New York, New York

Other sources of classical literature
Microcard Foundation, Washington, D.C.
International Documentation Center AB, Tumba, Sweden
Scripps Institution Library, La Jolla, California, can furnish positives of the
Dawson microfilm of algal literature from the University of California,
Berkeley

Recent and current phycological literature
Compilations of the world's phycological literature for successive years be-
ginning with 1956, by P.C. Silva, in the *Phycological Society Bulletin* and in
Phycologia

Regional floras useful in the study of North American benthic algae
Taylor, W. R. 1957. *Marine Algae of the Northeastern Coast of North America.*
Ann Arbor: Univ. of Michigan Press. ix + 509 pp., 60 pls.
Taylor, W. R. 1960. *Marine Algae of the Eastern Tropical and Subtropical Coasts
of the Americas.* Ann Arbor: Univ. of Michigan Press. ix + 870 pp., 30 pls.
Smith, G. M. 1944. *Marine Algae of the Monterey Peninsula, California.* Stanford:
Stanford University Press. vii + 622 pp., 98 pls. (with addendum by I.A.
Abbott and G.J. Hollenberg, 1966)
Setchell, W. A., and N. L. Gardner. 1919–1925. Marine algae of the Pacific
Coast of North America. *Univ. Calif. Publ. Botany,* 8(1): 1–138, 1919; 8(2):
139–374, 1920; 8(3): 383–898, 1925.
Dawson, E. Y. 1961. A guide to the literature and distributions of Pacific
benthic algae from Alaska to the Galapagos Islands. *Pacific Sci.* 15:
370–461.
Dawson, E. Y. 1953–1963. Marine red algae of Pacific Mexico. *Allan Han-
cock Pac. Exped.,* 17: 1–398; 26: 1–208. *Pacific Naturalist,* 2: 1–126; 189–375.
Nova Hedwigia, 5: 437–476; 6: 401–481.
Dawson, E. Y. 1965. Some marine algae in the vicinity of Humboldt State
College, California. (with keys). Arcata, Calif.: Humboldt State College.
76 pp.
Dawson, E. Y., I. A. Abbott, G. J. Hollenberg and P. C. Silva. *The Marine
Algae of California.* Stanford: Stanford University Press (in preparation).
Doty, M. S. 1947. Marine algae of Oregon. *Farlowia,* 3: 1–65; 159–215.
Kylin, H. 1925. The marine red algae in the vicinity of the biological station
at Friday Harbor, Wash. Lunds Univ. Årsskr., N.F., Avd. 2, 21(9): 1–87.
Hoyt, W. D. 1920. Marine algae of Beaufort, N.C. and adjacent regions.
Bull. U.S. Bur. Fisheries, 36 (1917–1918): 367–556.

Major supply houses furnishing marine algal materials
Carolina Biological Supply Co., Burlington, North Carolina (materials
mainly from North Carolina and from Oregon)
Wards Natural Science Establishment, Inc., Rochester, New York and
Monterey, California (materials mainly from central California and from
Maine)

Marine laboratories and near-shore marine botanical facilities
Pacific Coast Stations
University of Alaska, Douglas Island Marine Station, Institute of Marine Science, College, Alaska

University of British Columbia, Department of Botany, Vancouver 8, Canada

University of Washington, Friday Harbor Laboratories, San Juan Island, Washington

University of Washington, Department of Botany, Seattle, Washington

Whidbey Island Marine Station, Seattle Pacific College, Seattle 99, Washington

Walla Walla College Biological Station (Anacortes), College Place, Washington

University of Oregon Institute of Marine Biology, Charleston, Oregon

Humboldt State College Marine Laboratory, Arcata, California

Mendocino Biological Field Station, Albion, Calif. (Pacific Union College, Angwin, California)

Pacific Marine Station (University of the Pacific), Dillon Beach, California

University of California Marine Station, Bodega Head, California

University of California, Department of Botany, Berkeley, California

Hopkins Marine Station (Stanford University), Pacific Grove, California

Marine Laboratory, University of California at Santa Barbara, Goleta, California

Allan Hancock Foundation, University of Southern California, Los Angeles, California

University of California at Los Angeles, Department of Botany, Los Angeles, California

Kerckoff Marine Laboratory (California Institute of Technology), Corona del Mar, California

Scripps Institution of Oceanography, La Jolla, California

Escuela Superior de Ciencias Marinas, Universidad Autonoma de Baja California, Ensenada, Baja California, Mexico
Tropical Pacific Stations
University of Hawaii Marine Laboratory, Honolulu, Hawaii

Estacion de Biología Marina de Mazatlán, Casa del Marino, Paseo Claussen, Colonía los Pinos, Mazatlán, Sinaloa, Mexico
East Coast Stations
Biological Station, St. Johns, Newfoundland

Nova Scotia Research Foundation, Halifax, Nova Scotia

Quebec Départment des Pêcheries, Station de Biologie Marine, Grande-Rivière, Gaspé, Quebec

Mount Desert Island Biological Laboratory, Salisbury Cove, Maine

Biological Laboratory, Boothbay Harbor, Maine

Farlow Herbarium, Harvard University, Cambridge, Massachusetts
Marine Biological Laboratory, Woods Hole, Massachusetts
University of Connecticut Marine Research Laboratory, Noank, Connecticut
Narragansett Marine Laboratory, University of Rhode Island, Kingston, Rhode Island
Biological Laboratory, Milford, Connecticut
Bingham Oceanographic Laboratory, Yale Station, New Haven, Connecticut
Herbarium of the New York Botanical Garden, Bronx Park, New York, New York
Sandy Hook Marine Laboratory, Highlands, New Jersey
Academy of Natural Sciences of Philadelphia, Philadelphia, Pennsylvania
University of Delaware Marine Laboratory, Lewes, Delaware
Biological Laboratory, Oxford, Maryland
Chesapeake Bay Institute, Annapolis, Maryland
Chesapeake Biological Laboratory, Solomons, Maryland
Smithsonian Institution, Department of Botany, Washington, D.C.
Virginia Institute of Marine Science, Gloucester Pt., Virginia
Duke University Marine Laboratory, Beaufort, North Carolina
Fort Johnson Marine Biological Laboratory, Charleston, South Carolina
Biological Laboratory, Brunswick, Georgia
University of Georgia Marine Institute, Salpelo Island, Georgia
Marineland Research Laboratory, St. Augustine, Florida
University of Miami Marine Laboratory, Virginia Key, Miami, Florida

Gulf Coast Stations

Cape Haze Marine Laboratory, Sarasota, Florida
Florida State Board of Conservation Marine Laboratory, Bayloro Harbor, St. Petersburg, Florida
University of Florida Marine Laboratory, Alligator Point, Crawfordsville, Florida
Sabine Island Biological Laboratory, Gulf Breeze (Pensacola), Florida
Alabama Marine Laboratory, Bayon La Batra, Alabama
Gulf Coast Research Laboratory, Ocean Springs, Mississippi
A&M College of Texas Marine Laboratory, Fort Crockett, Galveston, Texas
University of Texas Institute of Marine Science, Port Arkansas, Texas

Tropical Atlantic Stations

Bermuda Biological Station for Research, Inc., St. George West, Bermuda
American Museum of Natural History Lerner Marine Laboratory, Bimini, Bahamas
University of Puerto Rico Institute of Marine Biology, Mayaguez, Puerto Rico
Instituto Tecnológico de Veracruz, Estacion de Biología Marina, Veracruz, Mexico

The University of Washington's Friday Harbor Laboratories on San Juan Island, Puget Sound, 1963.

Appendix B

Synopsis of the North American Benthic Marine Algae and Phanerogams

The following list, representing a flora of over 2000 species, attempts to summarize the families and genera of green, brown, and red algae and marine phanerogams, known to occur along, or adjacent to, the Pacific and Atlantic shores of continental North America (excluding Bermuda, the Caribbean islands, and the far off-lying Pacific Islands). It is intended to serve as a systematic and geographic guide and as an orienting checklist for those who encounter these names in connection with their marine botanical studies. The number of species recognized is according to current floristic accounts. The ranges indicated are very general and indicative only of gross regional occurrence without suggestion of frequency or abundance.

CHLOROPHYTA

VOLVOCALES
  Palmellaceae
    Gloeocystis, 2 species, temperate Atlantic
    Urococcus, 1 species, temperate Atlantic
  Chlorangiaceae
    Prasinocladus, 2 species, temperate Atlantic and Pacific

ULOTRICHALES
Ulotrichaceae
Hormidium, 1 species, Oregon
Stichococcus, 1 species, temperate Atlantic
Ulothrix, 5 species, temperate Atlantic and Pacific
Chaetophoraceae
Acrochaete, 1 species, temperate Atlantic
Bolbocoleon, 1 species, temperate Atlantic and Pacific
Endophyton, 1 species, temperate Pacific
Entocladia, 9 species, cosmopolitan
Internoretia, 1 species, temperate Pacific
Ochlochaete, 1 species, temperate Atlantic
Phaeophila, 4 species, temperate-tropical Atlantic and Pacific
Protoderma, 1 species, tropical Atlantic
Pseudendoclonium, 1 species, temperate Atlantic
Pseudodictyon, 1 species, temperate Pacific
Pseudopringsheimia, 1 species, temperate Pacific
Pseudulvella, 3 species, temperate Pacific
Tellamia, 1 species, temperate Atlantic
Ulvella, 2 species, temperate Pacific and tropical Atlantic
Chroolepidaceae
Pilinia, 6 species, temperate-tropical Atlantic and Pacific
Trentepohlia, 1 species, California
Monostromaceae
Blidingia, 1 species, temperate Pacific
Monostroma, 14 species, temperate-boreal Atlantic and Pacific
Ulvaceae
Capsosiphon, 1 species, temperate Atlantic
Collinsiella, 1 "species", temperate Pacific
Enteromorpha, about 18 species, cosmopolitan
Percursaria, 1 species, temperate Atlantic and Pacific
Ulva, about 13 species, cosmopolitan

SCHIZOGONIALES
Prasiolaceae
Prasiola (incl. *Schizogonium*), 5 species, temperate Atlantic and Pacific
Rosenvingiella, 2 species, temperate Pacific

CHLOROCOCCALES
Chlorococcaceae
Chlorochytrium, 5 species, temperate Pacific
Codiolum, 4 "species," temperate Pacific and Atlantic
Gomontiaceae
Gomontia, 1 "species," temperate-tropical Atlantic and Pacific
Oocystaceae
Palmellococcus, 1 species, temperate Atlantic

CLADOPHORALES
  Cladophoraceae
    Chaetomorpha, 18 species, cosmopolitan
    Cladophora, about 32 species, cosmopolitan
    Lola, 1 species, temperate-tropical Pacific
    Rhizoclonium, 6 species, cosmopolitan
    Spongomorpha, 9 species, temperate-boreal Atlantic and Pacific
    Urospora, 8 species, temperate-boreal Atlantic and Pacific
  Anadyomenaceae
    Anadyomene, 2 species, tropical Atlantic and Gulf
    Cystodictyon, 1 species, Florida
    Microdictyon, 3 species, tropical Atlantic and subtropical Pacific
    Valoniopsis, 2 species, tropical Atlantic and Pacific
SIPHONOCLADALES
  Valoniaceae
    Dictyosphaeria, 4 species, tropical Atlantic and Pacific
    Valonia, 5 species, tropical Atlantic
  Siphonocladaceae
    Cladophoropsis, 5 species, temperate-tropical Atlantic and Pacific
    Ernodesmis, 1 species, tropical Atlantic and Pacific
    Petrosiphon, 1 species, tropical Atlantic
    Siphonocladus, 3 species, tropical Atlantic and subtropical Pacific
  Boodleaceae
    Boodlea, 2 species, tropical Atlantic and Pacific
    Struvea, 3 species, tropical Atlantic and Pacific
SIPHONALES
  Chaetosiphonaceae
    Blastophysa, 1 species, temperate-tropical Atlantic
  Derbesiaceae
    Derbesia, 7 "species," temperate-tropical Pacific and Atlantic
    Halicystis, 2 "species," temperate Pacific; tropical Atlantic
  Bryopsidaceae
    Bryopsis, 9 species, temperate-tropical Pacific and Atlantic
  Caulerpaceae
    Caulerpa, about 18 species, tropical Pacific and Atlantic
  Codiaceae
    Avrainvillea, 5 species, tropical Atlantic
    Boodleopsis, 2 species, tropical Pacific and Atlantic
    Chlorodesmis, 2 species, tropical Pacific
    Codium, about 23 species, cosmopolitan
    Geppella, 1 species, Gulf of California
    Halimeda, about 10 species, tropical Atlantic and Pacific
    Penicillus, 4 species, tropical Atlantic
    Rhipilia, 1 species, tropical Atlantic
    Rhipocephalus, 2 species, tropical Atlantic
    Udotea, 8 species, tropical Atlantic

DASYCLADALES
Dasycladaceae
Acetabularia, 6 species, tropical Atlantic and Pacific
Acicularia, 1 species, tropical Atlantic
Batophora, 1 species, tropical Atlantic
Chalmasia, 1 species, tropical Atlantic
Cymopolia, 1 species, tropical Atlantic
Dasycladus, 1 species, tropical Atlantic
Neomeris, 4 species, tropical Atlantic and Pacific

XANTHOPHYTA

VAUCHERIALES
Vaucheriaceae
Vaucheria, 4 species, cosmopolitan
Phyllosiphonaceae
Ostreobium, 2 species, cosmopolitan

PHAEOPHYTA

ECTOCARPALES
Ectocarpaceae
Acinetospora, 1 species, temperate-tropical Atlantic
Bachelotia, 1 species, temperate-tropical Atlantic
Ectocarpus, about 33 species, cosmopolitan
Giffordia, about 22 species, cosmopolitan
Herponema, 1 species, Florida
Isthmoplea, 1 species, temperate Atlantic
Mikrosyphar, 1 species, temperate Atlantic
Phaeostroma, 1 species, temperate-tropical Atlantic
Pylaiella, 6 species, temperate Pacific and Atlantic
Sorocarpus, 1 species, temperate Atlantic
Streblonema, 22 species, temperate-boreal Atlantic and Pacific
Ralfsiaceae
Hapalospongidion, 1 species, temperate-tropical Pacific
Hapterophycus, 1 species, temperate Pacific
Lithoderma, 1 species, boreal Atlantic and Pacific
Ralfsia, 11 species, cosmopolitan
Sorapion, 1 species, boreal Atlantic
SPHACELARIALES
Sphacelariaceae
Chaetopterus, 1 species, boreal Atlantic
Sphacelaria, 16 species, cosmopolitan
Stypocaulaceae
Halopteris, 1 species, boreal Atlantic
Cladostephaceae
Cladostephus, 1 species, temperate Atlantic

TILOPTERIDALES
Tilopteridaceae
Haplospora, 1 species, temperate Atlantic
Masonophycus, 1 species, tropical Pacific
Tilopteris, 1 species, temperate Atlantic
CUTLERIALES
Cutleriaceae
Cutleria, 1 species, Gulf of California
DICTYOTALES
Dictyotaceae
Dictyopteris, 9 species, temperate-tropical Pacific and Atlantic
Dictyota, 14 species, temperate-tropical Pacific; tropical Atlantic
Dilophus, 4 species, tropical Pacific and Atlantic
Pachydictyon, 1 species, temperate Pacific
Padina, 10 species, tropical Pacific and Atlantic
Pocockiella, 1 species, tropical Pacific and Atlantic
Spatoglossum, 4 species, tropical Pacific and Atlantic
Stypopodium, 1 species, tropical Atlantic
Syringoderma, 1 species, temperate Pacific
Taonia, 1 species, temperate Pacific
Zonaria, 2 species, temperate Pacific and Atlantic
CHORDARIALES
Myrionemataceae
Ascocyclus, 2 species, temperate Atlantic
Compsonema, 17 species, temperate Pacific
Hecatonema, 3 species, temperate Pacific and Atlantic
Microspongium, 1 species, Maine
Myrionema, 13 species, temperate-tropical Pacific and Atlantic
Elachisteaceae
Elachistea, 4 species, temperate Atlantic and Pacific; tropical Atlantic
Giraudia, 1 species, Massachusetts
Gonodia, 2 species, Gulf of California
Halothrix, 1 species, temperate Atlantic and Pacific
Leptonema, 1 species, Maine
Myriactula, 2 species, temperate Atlantic
Symphoricoccus, 1 species, New Jersey
Corynophloeaceae
Leathesia, 2 species, temperate Pacific and Atlantic
Petrospongium, 1 species, temperate Pacific
Chordariaceae
Chordaria, 3 species, boreal Atlantic and Pacific
Cladosiphon, 1 species, tropical Atlantic
Eudesme, 2 species, temperate Pacific and Atlantic
Haplogloia, 2 species, temperate Pacific
Heterochordaria, 1 species, temperate Pacific

Mesogloia, 1 species, temperate Atlantic
Saundersella, 1 species, boreal Pacific
Spermatochnaceae
Nemacystus, 2 species, tropical Pacific and Atlantic
Acrothricaceae
Acrothrix, 1 species, temperate Atlantic
Stilophoraceae
Stilophora, 1 species, tropical-temperate Atlantic

SPOROCHNALES
Sporochnaceae
Carpomitra, 1 species, subtropical Pacific
Nereia, 1 species, tropical Atlantic
Sporochnus, 2 species, subtropical-tropical Pacific and Atlantic

DESMARESTIALES
Desmarestiaceae
Arthrocladia, 1 species, temperate Atlantic
Desmarestia, 20 species, temperate Atlantic and Pacific

DICTYOSIPHONALES
Striariaceae
Phloeospora, 1 species, temperate Atlantic
Stictyosiphon, 2 species, temperate Pacific and Atlantic
Striaria, 1 species, temperate Atlantic
Punctariaceae
Desmotrichum, 2 species, temperate Atlantic
Halorhipis, 1 species, temperate Pacific
Ishige, 1 species, Gulf of California
Litosiphon, 1 species, temperate Atlantic
Myelophycus, 1 species, temperate and boreal Pacific
Myriotrichia, 3 species, temperate Atlantic
Phaeostrophion, 1 species, temperate Pacific
Punctaria, 8 species, temperate and boreal Atlantic and Pacific
Rhadinocladia, 2 species, temperate Atlantic
Soranthera, 1 species, temperate and boreal Pacific
Scytosiphonaceae
Asperococcus, 1 species, temperate Atlantic
Colpomenia, 3 species, cosmopolitan
Delamarea, 1 species, temperate Atlantic
Endarachne, 1 species, temperate Pacific
Hydroclathrus, 1 species, tropical Pacific and Atlantic
Omphalophyllum, 1 species, boreal Atlantic
Petalonia, 1 species, temperate-boreal Pacific and Atlantic
Phaeosaccion, 1 species, temperate Atlantic
Rosenvingea, 4 species, tropical Atlantic and Pacific
Scytosiphon, 5 species, cosmopolitan

Chnoosporaceae
Chnoospora, 3 species, tropical Atlantic and Pacific
Dictyosiphonaceae
Coilodesme, 8 species, temperate-boreal Pacific
Dictyosiphon, 7 species, temperate-boreal Pacific and Atlantic

LAMINARIALES
Chordaceae
Chorda, 2 species, temperate-boreal Atlantic; boreal Pacific
Laminariaceae
Agarum, 2 species, temperate-boreal Pacific and Atlantic
Arthrothamnus, 1 species, temperate-boreal Pacific
Costaria, 2 species, temperate Pacific
Cyamathere, 1 species, temperate Pacific
Hedophyllum, 2 species, temperate-boreal Pacific
Laminaria, 20 species, temperate-boreal Atlantic and Pacific
Phyllaria, 1 species, temperate-boreal Atlantic
Pleurophycus, 1 species, temperate-boreal Pacific
Thalassiophyllum, 1 species, temperate Pacific
Lessoniaceae
Dictyoneuropsis, 1 species, temperate Pacific
Dictyoneurum, 1 species, temperate Pacific
Lessoniopsis, 1 species, temperate-boreal Pacific
Macrocystis, 2 species, temperate-boreal Pacific
Nereocystis, 1 species, temperate-boreal Pacific
Pelagophycus, 3 species, temperate Pacific
Postelsia, 1 species, temperate Pacific
Alariaceae
Alaria, 12 species, temperate-boreal Pacific and Atlantic
Egregia, 3 species, temperate Pacific
Eisenia, 3 species, temperate Pacific
Pterygophora, 1 species, temperate Pacific

FUCALES
Fucaceae
Ascophyllum, 2 species, temperate-boreal Atlantic
Fucus, about 9 species, temperate-boreal Atlantic and Pacific
Hesperophycus, 1 species, temperate Pacific
Pelvetia, 1 species, temperate Pacific
Pelvetiopsis, 2 species, temperate Pacific
Cystoseiraceae
Cystophora, 1 species, temperate Pacific
Cystoseira, 4 species, temperate Pacific
Halidrys, 1 species, temperate Pacific
Sargassaceae
Sargassum, about 23 species, tropical Pacific and Atlantic

RHODOPHYTA
Class Bangiophycidae

GONIOTRICHALES

Goniotrichaceae

Asterocytis, 1 species, temperate-tropical Atlantic

Goniotrichopsis, 1 species, California

Goniotrichum, 2 species, temperate-tropical Atlantic and Pacific

BANGIALES

Erythropeltidaceae

Erythrocladia, 5 species, temperate-tropical Atlantic and Pacific

Erythropeltis, 1 species, temperate Pacific and Atlantic

Erythrotrichia, 15 species, temperate-tropical Atlantic and Pacific

Porphyropsis, 1 species, temperate Atlantic and Pacific

Smithora, 1 species, temperate Pacific

Bangiaceae

Bangia, 6 species, temperate-tropical Atlantic and Pacific

Colaconema, 1 species, temperate Atlantic

Conchocelis, 1 "species," temperate Pacific; temperate-boreal Atlantic

Porphyra, 19 species, cosmopolitan

Porphyrella, 2 species, temperate Pacific

Class Florideophycidae

NEMALIONALES

Acrochaetiaceae

Acrochaetium, about 61 species, cosmopolitan

Audouinella, 1 species, temperate Atlantic and Pacific

Kylinia, 11 species, temperate-tropical Atlantic and Pacific

Rhodochorton, 4 species, temperate-boreal Atlantic and Pacific

Helminthocladiaceae

Cumagloia, 1 species, temperate Pacific

Dermonema, 1 species, tropical Pacific

Helminthocladia, 3 species, temperate Pacific; tropical Atlantic

Helminthora, 2 species, temperate Pacific

Liagora, 11 species, tropical Atlantic and Pacific

Nemalion, 3 species, temperate-tropical Atlantic and Pacific

Chaetangiaceae

Galaxaura, 18 "species," tropical Atlantic and Pacific

Pseudogloiophloea, 2 species, temperate-tropical Pacific; tropical Atlantic

Pseudoscinaia, 1 species, temperate Pacific

Scinaia, 7 species, temperate-tropical Atlantic and Pacific

Whidbeyella, 1 species, temperate Pacific

Naccariaceae

Naccaria, 1 species, tropical Atlantic

Bonnemaisoniaceae

Asparagopsis, 1 species, tropical Atlantic and Pacific

Bonnemaisonia, 3 species, temperate Pacific

Falkenbergia, 1 "species," temperate-tropical Pacific; tropical Atlantic

Trailliella, 1 "species," temperate Pacific and Atlantic

GELIDIALES

Gelidiaceae

Gelidium, 28 species, temperate and tropical Pacific and Atlantic

Pterocladia, 9 species, temperate-tropical Atlantic and Pacific

Gelidiellaceae

Gelidiella, 9 species, tropical Atlantic and Pacific

Wurdemanniaceae

Wurdemannia, 1 species, tropical Atlantic and Pacific

CRYPTONEMIALES

Dumontiaceae

Acrosymphyton, 1 species, tropical Atlantic

Constantinea, 3 species, temperate-boreal Pacific

Cryptosiphonia, 1 species, temperate-boreal Pacific

Dilsea, 1 species, temperate-boreal Pacific

Dumontia, 2 species, boreal Atlantic and Pacific

Farlowia, 2 species, temperate Pacific

Leptocladia, 2 species, temperate Pacific

Neodilsea, 1 species, boreal Atlantic

Pikea, 2 species, temperate Pacific

Thuretellopsis, 1 species, temperate Pacific

Weeksia, 4 species, temperate Pacific

Rhizophyllidaceae

Ochtodes, 1 species, tropical Atlantic

Polyides, 1 species, temperate-boreal Atlantic

Gloiosiphoniaceae

Gloiosiphonia, 3 species, temperate-boreal Pacific and Atlantic

Schimmelmannia, 1 species, temperate Pacific

Endocladiaceae

Endocladia, 1 species, temperate Pacific

Gloiopeltis, 2 species, temperate-boreal Pacific

Squamariaceae

Asymmetria, 1 species, California

Contarinia, 1 species, temperate-tropical Atlantic

Cruoriella, 4 species, temperate-tropical Pacific

Ethelia, 1 species, tropical Pacific

Peyssonelia, 9 species, temperate-tropical Pacific and Atlantic

Rhodophysema (Rhododermis), 4 species, temperate-boreal Atlantic; temperate Pacific

Hildenbrandiaceae

Hildenbrandia, 3 species, cosmopolitan

Corallinaceae

Amphiroa, 19 species, tropical Atlantic and Pacific

Archeolithothamnium, 4 species, tropical Atlantic and Pacific

    Bossiella, 11 species, temperate Pacific
    Calliarthron, 4 species, temperate Pacific
    Choreonema, 1 species, temperate-tropical Pacific
    Clathromorphum, 3 species, boreal Pacific and Atlantic
    Corallina, 11 species, temperate-boreal Atlantic and Pacific
    Dermatolithon (Tenarea), 5 species, temperate-tropical Atlantic and Pacific
    Fosliella, 3 species, temperate-tropical Atlantic and Pacific
    Goniolithon, about 8 species, tropical Atlantic and Pacific
    Heteroderma, 7 species, temperate-tropical Atlantic and Pacific
    Hydrolithon, 4 species, tropical Pacific
    Jania, 10 species, tropical Atlantic and Pacific
    Litholepis, 3 species, tropical Pacific
    Lithophyllum, about 23 species, temperate-tropical Atlantic and Pacific
    Lithothamnium, about 28 species, cosmopolitan
    Lithothrix, 1 species, temperate Pacific
    Melobesia, 4 species, temperate-tropical Atlantic and Pacific
    Pachyarthron, 1 species, boreal Pacific
    Phymatolithon, 3 species, temperate-boreal Atlantic
    Polyporolithon, 3 species, temperate Pacific
    Porolithon, 2 species, tropical Pacific and Gulf of California
    Pseudolithophyllum, 1 species, temperate-boreal Atlantic
    Serraticardia, 1 species, temperate Pacific
Dermocorynidaceae
    Dermocorynus, 1 species, temperate Pacific
Cryptonemiaceae
    Aeodes, 1 species, temperate Pacific
    Carpopeltis, 3 species, temperate-tropical Pacific
    Corynomorpha, 1 species, tropical Atlantic
    Cryptonemia, 10 species, temperate-tropical Pacific; tropical Atlantic
    Grateloupia, 17 species, temperate-tropical Pacific; tropical Atlantic
    Halymenia, 12 species, temperate-tropical Pacific; tropical Atlantic
    "Lobocolax", 1 species, temperate Pacific
    Prionitis, 11 species, temperate-tropical Pacific
Kallymeniaceae
    Callocolax, 2 species, temperate Pacific
    Callophyllis, 21 species, temperate Pacific
    Erythrophyllum, 3 species, temperate-boreal Pacific
    Euthora, 2 species, temperate-boreal Atlantic and Pacific
    Kallymenia, 9 species, temperate-boreal Atlantic and Pacific; tropical
       Atlantic
    Pugetia, 1 species, temperate Pacific
Choreocolacaceae
    Ceratocolax, 1 species, boreal Atlantic
    Choreocolax, 1 species, temperate-boreal Atlantic and Pacific
    Gelidiocolax, 1 species, temperate Pacific
    Harveyella, 1 species, temperate Atlantic

GIGARTINALES
  Cruoriaceae
    Cruoria, 3 species, temperate Pacific; boreal Atlantic
    Cruoriopsis, 4 species, temperate-tropical Pacific; temperate-boreal Atlantic
    Haematocelis, 1 species, temperate Pacific
    Petrocelis, 5 species, temperate-boreal Pacific and Atlantic
  Nemastomaceae
    Platoma, 2 species, temperate Atlantic and Pacific
    Predaea, 2 species, tropical Pacific
    Schizymenia, 2 species, temperate Pacific
    Titanophora, 1 species, Florida
  Solieriaceae
    Agardhiella, 2 species, temperate-tropical Atlantic and Pacific
    Eucheuma, 5 species, Gulf of California; tropical Atlantic
    Gardneriella, 1 species, temperate Pacific
    Meristotheca, 1 species, tropical Atlantic
    Opuntiella, 1 species, temperate-boreal Pacific
    Sarcodiotheca, 4 species, temperate and tropical Pacific
    Turnerella, 2 species, temperate-boreal Pacific; boreal Atlantic
  Rhabdoniaceae
    Catenella, 2 species, tropical Atlantic
  Rhodophyllidaceae
    Cystoclonium, 1 species, temperate-boreal Atlantic
    Rhodophyllis, 1 species, temperate and boreal Atlantic
  Hypneaceae
    Hypnea, 11 species, temperate-tropical Atlantic and Pacific
    Hypneocolax, 1 species, subtropical Atlantic and Pacific
  Plocamiaceae
    Plocamiocolax, 1 species, temperate Pacific
    Plocamium, 4 species, temperate and tropical Pacific
  Sphaerococcaceae
    Caulacanthus, 2 species, tropical Pacific
    Taylorophycus, 1 species, subtropical Pacific
  Gracilariaceae
    Gelidiopsis, 3 species, tropical Atlantic and Pacific
    Gracilaria, 27 species, temperate and tropical Atlantic and Pacific
    Gracilariophila, 2 species, temperate Pacific
    Gracilariopsis, 7 species, temperate and tropical Atlantic and Pacific
  Dicranemaceae
    Dicranema, 1 species, tropical Pacific
  Phyllophoraceae
    Ahnfeltia, 3 species, cosmopolitan
    Gymnogongrus, 12 species, temperate-tropical Atlantic and Pacific
    Petroglossum, 2 species, temperate Pacific
    Phyllophora, 6 species, temperate Atlantic and Pacific; boreal Atlantic
    Stenogramme, 1 species, temperate-tropical Pacific

Gigartinaceae
  Besa, 1 species, California
  Chondrus, 1 species, temperate-boreal Atlantic; boreal Pacific
  Gigartina, about 29 species, temperate-boreal Atlantic and Pacific
  Iridaea, 16 species, temperate-boreal Pacific
  Rhodoglossum, 11 species, temperate Pacific

RHODYMENIALES
Rhodymeniaceae
  Agardhinula, 1 species, subtropical Atlantic
  Botryocladia, 10 species, temperate-tropical Pacific; tropical Atlantic
  Chrysymenia, 2 species, tropical Atlantic
  Cryptarachne, 2 species, tropical Atlantic
  Fauchea, 4 species, temperate-tropical Pacific
  Faucheocolax, 1 species, temperate Pacific
  Fryeella, 1 species, temperate Pacific
  Gloioderma, 1 species, Gulf of California
  Halosaccion, 3 species, temperate-boreal Pacific and Atlantic
  Leptofauchea, 2 species, temperate Pacific
  Maripelta, 1 species, temperate Pacific
  Microphyllum, 1 species, tropical Pacific
  Rhodymenia, 13 species, temperate and boreal Atlantic and Pacific
  Rhodymeniocolax, 1 species, temperate Pacific
  Sciadophycus, 1 species, temperate Pacific
Champiaceae
  Binghamia, 2 species, temperate Pacific
  Champia, 2 species, temperate-tropical Atlantic; tropical Pacific
  Coeloseira, 3 species, temperate Pacific
  Coelothrix, 1 species, tropical Atlantic; Gulf of California
  Gastroclonium, 1 species, temperate Pacific
  Lomentaria, 5 species, temperate-tropical Atlantic and Pacific
  Reticulobotrys, 1 species, temperate Pacific

CERAMIALES
Ceramiaceae
  Aglaothamnion, 2 species, subtropical Pacific
  Antithamnion, 34 species, cosmopolitan
  Callithamnion, 27 species, cosmopolitan
  Centroceras, 3 species, temperate-tropical Atlantic and Pacific
  Ceramium, about 47 species, cosmopolitan
  Crouania, 2 species, tropical Atlantic; subtropical and tropical Pacific
  Griffithsia, 6 species, temperate-tropical Atlantic and Pacific
  Gymnothamnion, 1 species, temperate-tropical Pacific; tropical Atlantic
  Haloplegma, 1 species, tropical Pacific
  Lejolisia, 1 species, tropical Pacific
  Microcladia, 3 species, temperate-boreal Pacific
  Neoptilota, 3 species, temperate-boreal Pacific

Platythamnion, 5 species, temperate-tropical Pacific
Pleonosporium, 12 species, temperate-tropical Atlantic; tropical-temperate-
boreal Pacific
Plumaria, 1 species, temperate-boreal Atlantic
Ptilota, 4 species, temperate-boreal Atlantic and Pacific
Seirospora, 2 species, temperate-tropical Atlantic
Spermothamnion, 4 species, temperate-tropical Pacific and Atlantic
Spyridia, 3 species, tropical Atlantic and Pacific; temperate Atlantic
Tiffaniella, 1 species, subtropical Pacific
Wrangelia, 3 species, tropical Atlantic and Pacific
Delesseriaceae
Acrosorium, 2 species, temperate-tropical Pacific
Anisocladella, 1 species, temperate Pacific
Botryoglossum, 2 species, temperate Pacific
Branchioglossum, 2 species, temperate Pacific
Caloglossa, 1 species, temperate-tropical Atlantic; tropical Pacific
Cottoniella, 1 species, Florida
Cryptopleura, 7 species, temperate Pacific
Cyclospora, 1 species, Florida
Delesseria, 1 species, temperate Pacific
Erythroglossum, 2 species, temperate Pacific
Gonimophyllum, 1 species, temperate Pacific
Grinnellia, 2 species, Gulf of California; temperate Atlantic
Haroldia, 1 species, temperate Pacific
Holmesia, 1 species, temperate Pacific
Hymenena, 7 species, temperate Pacific and Atlantic
Hypoglossum, 4 species, temperate-tropical Atlantic and Pacific
Martensia, 1 species, tropical Atlantic
Membranoptera, 9 species, temperate-boreal Atlantic and Pacific
Myriogramme, 7 species, temperate Pacific
Nienburgia, 2 species, temperate Pacific
Nitophyllum, 2 species, temperate Pacific
Pantoneura, 3 species, boreal Atlantic and Pacific
Phycodrys, 8 species, temperate-boreal Atlantic and Pacific; tropical Atlantic
Platysiphonia, 2 species, temperate Pacific
Polycoryne, 1 species, temperate Pacific
Polyneura, 1 species, temperate Pacific
Polyneurella, 1 species, Gulf of California
Pseudophycodrys, 1 species, boreal Pacific
Schizoseris, 1 species, subtropical Pacific
Sorella, 3 species, temperate Pacific
Taenioma, 2 species, tropical Atlantic and Pacific
Dasyaceae
Dasya, 10 species, temperate-tropical Atlantic and Pacific
Dasyopsis, 1 species, tropical Atlantic
Dictyurus, 1 species, tropical Atlantic

Halodictyon, 1 species, tropical Atlantic
Heterosiphonia, 5 species, temperate-tropical Atlantic and Pacific
Pogonophorella, 1 species, temperate Pacific
Rhodoptilum, 2 species, temperate Pacific

Rhodomelaceae

Acanthophora, 2 species, tropical Atlantic
Amansia, 1 species, tropical Atlantic
Amplisiphonia, 1 species, temperate Pacific
Bostrychia, 9 species, temperate-tropical Atlantic and Pacific
Bryocladia, 2 species, tropical Atlantic
Bryothamnion, 3 species, tropical Atlantic and Pacific
Chondria, 19 species, temperate-tropical Atlantic and Pacific
Digenia, 1 species, tropical Atlantic and Pacific
Enantocladia, 1 species, tropical Atlantic
Erythrocystis, 1 species, temperate Pacific
Herposiphonia, 9 species, temperate-tropical Pacific; tropical Atlantic
Janczewskia, 4 species, temperate Pacific
Jantinella, 1 species, temperate-tropical Pacific
Laurencia, about 34 species, temperate-tropical Atlantic and Pacific
Levringiella, 1 species, California
Lophocladia, 1 species, tropical Atlantic
Lophosiphonia, 5 species, temperate-tropical Pacific; tropical Atlantic
Micropeuce, 1 species, tropical Atlantic and Pacific
Murrayella, 1 species, tropical Atlantic
Murrayellopsis, 1 species, temperate Pacific
Odonthalia, 7 species, temperate-boreal Atlantic and Pacific
Polysiphonia, about 50 species, cosmopolitan
Pterochondria, 1 species, temperate Pacific
Pterosiphonia, 8 species, temperate-tropical Atlantic and Pacific
Pterosiphoniella, 1 species, subtropical Pacific
Rhodomela, 5 species, temperate-boreal Atlantic and Pacific
Rhodosiphonia, 1 species, temperate-tropical Pacific
Tayloriella, 2 species, tropical Pacific
Veleroa, 1 species, Gulf of California
Vidalia, 1 species, tropical Atlantic
Wrightiella, 1 species, tropical Atlantic

MARINE PHANEROGAMS

Hydrocharitaceae

Halophila, 3 species, tropical Atlantic and Pacific
Thalassia, 1 species, tropical Atlantic

Potamogetonaceae

Halodule, 4 species, tropical Atlantic and Pacific
Phyllospadix, 2 species, temperate Pacific
Ruppia, 1 species, temperate Atlantic and Pacific
Syringodium, 1 species, tropical Atlantic
Zostera, 1 species, temperate Atlantic and Pacific

Glossary

Å: an angstrom unit equal to one ten-thousandth of a micron, used in expressing the length of light waves.

abaxial: in the direction or position away from the axis.

accessory: additional or auxiliary.

adaxial: in the direction of, or position toward, the axis.

adelphoparasite: a parasite closely related phylogenetically to the host.

adventitious: arising from other than the usual place.

aerotactic: showing an accelerative or depressant response to the presence of oxygen (in aerobic and anaerobic microorganisms).

aestival: developing during summer.

agar: a dry, amorphous, gelatin-like, nonnitrogenous phycocolloid obtained from red algae, mainly *Gelidium*.

agarphyte: an alga from which agar can be obtained.

akinetes: single cells whose walls thicken and separate off from the vegetative thallus to form nonmotile reproductive bodies.

algin: the soluble sodium salt of alginic acid, being a complex organic phycocolloid obtained from large brown algae, especially *Macrocystis*.

alloparasite: a parasite showing no particular relationship to its host.

alternation of generations: the reproduction by organisms that do not necessarily or precisely resemble the parent, but instead resemble the grandparent; applied especially to the regular succession of gametophyte and sporophyte phases.

alveolae: minute pits or depressions.

anaerobic: living or active in the absence of free oxygen.

anaphase: the stage in nuclear division following metaphase at which the daughter nuclei form.

anisogamy: union of 2 gametes of unlike size, both usually motile (but see Chapter 4 for a special usage in diatoms.)

amylogenic: giving rise to starch.

annulate: furnished with or composed of rings.

anterior: positioned in front.

antheridium: the sex organ producing motile male gametes.

antherozoid: a spermatozoid; motile male gamete.

anticlinal: perpendicular to the circumference.

apical: at the apex.

aplanogametes: nonmotile sexual bodies, usually accomplishing fusion within a common gelatinous envelope.

apophysis: the region of expansion between stipe and blade.

appressed: lying flat against something.

areola: minute cells, cavities, or spaces.

ascocarp: the sporocarp of Ascomycetes producing asci and ascospores.

ascus: a large cell, usually the swollen end of a hyphal branch in the ascocarp, in which usually 8 spores are produced.

asexual: reproduction that does not involve a union of gametes.

assimilatory shoots: erect or free parts serving mainly for photosynthesis and the incorporation of food materials into the protoplasm.

autogamous: capable of self-fertilization.

autogamy: fusion of 2 nuclei from the same parent cell.

autophytic (autotrophic): the capacity of a plant to be independent of organized food materials.

auxiliary cell: in the Florideophycidae, a cell that receives a nucleus from the zygote and then produces gonimoblasts.

auxospore: the spore in diatoms formed as a result of sexual fusion.

axial: relating to the morphological axis as distinct from its appendages.

axile: situated in the axis.

blade: the more or less broad, flattened, foliose part of an erect alga; lamina.

bloom: an abundant development of plankton.

bullate: appearing as if blistered, or as a blister.

calyptra: a cap-like or lid-like structure.

carpogonial branch (or filament): a reproductive filament or row of cells terminating in a carpogonium (in Florideophycidae)

carposporophyte: a generation following sexual fusion in the Florideophycidae, consisting of the gonimoblast filaments and the carposporangia borne on them.

carrageenin (or carragheen): a gelatin-like phycocolloid resembling agar, but obtained from *Chondrus* and other red algae of the family Gigartinaceae.

caulicle: the initial region between the radicle and the cotyledons of an embryo; the hypocotyl.

cellulolytic: capable of hydrolyzing cellulose.

centripetal: toward the center.

chimaera: a product of mechanical coalescence of the meristems of 2 parental forms.

chitin: the organic substance forming the chief constituent of the exoskeletons of insects and crustacea, but also, in somewhat different composition, found in fungi and in some green algae.

chromatophore: one of the pigment-containing bodies or plastids found in plant cells.

ciguatera: a form of ichthyosarcotoxism, or poisoning resulting from human ingestion of the flesh of certain marine fishes.

circinate: curled downward from the apex like a fiddlehead.

coalesced: grown together.

coenocyte: a term traditionally applied to an organism consisting of a number of united protoplasts, or to an alga with multinucleate cell or cells.

commensal: one of 2 organisms living in mutual beneficent relations.

compensation point: the point at which photosynthetic activity of a plant is exactly balanced by respiratory activity.

complanate: flattened.

conceptacle: a cavity opening to the thallus surface and containing reproductive organs.

conidium: an asexual spore produced by abstriction from the tip of a specialized hypha.

conjugation: fusion of 2 gametes to form a zygote, especially when the gametes are similar.

contractile: capable of actively shrinking in volume or dimensions and expanding again.

copulation: union of sexual cells (usually motile ones).

coralline: a calcareous red alga of the family Corallinaceae.

coronate: crowned; having a corona.

cortex: the outermost cell layer or tissue of an algal thallus.

cortication: the development or production of an outer covering layer of cells or tissue over part or all of an algal thallus.

cruciate: having the contents of the tetrasporangium divided in 2 or 3 planes at right angles to one another.

crustose: in the form of a crust.

cryptostomata: minute cavities in the outer cortex of Fucales, bearing tufts of hairs.

cystocarp: the "fruit" resulting from fertilization in Rhodophyta; in Bangioideae consisting only of carpospores; in Florideophycidae consisting of gonimoblast filaments and carpospores usually within a pericarp.

cytokinesis: the cytoplasmic changes involved in mitosis, meiosis, and fertilization as distinguished from nuclear changes.

cumatophyte: a surf-inhabiting plant.

daughter cells: the cells derived from the division of an older one (the mother cell).

deciduous: falling off or shed at maturity.

decumbent: reclining on the substrate.

denitrification: a process by which nitrates or nitrites are reduced, with the formation of nitrites, oxides of nitrogen, ammonia, or free nitrogen.

dentate: toothed.

determinate: having limited growth.

diffluent: tending to dissolve.

diplohaplont: a type of life history in which there is an alternation of a diploid and a haploid multicellular phase.

diploid: having in each cell double the number of chromosomes characteristic of the gamete.

dioecious: with male and female organs borne on separate thalli.

diphasic: with 2 phases in the life history.

diplont: a type of algal life history in which the gametes are the only haploid cells.

discoid: resembling a disc.

distal: remote from the place of attachment; converse of proximal.

distichous: in 2 ranks.

distromatic: having the cells in 2 layers.

dorsiventral: having distinct dorsal and ventral surfaces.

eclipsophycean: an alga found during part of the year as a microscopic form and during part of the year as a macroscopic form.

ecophene: a morphological form of a plant representing response to the environment.

egg: a large, nonmotile female gamete.

endemic: peculiar to a particular locality.

endolithic: living within stone.

endophyte: a plant which grows within another plant.

endospores: spores formed within the parent cell by division of the entire protoplast.

endosymbiont: an organism living internally in another in a state of symbiosis.

endozootic (endozoic): living in an animal.

entire: having the margin continuous and not broken by divisions, teeth, or serrations.

epitheca: the larger, outer valve of a diatom frustule, including the connecting band.

epilithic: living on rock.

epiphyte: a plant that grows upon another plant but is not parasitic.

epizootic (epizoic): living on an animal.

eucarpic: producing several successive fructifications from the same thallus.

exogenous: arising from the outer or superficial tissue.

eyespot: a colored spot in a motile cell.

facultative: having the power to live under different conditions of life.

fascicle: a small bundle.

flagellum: a thread-like cytoplasmic outgrowth by which a swimming cell moves through the water.

floristic: pertaining to the composition of a flora.

foliose: leaf-like.

forcipate: incurved like a pair of pincers.

fructification: the bearing of sexual or asexual reproductive structures in the algae.

frustule: a whole diatom cell wall.

galenophilic: favoring a calm situation.

gametangium: a cell producing gametes (multicellular in some plants).

gametogenesis: the origin and development of gametes.

gametophyte: a plant that produces gametes.

geniculum: an uncalcified joint between segments in a coralline alga.

girdle: that portion of the diatom frustule that unites the valves.

gonimoblast: a carposporangium-producing filament or group of filaments growing from the carpogonium or from an auxiliary cell in the Florideophycidae.

Gram-negative: certain bacteria recognized according to Gram's method in which the organisms are treated with Gram's solution after being stained with gentian violet. Following treatment with alcohol and washing with water, Gram-positive bacteria retain the dye and Gram-negative ones are decolorized.

halocline: a salinity gradient, especially a marked one.

halophytes: plants that grow within the influence of salt water.

haploid: having in each cell the number of chromosomes usually characteristic of the gamete (a single set).

haplont: a type of algal life history in which the zygote is the only diploid cell.

hapteron: a basal multicellular outgrowth forming part of a holdfast.

haustorium: the appendage of a parasitic plant that enters the host and absorbs nutriment.

hemiparasitic: partially or incompletely parasitic.

herpophyte: a creeping plant.

heterocyst: a cell distinctly larger than, or different from its neighbors.

heterogamous: having dissimilar gametes.

heteromorphic: having different form or appearance.

heterotrichous: a highly evolved type of filamentous habit in the algae; or an initial filamentous stage in brown and red algae, consisting of a prostrate system and an erect or projecting system.

heterotrophic: capable of nutrition through absorption of organic substances from the external medium rather than by synthesis of them.

hexose: any of a class of sugars containing 6 atoms of carbon, as glucose.

holdfast: the basal attachment organ of an alga.

holocarpic: applied to those fungi in which the whole body of the plant goes to form the sporangium.

holozoic: wholly or distinctly like an animal as to nutrition; ingesting protein matter.

homothallic: with male and female organs borne on the same plant: monoecious.

hormogonia: portions of a blue-green algal filament that become detached by heterocysts or other means and develop into new plants.

hydrolyzed: having undergone hydrolysis, a kind of chemical decomposition in which a compound is resolved into other compounds by taking up the elements of water.

hypertonic: having a greater osmotic pressure than an isotonic fluid.

hypha: the cylindric, thread-like element of a fungus thallus.

hypotheca: the smaller, inner valve of a diatom frustule, including its connecting band.

immutability: incapable of change; unalterable.

indeterminate: having more or less unlimited growth.

infralittoral: below low tide level.

initial: the early stage of a cell, tissue, or organ.

insolation: exposure to the sun's rays.

intercalary: neither basal nor terminal, but between these extremes.

intergenicula: the calcified segments between the uncalcified joints in a coralline alga.

involucre: a sterile envelop or group of branchlets around a reproductive structure.

isogamy: union of 2 gametes of similar size and appearance.

isomorphic: having the same form or appearance.

isothere: a line joining points on the earth's surface having the same mean summer temperature.

isotonic: having the same or equal osmotic pressure.

karyogamy: fusion of nuclei.

lamina: the more or less broad, flattened, foliose part of an erect alga; blade.

laminarin: a polysaccharide formed in the Phaeophyta.

lenticular: in the form of a lens, especially a doubly convex one.

leucoplast: a colorless plastid.

lignicolous: living in wood.

lithothamnium ridge: the raised margin of an actively growing atoll, usually dominantly composed of calcareous red algae of the genus *Porolithon*, hence, more correctly, porolithon ridge.

lux: the international unit of illumination, being the direct illumination on a surface which is everywhere 1 meter from a uniform point source of one international candle, equal to 1 lumen per square meter, or 0.0929 foot candles.

mannan: any of certain hexosans found as reserve carbohydrates in plants and yielding mannose upon hydrolysis.

marginal: at the margin.

marl: an earthy deposit of clay and calcium carbonate.

meiosis: that type of nuclear division in which the number of chromosomes is halved; reduction division.

meiospore: a spore produced by meiotic division.

meiosporophyte: the diploid portion of a sexual plant in *Prasiola* which gives rise to meiospores and in turn to a patchwork of intact male and female gametophytic tissues.

meristoderm: a meristematic surface layer of tissue in the Laminariales.

mesocarp: the middle layer of a pericarp.

mesochite: the middle, gelatinous layer of the female gametangium in Fucaceae.

metaphase: the stage in nuclear division at which the daughter chromosomes separate.

metarrheophyte: a plant favoring a habitat in strong currents.

microfibril: one of the submicroscopic cellulose filaments making up the algal cell wall.

micron: one-thousandth part of a millimeter; μ.

mitosis: nuclear division in which there is no reduction in chromosome number, and in which division of the cytoplasm usually follows.

mitospore: a spore produced by mitotic rather than meiotic division.

monoecious: with female and male organs borne on the same plant.

monopodial: a mode of development in which the main or primary axis continues its original line of growth, giving off successive axes or lateral branches.

monospore: a spore formed singly within a monosporangium.

monostromatic: having the cells in a single layer.

multiaxial: a manner of thallus construction from multiple primary axial filaments.

mycelium: the vegetative portion of the thallus of a fungus.

mμ: millimicron; the thousandth part of a micron.

nemathecium: a wart-like elevation of the surface containing many reproductive organs (in Florideophycidae)

nematocyst: one of the minute stinging cells of hydrozoans and certain other aquatic organisms.

nitrification: the process of oxidation, especially by bacteria, of ammonia salts to nitrites and the further oxidation of nitrites to nitrates.

nitrogen fixing: having the power of converting free nitrogen into combined form.

node: that part of a stem that normally bears 1 or more leaves.

nullipores: certain nonarticulated, lime-secreting coralline algae.

obligate epiphyte: living in such close relationship on another plant that no alternate habitat is acceptable.

oöblast: a connecting filament through which the zygote nucleus moves from a carpogonium to an auxiliary cell (in Florideophycidae).

oögamy: union of 2 gametes, one of which (male) is motile and the other is a non-motile egg.

oögonium: a single-celled female sex organ containing 1 or more eggs.

operculate: furnished with a lid.

ostiole: a pore-like opening of a conceptacle or a pericarp.

palmelloid: consisting of cells arranged in a shapeless plate, mound or mass.

pan-tropical: occurring widely or throughout the tropics.

papilla: a small, superficial protuberance.

paraphysis: a modified cell or filament (often sterile) borne adjacent to a reproductive organ.

parenchymatous: consisting of comparatively undifferentiated, thin-walled cells of more or less isodiametrical form.

parietal: attached or positioned along a wall.

parthenogenetic: arising from a sex cell without fertilization.

peduncle: the stalk of an inflorescence.

peltate: having the stipe attached to the lower surface but not at the base or margin.

pericarp: a sterile envelope around a cystocarp (in Florideophycidae)

pericentral cell: one of a ring of cells cut off from and surrounding the central (axial) cell in the Rhodophyta.

periclinal: parallel with the circumference.

perithallium: the upper layer of tissue in a crustose alga.

perithecium: a receptacle in fungi enclosing spores that are naked or in asci.

_p_H: a symbol denoting the negative logarithm of the concentration of the hydrogen ion in gram atoms per liter (_p_H of 6 means 10^{-6} or .000001).

phosphorylation: the act or process of converting into a compound of phosphorus, as a sugar into a phosphoric acid ester.

photogenic: producing or generating light.

phototactic: responding by movement with respect to light as the directive factor.

phototropic: responding (as by bending) to the orienting stimulus of light.

phycocolloid: a colloidal substance obtained from seaweeds.

phylum: one of the primary divisions of the animal or plant kingdom.

pinnate: having the divisions arranged on each side of a common rachis (feather-like).

pit connection: a cytoplasmic strand connecting 2 adjoining cells through a pit in their respective walls.

plankter: an individual member of the plankton.

plankton: the passively floating or weakly swimming animal and plant life of a body of water.

planktont: any planktonic organism.

plasmodesmata: protoplasmic connections between 2 cells.

plasmogamy: fusion of cytoplasm.

plasmolysis: contraction or shrinking of the cytoplasm of a living cell due to loss of water.

pleomorphic life histories: those in which more than 1 morphological type occurs.

plethysmothallus: in certain brown algae, a small asexual, filamentous plantlet, usually of ectocarpoid form, arising from a zoospore and serving as an accessory method of reproducing the sporophyte generation vegetatively or by swarmers.

plumule: a primary leaf bud of an embryo.

plurilocular: with several or many cells, locules, or compartments.

pluriseriate: in more than 1 series.

pluristromatic: having the cells in several layers.

pneumatocyst: an air bladder.

polarity: the condition of having distinct poles.

polysiphonous: with many "siphons" or pericentral cells, as in *Polysiphonia*.

polystichous: in many ranks.

procarp: a female reproductive structure in the Florideophycidae in which the carpogonial branch is closely associated with an auxiliary cell to form a well-defined, unified organ.

proliferation: the development of regenerative offshoots, ordinarily in the sense of unusual position or abundance.

prophase: the first stage of nuclear division during which the chromosome threads contract and come to appear as distinct double bodies.

protandry: the condition in which the male reproductive organs develop before the female ones.

proterogyny: the production of receptive pistils before the anthers have ripe pollen, or of male reproductive cells before female ones.

psammophile: a plant favoring a sandy habitat.

pseudolateral: a lateral branch arising through sympodial development by the lateral displacement of the apical shoot.

pseudoparenchyma: a basically filamentous tissue having the appearance of parenchyma.

punctum: a dot-like marking on a diatom valve.

radial: developing uniformly around a central axis.

radicle: the rudimentary root of the embryo.

raphe: the median line or rib of a diatom valve.

receptacle: the specialized fertile portion of branches in Fucales containing conceptacles.

reticular: in the form of a network.

rhizoid: a slender, "root-like" attachment filament usually of a single cell or of a row of cells.

rhizome: a rootstock or dorsiventral stem, usually prostrate, producing roots as well as stems or leaves.

rostrum: a beak-like extension.

rotate: in the form of a wheel.

saccate: in the form of a sac.

saprobic (saprophytic): living on decaying organic matter.

saxicolous: inhabiting rocks.

sciophilic: favoring dim light.

scuba: self-contained underwater breathing apparatus.

secund: arranged along 1 side of an axis.

segments: the divisions of a jointed, segmented, or divided thallus; the cells cut off from an apical cell; the multinucleate units of coenocytes.

septate: provided with partitions or walls.

seriate: in a series.

sessile: without a stipe or stalk.

setae: bristles or stiff hairs.

sieve filament: a series of elongated cells having perforated end walls, in the inner cortex and medulla of stipes of certain Laminariales.

sigmoid: curved in 2 directions as in the letter S.

simple: without branches.

sinter: a calcareous deposit in springs and geysers.

siphonaceous (siphonous; siphoneous): possessing tubular structure (as in certain multinucleate green algae).

sorus: a group or cluster of reproductive organs.

spadix: a kind of flower spike with a fleshy axis.

spathe: a large bract enclosing a flower cluster (spadix).

spermatium: a nonmotile male gamete in the red algae.

spermatozoid: a flagellated male gamete.

spindle: the spindle-shaped figure of fibers of achromatic substance formed during mitosis or meiosis.

spontaneous generation: the assumed generation of living from nonliving matter; that organisms found in putrid organic matter presumably arise spontaneously from it.

spongiose: sponge-like.

sporangium: a spore-producing structure.

sporogenesis: the origin and development of spores.

sporophyll: a blade producing sporangia.

sporophyte: a plant or generation in the life history that produces spores.

stellate: star-shaped.

stenohaline: favoring little salinity variation.

stenomesothermic: enduring a narrow temperature amplitude in the median temperature range.

stenophotic: favoring uniform light intensity.

stichidium: an inflated or expanded, specialized branch bearing tetrasporangia (in some Florideophycidae).

stipe: the stem-like, usually basal part of a thallus.

stolon: a branch or shoot growing out from the base of a parent plant and capable of producing another shoot.

stoloniferous: provided with stolons.

stupose: having tufted or matted filaments.

subclavate: shaped somewhat like a club.

subcortical: beneath or within the cortex (usually a tissue between cortex and medulla).

subspecies: in classification, the rank below the species.

sulcus: a groove in a dinoflagellate cell.

supralittoral fringe: the shore area just below and just above the level of extreme high water of spring tides.

swarmers: zoospores or zoogametes.

symbiosis: the living together of 2 unlike organisms in a mutually advantageous manner.

sympodial: a mode of development in which the apparent main axis is not developed by continuous terminal growth, but is made up of successive secondary axes, each representing a branch.

syngamy: the fusion of 2 sexual cells or gametes.

synonymy: all that relates to synonyms (superceded, unused, or rejected names).

systematist: one who studies the orderly classification of organisms according to a phylogenetic or other system.

taxonomist: one concerned with classification and naming of organisms.

tenaculum: a specialized secondary attachment structure.

tetrahedral: having the contents of a tetrasporangium triangularly divided so that only 3 of the tetraspores can be seen in one view.

tetraspore: a spore formed in a group of 4 in a tetrasporangium.

tetrastichous: in 4 ranks.

thallus: the whole plant body of an alga or fungus.

thermocline: a temperature gradient, especially one showing sharp change.

trabeculum: a special wall structure projecting into or traversing a cell cavity (mainly in coenocytes).

transection: a section cut transversely.

trichoblast: a simple or branched filament arising from the apex of a plant in the Rhodomelaceae.

trichogyne: the hair-like apical prolongation of a carpogonium.

trichome: an entire row of cells of a blue-green algal filament, but not including the sheath.

trichothallic: a method of growth in which thallus development is initiated at the base of one or more filaments (in certain Phaeophyta).

trumpet hyphae: elongate cells in the central tissues of the stipes of certain Laminariales, having enlarged ends with pitted septa.

tufa: a form of porous limestone.

turbidity: a condition of cloudiness of water due to impurities.

undulate: wavy.

uniaxial: a manner of thallus construction in which there is a single primary axial filament.

unilocular: with a single cell, compartment, or locule.

uniseriate: in a single series.

unistratose: consisting of a single layer.

upwelling: the ascent of water of greater density and lower temperature toward the surface in ocean regions of diverging currents, especially along western coasts of continents where prevailing winds carry surface waters away from the shore.

utricle: a vesicle-like cell, or the terminal bulge of a superficial filament forming a kind of tissue as in *Codium* or *Galaxaura*.

verticillate: whorled; arising from the same point on the axis.

vesicle: a bladder-like structure.

zonate: having the contents of a tetrasporangium divided by 3 parallel planes so that the tetraspores lie in a series.

zoogametes: motile sexual cells.

zoosporangium: a sporangium producing zoospores.

zoospore: a motile spore with one or more flagella or cilia by the vibration of which it swims.

μ: one-thousandth of a millimeter; micron.

μg: microgram; one-millionth of a gram.

Index

(Illustrations and tables are indicated in italics)